Kiss Daddy Goodbye

Kiss Daddy Goodbye

Thomas Altman

NELSON DOUBLEDAY, INC.
Garden City, New York

To E.,
for the first salvage
And Peter Gethers,
the second

Chapter One

1.

She hurried past the Keep Out sign, her face lowered against the rain that blew down through the darkness. When she came to the barbed-wire fence she carefully separated the rusted strands to make an opening for herself. She caught her finger on a barb, drawing blood quickly to the surface of the skin. She paused, sucked on the broken skin, tasting not blood but rain in her mouth. Metallic and cold. And then she was through the fence and moving along the slope that led down to the edge of the canal. She drew up the collar of her coat, wondering if she might miss the place in the dark, if she would lose herself in the grass that grew steadily longer the closer you got to the bank. It reached up now around her thighs, as if it sought to restrain her. And the mud underfoot pulled at her shoes, dragging at her.

She stopped again.

Somewhere near here, she thought. Somewhere close.

She peered through the dark. She could hear the sudden swirl of water, then she went down the slope slowly, easily, knowing that when she reached the edge of the reeds she wouldn't have far to go. She took a flashlight from the pocket of her coat but she didn't switch it on. Underfoot, an empty beer can, squashed and battered, slid away from her.

Now the sound of water was stronger than before. She knew she was close to the old lock. She hurried again. A squall blew the rain back at her, misting her eyes, making her lips cold. Around her she could hear noises—rain, canal rats scuttling through the rushes. Small panicked noises. As if something had been disturbed.

She reached the sign that said Dangerous Beyond This Point, flashed the light at it a moment, then killed the beam. Dangerous—but it wasn't, it wasn't dangerous at all, if you knew where you were going and what you were doing. Far in the eastern sky there was a flare of sudden lightning. Brief, distorted. She waited for the sound of thunder but it didn't come. Then she was standing above the lock where the water foamed against the old brick banks. Once, this canal had been part of a system of inland waterways, a branch of the Erie Canal, but now it was no longer used. Momentarily she tried to imagine it as it once must have been—the lock gates opening and closing, barges sliding slowly through. But that had been forty years ago and now there was only the rain and the foaming water and the scent of moss growing out of the bricks. Empty. Stagnant.

Without any purpose, she thought.

She parted the clinging reeds, shoving them aside. Faintly, a black outline set against a blacker sky, she could see the building. She stopped and stared and she thought, I shouldn't have come here. I shouldn't have come.

But you have to return to the scene, don't you?

You have to go back.

And then she was moving quickly towards the building, her head bent against the increasing wind that cracked the reeds like whips.

It was a small brick construction. From here the opening and closing of the lock gates had been controlled. Now the windows were broken and the roof shot and the floors scattered with the debris of teenage parties that had taken place before the barbed wire went up and the warning notices posted. She pushed the door, which whined on its rotted hinges. She turned on her flashlight, conscious of the quick sound of her own breathing. Relax, she told herself. There's nothing here to frighten you. Nothing at all.

The thin beam crossed the floor, picking out the broken slats of old wood crates, empty cobwebbed beer bottles, an item of old clothing which might once have been a girl's blouse. She moved slowly. Rain hammered on the roof, dripping through spaces in the roof and creating small dark pools on the floor.

Why did you want me to come here? I mean, here of all places? We could've talked someplace less crummy.

The echoes.

She lowered the flashlight to her side and went across the floor. *We could've talked someplace less crummy. . . .* Yes, Nick, dear Nick, we could have done that. But that wasn't how I wanted it, was it? That wasn't exactly it, my love. She closed her eyes for a second, imagining all the things that might have happened in this small building. A lock keeper lighting his pipe and watching the canal through the window. A radio playing—maybe one of Roosevelt's fireside talks. And then time passing, the canal being closed but never drained. Kids coming out here to party. Maybe some furtive liaisons took place, quick couplings under the rotted roof, small savage acts of passion. Maybe.

Her head ached suddenly. A brief flare-up of the old pain. Not now, she thought. She wouldn't give in to it now.

She listened to the wind flap the scrap of brown paper somebody had stuck over a broken pane of glass. Then she followed the beam of the flashlight to the other side of the room. The door was here. The door down. And then she remembered when she'd discovered this place. Walking one summer night, trying to think her life out, trying to silence the goddam scream of the past—and she'd come across it because she'd blindly ignored the signs, because the wire fence had parted easily for her.

It was Her Place.

She opened the door and turned the flashlight on the steps that led down to a small cellar room. There was a rushing smell of dampness, sickening, a stale trapped perfume of mildewed wood and sodden canvas. The steps shook under her as she went down. She held the handrail tightly. You could fall, she thought, and just maybe they'd never find you. But you wouldn't be alone, after all. You wouldn't be alone down here.

She reached the bottom, breathing hard. The flashlight played around the room. Discarded pieces of shelving, an ancient pair of leather gloves hanging from a hook, an old sou'wester spread across the floor. Scraps of cracked tarpaulin littered around.

A pile of canvas bags stacked untidily in one corner.

She stopped. Again she thought, I shouldn't have come here. Why then? Why did you?

She could almost taste the answer in her mouth.

She moved across the floor, stepping over small puddles of water to reach the canvas sacks. Her hand shook. She almost dropped the flashlight but caught it against her knee. Look, she thought. Go ahead and look. There's nothing new to see, no surprises here for you. Just look.

Savor it, that strange sense of triumph, of a wrong set right.

With one hand she began to pull the canvas sacks away. They were wet and stuck to her fingers. She kept going, drawing them back one by one, her hand still shaking, her head beginning to hurt. Then she stopped and caught her breath and swung the flashlight into the corner.

He was staring at her with a certain surprised sadness, a mild look of accusation, even a vague touch of peacefulness. It wasn't a look she'd ever seen on his face during his life.

Nick. Nick, she thought.

Something moved across the front of his shirt, something it took her a second to recognize. She stepped back quickly. Across the wound, where the blood had blackened and hardened, a great gray slug was feeding. She raised her foot, knocking the thing aside, feeling its softness even through the leather of her shoes. She heard it land somewhere with a noise no louder than a whisper.

A creature feeding on a dead body—wasn't that natural? Wasn't that a part of the same endless cycle, the same rhythm, that affects us all? She bent down and turned the light full on Nick's face. There were marks on the skin, like small contusions. The mouth was half open and set in a stiff way. One hand was twisted under his jaw, the fingers discolored.

She said his name a couple of times, then she began to pick up the sacks again, strewing them over him. She remembered something now—how, when she'd waken sometimes in the dawn and find him lying uncovered in the bed beside her, she'd draw the blankets up around him and kiss him softly on the side of the forehead so as not to disturb him. Where had all that tenderness gone? When had that died?

She shut her eyes. She recalled a dream of ice-blue water and the sound of a child crying, as if the dream were taking place in an endless corridor filled with its own weird echoes. She followed the cry through the whole dream, never finding the child, awakening suddenly in her own bed and staring at the ceiling and trying not to bring it back, not to resurrect the pain. When she opened her eyes her head was pounding, a firework going off again and again inside her skull, a pulse she knew would expand to fill her entire head, distending the bones, pressing behind the eyes, ringing in the ears.

Nick, she thought.

Does it ever have an end?

Does the dream of ice-blue water have an end?

Back inside her car she quickly opened the glove compartment and took out a small prescription bottle, pouring a tablet into her hand. It tasted bitter as it broke against the back of her throat. She raised her hand to the side of her head, massaging herself lightly. *You can expect pain, of course. That's when the pills should help.* Doctor Spassky had told her that, confident with his arcane understanding of the mind, smug with his comprehension of chemicals. But the pills didn't help. Sometimes the pain blinded, cut the skull bone like a razor blade, like a surgeon's knife. Sometimes there was nothing else but the pain. As if you became the pain, or it became you— your whole life controlled by a single sensation. Zigzagging lines across the eyes, a tight band of cold metal around the head, sweat running everywhere.

She turned the key and drove slowly through the rain, the slick streets. She crossed a thoroughfare, unaware of the red light burning against her, and she drove until she came to a shopping plaza, a place of relentless neon blurred in the rain. She parked outside a Safeway market and for a time she didn't move, she sat listening to the tapping of rain on the roof of the car. It might have been falling inside her head. The Fiorinal tasted bad. But she wasn't going to be sick, she was determined not to be.

She watched a man push a shopping cart through the automatic doors of the market. Then she got out of the car, crossing the wet parking lot. Faintly, she heard Muzak from inside the supermarket. It was "Charmaine." The door slid open and she went inside, where the bright fluorescent lights touched everything like frost. At the drinking fountain she inclined her head to the tiny jet of cold water. Her throat was dry.

She moved along the aisles, hardly aware of herself now, seeming to glide through the air like her body had no contact with the world. She paused at the toy section.

And the pain began again in her skull, starting with a shudder that ran across her scalp, then burrowing beneath the surface like some small enraged animal. The toy section. The toys that gazed at you from their cellophane containers, the miniature figures, the farmyard animals, the stuffed bears and giraffes that seemed to accuse you of something. She felt her body tighten. No, she thought. Not here. Move. Move away from this, for Christ's sake. She was paralyzed a moment, unable to shift her feet, to pull herself away from the ugly display. Charlie, she thought. Dear God, where are you?

Then she heard a kid say *I wanna get this I wanna get this* and it was as if some spell had been broken. She moved back towards the doors, stopping briefly in front of the community bulletin board.

She gazed at the little white cards thumbtacked into cork.

There was one that caught her attention.

2.

Ted was hammering at something in the back yard. With her arms folded, Emily watched from the kitchen window. A trellis, she thought. Why a trellis, of all things? Slats of wood lay all around him; he worked with furious concentration, his dark hair falling across his brow, the sleeves of his plaid shirt rolled up high above the elbows. He was holding nails between his lips and sometimes he would pause, let the hammer droop, and take one of the nails from his teeth as though it were a piece of undigested food.

She opened the kitchen door and stepped outside. She could still smell yesterday's rain in the air; the late afternoon sky was dismal, banks of clouds that scudded with the wind. She walked a little way towards Ted and watched the hammer rising and falling. She saw the muscle in his arm tighten and slacken with the motion of the tool. Sometimes he'd stop to wipe the hair from his forehead with his knuckles—a tiny characteristic she found endearing. And she thought: He hasn't changed much in thirteen years, he hasn't gone to fat like some men do, he hasn't lost his hair. He was the same Ted in any number of ways; she might have been looking at an old wedding photograph.

She moved up behind him, then put her hands over his eyes, blinding him.

"Three guesses," she said.

"You could've scared me into swallowing these nails," he said, turning to her, smiling.

She watched the nails fall onto the grass and she laughed. Then she walked around the trellis and peered at him through the criss-crossing beams of white wood. "You think we really need this thing, Ted?" she said.

"It enhances the property," he said.

She stood behind him again and laid her hands on his shoulders and began lightly to massage his muscles. *It enhances the property*. The phrase had become a standing joke between them. Every one of

Ted's improvements enhanced the property. The extra room he'd built where none was really needed. The loft he'd converted into a guest bedroom. The tool shed. And now this trellis where presumably he imagined roses growing in some future season. She looked across the back yard. Beyond rows of withered cornstalks and the ruins of a flower bed there was a weathered cedar fence. The gate was open and she could hear the sounds of the children in the back alley. If she closed her eyes she could have identified a multitude of noises —the distant rattle of a motorcycle being revved, a lawn mower humming, a pool filter throbbing somewhere, the shifting of wind in the maple trees, the faraway drone of the freeway that encircled the suburb. But it was the kids she was listening for. Their thin voices. The quiet comfort of knowing they were near.

That's mine.

Finders keepers losers weepers.

Ted put his hammer down and looked at her. There was something in his expression, some small ghost of a thing that made her feel uneasy—and then she remembered: his trip. He was going away again on another of his trips and she had the feeling he was going to say something about it, ask some mundane question about whether he had enough clean shirts, clean socks, whatever. But he didn't say anything. Instead, he stood up and leaned forward and kissed her lightly on the side of her face.

"What did I do to deserve that?" she said. Those damn trips—why did she let them touch her like this? Why did his absence create such a hole in her life?

"Call it a casual impulse," Ted said. He put his arm around her shoulder. She stared past him at the open gate.

Finders keepers doesn't mean anything.

It's the law, little brother.

She thrust her hands into the pockets of her white jeans and she thought: This should be a perfect picture, a gorgeous suburban portrait in miniature—the voices of your kids in the back alley, the weight of your husband's arm around the shoulder. Comfort and protection and security. Except—

Except for the trips and the motel rooms and the strange little flashes of jealousy she experienced when Ted had to go away; it was almost as if she couldn't imagine him *always* being alone in those motel rooms. Small ghosts. Shadows. Why did she let these things

plague her anyhow? On the bottom line she couldn't *really* see Ted
with another woman, she couldn't really make a clear picture out of
Ted fumbling with another woman's clothes or his hands covering
another woman's breasts or envisage him entering somebody else.
She couldn't see any of these things: and yet when Ted was gone and
she was alone in the house with the two kids it was like some kind of
shadow falling across her mind.

She turned her face towards him and, reaching up, kissed him on
the mouth.

"Did I do something to *deserve* that?" Ted said.

"One casual impulse deserves another," she said. Momentarily,
she laid her face against his shoulder, conscious all at once of his
strength, of how much she had come to depend on that. And then
there was silence from the alley, as if the kids had stopped arguing
and were staring each other down. Overhead, clouds shredded in the
wind. She was suddenly cold. She did up the top button of her shirt
and she thought: *Don't even think about him going away in the
morning. Don't let it enter your mind.*

She watched him bend to pick up his hammer.

He sneezed abruptly.

"Gesundheit," she said.

"I hope I'm not coming down with something." He took a large
handkerchief from his pants and rubbed his face with it.

"Then you'd have to cancel your trip," she said. "Which would be
terrible."

He folded the handkerchief. He doesn't even hear me, she thought.
Sarcasm thick as peanut butter and he doesn't hear it. She turned,
shivering, and walked towards the kitchen door. Inside, she sat down
at the table and lit a cigarette. Maybe some people just lost their
sense of humor with the passing of time. Once, Ted would have
taken her remark and turned it around and thrown it back at her and
they would have laughed together. Maybe people were like houses:
their foundations settled, their creaking idiosyncrasies became silent
and complacent, and dust grew thick in their attics.

Maybe.

She heard the sounds of the kids laughing in the back yard and she
looked through the window and she saw Frankie tapping a nail into
the trellis with Ted's hammer while Charlotte stood pulling faces
through the slats. For a moment she felt a good sense of warmth, a

feeling that spread through her like a rush of blood, a time of belonging and of understanding what it was that you belonged to. This family. The sum of things. A sudden blur of memories then—the camping trip two years ago when they'd had their tent blown away by a storm in the Adirondacks, the vacation in Virginia the year before that when she and Ted had waited until the kids were asleep and then they'd gone out on to the motel balcony and made love over the sound of the Atlantic's squall, an old picture of Ted changing Frankie's diaper and puncturing his thumb and insisting he get a tetanus shot immediately. Pictures. Cameo shots. Moments of loving, of being loved. Times of understanding what really lay in the crevices of the heart.

Then she was aware of Ted standing beside her. "I smell something good," he said, and he sniffed the air in an exaggerated way.

"Pot roast," she said.

"Ah. My juices are running." And he raised the lid of the saucepan, his face immediately engulfed in steam. Then he sat down at the other end of the table and looked at her in silence for a time. She suddenly imagined she could hear a clock ticking her life away. A cuckoo clock: it not only measured her life, it derided her too, as if it were saying that a world of grocery shopping, waxing floors, doing laundry, was too preposterous for speech. She could hardly see Ted's face in the darkening kitchen now, and she felt uneasy.

"How long will you be in Maine?" she asked.

"Oh. Four days max. Four nights." He took out his pipe and stuffed it with tobacco, then he made a great play of lighting it. Maine, she thought. Four nights max. Motel rooms—*no, goddam, I don't want to go in that direction.* She wanted to say: Is there something wrong with our marriage? Do I expect too much? Or do all marriages end the same way, running with the regularity of a metronome?

She said: "Can I ask a question?"

Ted knocked his pipe in the ashtray. "You've got that serious look on your face—"

"One small question, not too serious."

He nodded his head.

"Do you love me?" she asked.

He was silent for a time, then he tilted his head backwards and laughed. He got up from his chair and came around the table and sat beside her, holding both her hands, inclining his face forward to her. "Do you need to ask *that?*" he said.

"I need it answered," she said.

He looked bemused for a second, then he put his arm around her neck, drawing her face against him. "I love you," he said. "And you don't need to ask."

It dissolved inside her then—the sense of staleness, of sameness, the awareness of monotony. It melted inside her suddenly: and all it took was a touch of reassurance. She felt embarrassed, vulnerable, as if she'd revealed some absurd fear.

She was silent for a time. Then she said, "I better pack you some warm clothing, if you're going to Maine."

Ted released her from his hold and laid the palms of his hands on either side of her face. It seemed to her that he was about to say something, but he didn't. She went to the stove and poked at the slab of meat, watching pink juices run into the gravy.

"I'll pack your hammer too," she said. "Just in case you miss it."

"Funny," he said.

Funny, she thought. But he wasn't even smiling. Then the kids came in, noisy, clattering, both of them trying to talk at the same time. Ted was judiciously trying to settle some dispute. He was good at that.

I found it first, dad. I swear.

No way you found it first.

Ted banged his pipe on the table like a gavel. "Come on, kids," he was saying. "It's easy to settle. It's real easy."

Emily shoved the lid back on the saucepan, wiping her palms against the sides of her jeans.

It's like this, Ted.

Like what?

I send the kids off to school. I clean up. Maybe on a good day I've groceries to pick up. Then what? What do I do then?

You talked once about a part-time job. . . .

Maybe.

She got up from the bed and crossed the darkened room to the bathroom that adjoined the bedroom. She turned on the light and absently opened the medicine cabinet, briefly catching her own reflection in the sliding mirror. What was the point in replaying a conversation? A part-time job—such as? What am I cut out for? I could sell flowers. Help kids over crosswalks after school. Peddle photographic portraits by telephone.

But if there was going to be a job, even a part-time one, it was something she would have to ease herself into in a series of steps. You stay home and raise kids and you get rusty and that rust has to be scraped away. You lose a whole lot of self-confidence and that has to be restored somehow; and the tiny insecurities—they had to be destroyed. She couldn't just go out and find a job, not immediately. She had to begin what she thought of as her restoration in small ways at first.

She stared at the contents of the cabinet. A half-used bottle of Nivea Creme. A blunt stick of Brut deodorant. A bottle of Wrinkles Away. Aqua Velva. Encare Oval Contraceptive pills. She found a new roll of toilet paper, ripped a couple of squares off, folded them over and, reaching down between her legs, wiped away a slick of sperm. The boat leaks, she thought. A slick of cold sperm. She looked at herself in the mirror a moment, then turned to the open door.

Ted was sitting up with his hands behind his head.

"It isn't the money," he said.

"What isn't the money?"

"The idea of a part-time job." He moved his head, a dark shadow against the white pillows. "We don't really need the money."

She was silent.

"It would be for you, for your sake," he said. "I know it can't be easy being round the house all the time. And the kids . . ." He sighed and she wondered if he was being condescending, if he was just patting her on the head. There's a good girl, Em. Go out. Find yourself something to pass the time. *See, Ted, if I don't do something,* anything, *I can picture myself later and what I see is a Polaroid of myself when I'm a member of the Polygrip set and my diet is Geritol on the half shell. And I don't much like it.*

She switched off the light and went back to bed.

Ted said, "Seriously. It would be good for you."

From somewhere, maybe from the freeway, there was the sound of an ambulance slashing through the night. She stared at the thin drapes through which a streetlight could be seen. The wind blew at the big oak in the front yard. She wondered how many nights she'd lain in just this position, the other half of the bed empty, and imagined shapes in the outline of the oak's branches.

Bats. Weird flying mammals. Monstrous birds.

Other things.

Sometimes something scaled down the tree, growing as it descended, taking form, sometimes it reached the ground and moved between the shadows to the front door, a claw on the handle, the handle turning, the wood splintering downstairs—

And then it was inside, standing at the bottom of the stairs and looking up through the darkness.

Night fears.

When Ted is away. When Ted is in Maine or New Hampshire or wherever his territory takes him.

Why did he have to go away so often?

She turned towards him, laying her bare arm against his shoulder, thinking about the lovemaking that had taken place only a few minutes ago, how strangely urgent he had been, how quick to climax, as if the act were less one of passion than of getting something out of the way. Performing a duty. She rubbed the palm of her hand over his nipple and she thought: It wasn't always like that. There were still times when he could be slow and tender.

"When you go away . . ." She paused, listening again to the wind shake the oak in a sudden frenzy of leaves rattling. "I feel lost when you go away."

He folded his hand over hers, squeezing it lightly. He didn't speak.

"I feel threatened," she said. "I don't know how to explain it."

"Threatened by what?"

She shrugged. "I don't know." She was quiet a moment. Then she laughed in a soft way. "Tell me I'm high-strung, Ted. Tell me something like that."

"You're high-strung and I love you despite it," he said.

She pressed her face against the side of his arm. Secure, she thought. Secure for the moment. For tonight. And then tomorrow he's gone. She wanted to ask him to cancel his trip, to call it off just this one time.

He said, "A job would be more practical than that class."

Ah, the class. It surprised her that he hadn't forgotten.

"What do you expect to get out of poetry writing?" he asked.

"Mainly, I expect to get out of the house," she answered. "Every Wednesday night for two whole hours. Gallivanting around night school with Emily Dickinson hidden under my coat—"

"Seriously," Ted said.

She shut her eyes. It was with a faint feeling of embarrassment that she remembered showing him, before their marriage, the folder of poems she'd written in high school. It hadn't been embarrassing back then, but now—for some reason—the memory burned her. He'd forgotten it, though. He'd forgotten that folder. The amnesiac heart.

"Look, the class is just a start, that's all. It's just a start."

Ted said nothing. She shifted her head, opened her eyes, gazed once more at the curtains. Outside, the branches changed shape again. She tried not to think of being alone in this dark room.

"Anyhow, maybe I've got some talent in that direction," she said. "Who knows? Maybe I'm a late developer."

Ted laughed quietly. She couldn't tell about the laugh. A tiny ridicule? A jibe? She watched the branches shift, rearrange themselves, shadowy against the streetlight.

Don't think about the thing coming down out of the tree, the wood breaking, the sound of quick breathing at the bottom of the stairs.

There were locks after all. Good solid locks. Ted had put them on himself. Deadbolt locks and a door-viewer.

"I could see the benefit of auto mechanics," Ted said. "Think of the savings on garage bills."

"Or carpentry," she said. "Then we could erect a trellis together in record time—"

"And get our names in the Guinness Book of Records," Ted said. *"Mr. and Mrs. Ted Allbright of West Pastorville, New York, completed a garden trellis in eighteen point six minutes."*

She laughed. She liked it when there were still echoes of the old Ted, the one who had a sense of humor. But then he sighed, as if something troubled him, and she knew what was coming next. The part he didn't like. She waited, tensed.

"Are you still going ahead with that other project?" he said.

"Why not?"

"We went through the reasons before."

"I haven't forgotten your reasons, Ted." *Damn strangers in the house,* he'd said. *I don't like it. How can you trust them? How can you know anything about them?*

"But you don't consider them valid?"

She laid her hands flat on her belly, feeling the outline of the

Caesarian scar left by Frankie's birth. It felt strangely puckered, shriveled.

"I've had three calls already," she said. "There's quite a lot of interest in the idea of a baby-sitting cooperative—"

Ted scratched his head in the dark. "Look, you pin up a card in some supermarket, you put your name and your telephone number on it—I mean, Christ, do you ever stop to think what's out there?"

"Tell me what's out there, Ted—"

"Some goddam weird people—"

"Admittedly—"

"And sometimes you can't tell just by looking. Sometimes they look ordinary and—"

"Come on, Ted. You don't think I could tell? Give me just a little credit, okay?"

He was silent for a long time. When he spoke again his voice was calm. "I don't like it, Emily. I don't like you getting involved. I don't want you to go ahead with it. I mean, we're talking about *strangers* looking after our kids."

She turned her face towards him and said, "I'd die before I'd let any harm come to our kids, Ted."

He sighed again. "I know," he said. "I know."

"So let's not argue about it, okay?"

"I don't *want* to argue about it."

I don't, I don't, I don't—sometimes he could come off like a Victorian husband catching his wife puffing on that newfangled horror, the cigarette. There wasn't going to be any argument. Flat and final. It was her project and she was going ahead with it. And if Ted really thought about it, if he *really* thought about it, he'd understand that the whole project was dreamed up so they could go out more together, so they wouldn't have hassles over getting sitters, so they could enjoy themselves alone sometimes. . . . She stared at the faint outline of the half-open bathroom door, listening to the rising wind, the shake of the branches, imagining the wind blowing all across the suburb, from the ring of the freeway through the outlying shopping plazas, the new concrete malls, the all-night convenience markets, across West Pastorville Park and the Little League diamond and the empty bleachers, over the stagnant surface of the old canal, blowing down Central Street and past the modernistic spire of the Catholic church, the cinema complex, the high school, the vast empty parking lots, the cloned streets of tract housing, then the railroad tracks that led south to New York City and north to Utica.

"Friends?" Ted said.

"Yeah. Friends."

He leaned forward, kissed her gently on the forehead, rumpled her hair and then turned over onto his side.

She lay for a time with her eyes open.

It was weird—weird how she could feel close to him at one moment, then distant from him the next. Marriages didn't have to sink into dull exercises in familiarity, did they? They didn't need to be like that. She turned towards him, her arm falling across his side, and she heard him moan in a way that suggested pleasure, as if he were already on the edge of some good dream.

I love you, she thought.

Tomorrow you'll be gone and then I'll be alone with my kids and the deadbolt locks.

3.

In the cafeteria at Pastorville railroad station the kids had scrambled eggs while Emily smoked a cigarette and listened to a scratchy announcement over the PA system. She couldn't make out what it was. She stubbed her cigarette, noticing how her hand shook slightly, and she looked across the room. A couple of railroad workers were joking with the pretty girl behind the cash register. The smell of fried food was sickening. She sipped her tasteless coffee and watched the kids a moment, wondering why a strange silence fell over them whenever Ted left. Insecurity, she thought. They feel his absence.

Frankie put his fork down and reached for the ketchup bottle. His eggs were already smothered in red sauce.

"Don't you think you've got enough ketchup?" Emily said. Absently, she took another cigarette from her purse.

"Where's daddy now?" Frankie asked.

"Considering he's only just left, I'd say he's about ten miles away."

Frankie set the ketchup back. He stared at Emily for a while, his forehead creased, and she thought: How like Ted he is, a perfect miniature, the same firm set of the jawline, the same eyes. Seven years of age, she thought, and he's already devised an elaborate system of private retreats, small worlds of his own making. She watched his hand pick up the fork. The motion stopped in mid-air.

"How does he get to the airport in New York?"

"He takes a cab," Emily said.

"Then he flies," Frankie said.

"Then he flies. All the way to Bangor."

Across the table Charlotte had stopped eating, her plate pushed away, the eggs unfinished. She smoothed a strand of hair from her eyes. Pale blue eyes, vulnerable, dazzling at times. Emily sometimes wondered how she and Ted could have conspired to produce this beautiful child.

"When is he coming back?" Charlotte asked.

"Thursday or Friday. He'll call."

"Will it be morning or afternoon?" the girl said.

The questions, Emily thought. Such frantic interrogations. They needed to know, then they needed to know even more. She blew out smoke, making a ring accidentally.

"Morning, I guess. He'll call and let us know."

Charlotte, changing the subject, said, "Erika Strassman's parents are getting a divorce."

"Yeah?" Emily looked at her daughter. Why had that snippet of gossip come out just then? She tried to create a picture of Erika Strassman, but all she got was a long stringy girl with black hair and skinny legs.

"Her dad's got a girlfriend," Charlotte said.

"Too bad."

"I don't think Erika cares one way or another." The girl looked down at her plate and grimaced. "Those eggs are yucky."

"They're OK," Frankie said.

"How would *you* know? With all that ketchup."

Emily turned her head in the direction of the girl at the cash register, then she thought of Ted's train—ten, twenty miles to the south by this time. She tuned out the brief argument between the kids. *I like ketchup. A blind man could tell that, Frankie.* She wondered what rivalry of blood caused these flare-ups. It was like some weird competition in which they had to assassinate each other. But even so, there was a flip side to that coin—when they could demonstrate a strange tenderness, an odd concern for one another, as if what you had beneath the strata of conflict was a kind of shy love. And at that point it touched you in an awkwardly sentimental way.

She looked at them both again. Frankie had cleaned his plate. He was drinking Coke. At this time of morning, Emily thought—the sugar and caffeine rush. She wondered if she should have refused him the drink, but sometimes it took an extraordinary amount of energy to refuse, sometimes it was simpler to say yes, smile in a glazed way, and keep the somewhat fragile peace.

Charlotte said, "Erika says the divorce will be final in a month."

"Is that right?" Emily wondered why she was coming back to this topic. A divorce between strangers. She hadn't ever met Erika Strassman's parents, so why was Charlotte returning to the subject?

"She's going to spend one month every summer with her father, I guess," Charlotte said. She sighed, shaking her head.

Emily looked at the congealing stains of ketchup on Frankie's plate. "What do you think about it?" she asked.

"The divorce?" Charlotte shrugged. "Kinda sad. But then a lot of kids in my class have divorced parents. It's nothing new."

Nothing new, Emily thought. Was it some tiny strain of insecurity? Had the kid intuited something, some touch of awkwardness between her own parents? Kids. They picked up on things you thought invisible. They encountered phantasms. They had their antennae out all the time. She reached across the table and touched the back of Charlotte's hand as if to reassure her about something. The child smiled. Frankie finished his Coke and sucked loudly through the empty straw. Emily rose, picking up her purse.

"You guys ready?"

They followed her out of the cafeteria and along the platform to the exit gate. They passed below the faint Pastorville sign which hung aslant from a rusted chain. Then they were out in the parking lot, moving towards the station wagon. There was a strange autumnal sun low in the sky, white and bleached and watery: Emily saw it reflected in the maroon paint of the wagon. She unlocked the doors and the kids scrambled in back, Frankie climbing the rear seat and crawling over the luggage space to press his face against the back window.

Then she was thinking of Ted again, she was thinking of Ted on the train, then the flight to Bangor. Four nights max. You could divide it into time segments, mornings, afternoons, nights.

Nights.

Four nights max.

Like a clue in a crossword puzzle. A strange anagram.

No ax fright sum.

Did you ever really demolish this fear of the dark? Was there a time when suddenly you just grew up and the absence of light ceased to be terrifying? Ax fright, she thought. She looked into the driving mirror, catching the kids in reflection. And what she thought of all at once were those times when you were struck by an awareness of loving, the responsibility of caring, the spooky realization that there were at least two other human beings for whom you'd die—for whom you'd really sacrifice yourself. Sometimes, when it was dark and she was alone and the kids were sleeping, she'd consider this fact: *You would lay down your life for your kids.* It seemed preposterously natural, like some biological dictate. Like something you inherited with motherhood.

Philosophy in the station wagon, she thought. She smiled at herself.

Charlotte said, "Why are you turning here?"

Emily looked through the windshield. The shopping plaza on a Sunday morning in fall. A wasteland of vacant spaces and stores filled with artificial light. Only the dried dead leaves the wind had dragged suggested a season.

"We need milk and eggs," she said. "Your basics."

From the back Frankie said, "We're out of ketchup."

She parked the car and they got out, moving towards the supermarket.

There was Muzak inside, sounding strangely warped, whole phrases bent out of shape, as if the tape were twisted. Emily pushed her cart down the aisles, avoiding a brutal sales display of candies—a mountain of M & Ms lying in a great plastic container. There were canned goods to her left, health aids to her right. She picked up a can of baked beans and held it a moment. Baked beans. She caught herself staring at the price inked on top of the can, surprising herself with the realization that she was comparing this price to one she'd seen in some other supermarket. Did it come down to this in the end —staring at the prices of goddam baked beans? Perhaps even wandering supermarkets with a tiny calculator, tapping the buttons for

God's sake. Going loony in the aisles. *This way, lady. The van's waiting outside. Nobody's going to touch your calculator, I swear.*

She picked up milk and eggs and a box of Life cereal. She threw a tube of Crest and a bar of Dove Transparent Soap into the cart. Then, as she moved towards the checkout desk, she looked around for the kids. They were standing at the toy display, picking things up, putting them down—cheap plastic toys from Taiwan or Hong Kong. She called to them, smiled at the pallid checkout girl, saw the ribbon of paper come spitting out of the register, listened to the Muzak again. A bland infiltration of the eardrums.

She paid, took her change. Then she carried her bag to the exit, pausing to look at the community bulletin board. You could learn a lot from these tiny cards, she thought. You could learn about loneliness, the lack of money, or how to deal with a venereal disease. If you were fat you could join a club and shed pounds fast. If you smoked too many cigarettes, then you joined an encounter group dedicated to the kicking of a bad habit. *I can see the future. Call me for a private appointment. 436-4567.* Somewhere in the suburb, Jesus, a soothsayer. *Several sets of unused false teeth for sale. Going out of business.* She tried to imagine a drawer in somebody's attic stuffed with dentures. Did you try them on for size? *Must sell 1967 Mustang. Sacrifice. Leaving the district.* This written in a wretched hand that suggested someone with hasty fugitive intentions. *Make offer on unused baby clothes, crib, etc.* Unused, she thought. Something sad in there, some small cry.

She searched for her own card. She scanned the board for the one she'd left there about a week ago. But she couldn't see it. She felt a moment of anxiety, as if the disappearance of the card were of some great importance. But it wasn't important at all. She turned and saw a young man moving just behind her, a grocery clerk in an apron. He had a glorious case of acne and his glasses were thick, magnifying his eyes.

"I had a card here," she said.

The young man stopped and stared unblinkingly at the board. She looked at his name tag. Safeway, it said, and beneath it the name Jack.

"I don't see it now," she said. "Do the cards get changed regularly?"

The clerk said, "Ah, the thumbtack phantom strikes again."

"The who?"

The clerk took off his glasses and rubbed them on his apron and looked at Emily. "People are always stealing the tacks," he said. "They come in, write out a card, then they just take the tacks from some other card and throw it away so they can put up their own. If yours is missing why don't you write out a new one?"

She found a blank card and a Bic pen attached to the wall by a length of rotted string. She wrote the message out the way she had done before, took the thumbtacks from the soothsayer's card, and stuck her own into the soft board. Satisfied, she stepped back. It was placed between *Electric Weed Trimmer For Sale, Hardly Used* and a printed pamphlet of a religious nature, which said: *Are Ye Tired And Heavy Laden?* Sure I am, she thought. Sure. Then she called the kids and they went out through the automatic doors to the parking lot.

The thumbtack phantom, she thought.

What a weird notion.

4.

She stared at the closed door at the end of the landing and for a long time she didn't move, she was strangely conscious of herself as if from a point overhead, as if she were observing herself through a flawed telescope, seeing her own body staring at the closed door, noticing how tiny she seemed, how small and inadequate. From the corner of her eye she could see inside her father's bedroom. His mouth hung open in sleep. His black glasses lay on the bedside table propped up against a glass of stale water and a collection of prescription bottles. From beneath the bedsheet a thin white leg protruded. A wasted leg, beneath the flesh of which thick veins stood out.

She moved forward a little way, passing under a framed photograph which she glanced at quickly even though she knew it by heart, even though she knew it in each solitary detail. The dappled shadows cast by a tree over Charlie's face; the way Charlie was smiling. The sunglasses perched at the end of Nick's nose, like two old coins balanced there.

A photograph of another time.

She tried to remember where and when it had been taken, but the

memory was confused now. A park someplace, somewhere in the
area; a year ago, even more than that. She moved to the open door
of her own bedroom and looked inside. The unmade bed. The desk
at the window. A capped fountain pen. A glass paperweight set on
top of a drawing Charlie had done in her kindergarten class. And she
remembered all at once the words she'd written in her diary last night
—last night, the night before, the night before that; time had collapsed, had become incoherent—she remembered the pen flying
across blank paper, the words taking black shape as if her hand were
out of control: *There isn't any justice. Not really. There just isn't
anything worth a damn anymore. Nothing to make the effort worth-
while. Nothing. Nothing left to lose in the whole world.* She shut her
eyes tightly and heard her father moan in his sick room. Maybe he
was having a dream. A bad dream. Something terrible. Like a dream
of blue water, a dream of a young child. She hoped it was something
as bad as that. The sound stopped.

She forced herself to go as far as the closed door, afraid to turn
the handle, afraid to enter Charlie's world. Slowly, she thought. I
must go inside slowly.

She turned the doorknob a little way. There was another sound
now, coming from a place outside the house, the siren of a fire engine
flying past. A dark red sound, a wail. She waited for silence.

She twisted the handle, the lock clicked back. The door opened a
little way. For no good reason she was thinking now of Spassky, that
dark brown office with the white rug and the Naugahyde chairs—but
no sofa: weren't they supposed to have a sofa? She wanted to turn
Spassky out of her mind, not to think about him. *You never get over
it. I wouldn't delude you about that and I wouldn't want you to
delude yourself. It stays with you now and for the rest of your life.
The problem lies in coping.* Spassky, with his round staring eyes, the
curly hair that lay thick on his back collar. What the hell did he
know about *anything?*

She pushed the door wide and went inside the room. There was a
shelf of soft toys, pandas with glass eyes, stuffed bears, a giraffe with
a twisted neck. They seemed to be waiting for something in their frozen fashion. There was a set of picture books. *Playbook for Small
Fry. Things To Do Activity Book. Know Your Neighborhood.* She
crossed the floor, the circular orange rug, and she touched the toys,
her fingers drifting over surfaces.

On the shelf was a framed picture of Charlie on her fifth birthday, the conical hat above the yellow hair, a background of party favors, a half-eaten cake on a table.

She turned to look at the drawn curtains. Tumbling clowns and seals that balanced balls imprinted on bright cotton. She opened the curtains slowly and gazed down into the back yard.

The swimming pool.

Scummy green water. Dead leaves, sodden twigs, scraps of blown paper floating on a still surface. The white sun reflected dully.

Charlie, she thought.

Was it just dreaming? Dreaming of a cry in the dark?

She couldn't take her eyes from the pool. It held her, trapped her. For a moment she could see herself thrashing around in the murky water, her mouth filled with scum, her arms flailing and her legs, in a sudden panic, kicking upwards. And then she heard the fire engine again and the picture disintegrated. She dropped the curtain edge and turned to the narrow bed with the brass rails and the smooth pastel sheets.

She sat down on the bed.

Charlie, she thought.

Say something to me. Say anything.

Anything you like. It doesn't matter.

Dear sweet Charlie.

She heard her father calling her name, then the sound of a water glass being rapped on his bedside table. She didn't answer. I can't go to him, she thought. I can't go inside that room, the smells of sickness and decay and urine, the sick room, the dying room. She didn't want to look at his blind red eyes. She didn't want to see him turn his face towards the door, tilting it slightly in that strange vulnerable way of the blind. No, goddamit, no.

She closed the door of the child's bedroom and she went along the landing to her own room, ignoring the knock of the glass and the urgent sound of her own name being called. She stood over the desk and looked first at her diary, the pages moving in the breeze, then at the drawing beneath the paperweight. It was a sticklike figure who lacked proportion, dimension. In childish block letters there were the words: My Dad.

My dad, she thought.

She slid open the center drawer of the desk and removed some sheets of stationery, a box of envelopes, some paperclips, unpaid bills. The revolver, Nick's revolver, lay in the bottom of the drawer. She picked it up and she carried it into her father's room. The smells struck her immediately, like they always did. She wanted to smash the window open, let clean cold air flow into the stale passages of the room.

The revolver hung in her hand, loosely against her thigh.

"I've been hollering for you," he said, struggling to sit upright against his pillows. "Don't you hear?"

"I heard," she said. "I was resting."

"Resting?" He shook his head. The redness of his eyes, which seemed to have been forced back into his skull, disgusted her. "You weren't resting. I heard you. You were in *her* room. I heard you, I always hear you. *Always.*"

Always, she wondered.

"I'm hungry," he said.

Put your glasses on, she thought. For God's sake hide your eyes.

"I'm hungry," he said again. "I could lie here and starve, all you care."

She raised the revolver and pointed it directly at his head. He must have sensed something because he turned his face, blindly trying to locate her in the room, to fix her position.

"What the hell're you doing," he said. "What the hell're you up to?"

"Nothing," she said. She looked down the barrel of the gun, positioning the blind man against the sight. "Click," she said. "Click click click."

He reached out for his water, found the glass, sipped from it. "What are you talking about? Goddamit."

"Nothing," she said. "I'm not talking about anything."

She felt a strange sense of exultation. And behind that, like a shadow, like something masked by gauze, a form of apprehension.

"You going to fetch me something to eat?" he said.

"Sure. Sure I am."

"You want me to say please?" he said. "OK. I said it. Please."

She said nothing. She stared at the glass of water, the black glasses, the medications. The gun was suddenly a weight in her hand.

Her father turned in the bed, still struggling with his pillows, trying to make himself comfortable. When he was perfectly still he moved his face towards her, so that it seemed he was actually seeing her, looking at her. "Where's that husband of yours?" he said.

She didn't answer.

"Nick's left you, has he?"

She was silent for a time, listening to the ticking of an alarm clock in the room, the hapless buzzing of a fly against the window.

"He left," she said.

"Doing himself a favor," her father said.

"I'll get you some food," she said. She turned towards the door.

Her father said, "And no fancy spices either, mind. You know what I'm saying?"

In the doorway she paused. She heard it suddenly, a noise she couldn't mistake, a sound she had listened to in her dreams, in her waking moments, a sound that froze her where she stood. Charlie, she thought. Dear Christ. Charlie crying from behind that closed door. Her heart stopped. Her pulses became still. The blood ceased to run in her veins. She was cold. Cold to the bone.

She ran out of the bedroom, staring for a moment along the landing at the child's room, the white door shut tight. No. No, she thought. Why was she so tormented in this way? Why was she plagued by this? It was over and done with—

The crying stopped.

She stood alone on the landing, conscious of the revolver in her hand, conscious of her father's breathing in the room at her back, conscious of her own solitude, her own mad grief. *We can't go on together like this, baby.* Why not? I don't understand, Nick. *It's between us, all the fucking time, it's always fucking there.* I still don't understand. *I feel like I've been breathing bad air all my life, baby, and now I'm choking to death. Can't you see that?*

Her father said, "You're still there. I can hear you."

She didn't speak. She stared at the closed door. It isn't right, she thought. It isn't right, it isn't just. Something happens and suddenly your life is dead, everything is gone, you've got nothing left but echoes, empty echoes, a great black hole where you used to be. And that was all wrong, totally wrong.

She went back inside her own bedroom and put the revolver into the drawer, slamming it shut.

She looked at the kid's drawing again.

And then she noticed alongside it the tiny square of white cardboard covered with neat handwriting and she thought: Other lives continue, while mine has to stop.

There was no justice in that.

None.

She picked the card up and folded it neatly down the center and stuck it in the drawer beside the gun.

5.

Emily was reading a book, a novel of suspense, when she heard the sound of the front doorbell. The chimes, installed by Ted, simulated the sound of Big Ben. *Dee dah dee dah.* She put the book down and went to the door, peering out through the viewer. It was Mrs. De-Santis, who lived next door. Emily drew the bolt and opened the door. The kids, ensnared by some Sunday night network crap in the TV room, were silent for once.

Outside, Mrs. DeSantis stood clutching the collar of her coat against her throat.

"Hi," she said.

Mrs. DeSantis smiled. "I don't mean to trouble you, Emily."

"Come on in." Emily held the door wide and the other woman, still holding her collar as if she feared a display of flesh as much as the cold night air, stepped into the living room. "Can I get you anything? Coffee? Tea?"

Mrs. DeSantis shook her head. She always spoke in a whisper, like she was afraid of giving offense. Maybe, Emily thought, the sound of her own voice startles her. After all, she lived alone and her only pastime was that of spring-cleaning the house every other day. A life without contact. You wouldn't need to talk loudly.

"You want to sit down?" Emily said.

"No, this is fine," the other woman said.

A complaint was coming. Emily could sense it. It would be offered almost apologetically, the voice growing more and more hushed until it was almost inaudible. What have my kids destroyed now? she wondered. Mrs. DeSantis looked round the room, a vague expression of disapproval on her face. Ah, Emily thought, she doesn't like the un-tidiness—books lying open, cluttered ashtray, shoes kicked off and lying on the rug, pillows scattered.

"Is something wrong?" Emily said.

"Not wrong, not really," the woman said. She fingered her listless colorless hair a moment. She moved her lips and her upper dentures made a clicking noise. "One of your kids trampled through my shrubbery, that's all."

"Which one?"

"I didn't really see. It was almost dark."

Emily shrugged and sighed. "Kids," she said.

"I had three of my own and I know you can't keep them in strait-jackets, for sure," said Mrs. DeSantis.

"I'll talk with them," Emily said.

"It's just that they ought to have some, well, respect for the property of other people," the neighbor said. "It's harmless, I know. And they don't mean anything wrong."

Emily watched her neighbor for a time, wondering about her life, that immaculate isolation, that spotless, sterile house. The woman even looked vaguely waxen herself, like she had built up an accumulation of her own floor polish over the years. Mrs. DeSantis lowered her hand from her coat and Emily could see the floral nightgown underneath.

"Kids like you to be firm with them," the woman said quietly. "I think they expect it. Structure, I mean."

"Yeah, I'm sure," Emily said.

Mrs. DeSantis was silent a moment. Then she said, "Your husband away?"

Emily nodded. "Business."

"Mine used to go away a lot," the other woman said.

Emily didn't know what to say. She felt the way she did when Jehovah's Witnesses stood on her doorstep and talked about God, or fresh young Mormons tried to convert her, young men with shaved faces and shaved minds, who grinned at you politely, despite your sins, and talked of life and eternity as if they had been equipped with looped tapes in some Salt Lake City basement. The quiet flow of people who came to the door selling God or encyclopedias or Girl Scout cookies or flowers for Moonies: she never knew what to say to any of them. Even those double-knit realtors who wanted to know if you were thinking of selling. Maybe there's a mark on the sidewalk, she thought, a coded sign saying that this house is an easy touch.

"Still," said Mrs. DeSantis. "It's water under the bridge."

Emily picked up her book and stared at the crumpled empty cigarette pack she'd used as a mark. "I'll talk to them. I really will. You have my word."

Mrs. DeSantis went to the door. "You don't mind, do you?"

"Of course I don't. Kids oughtn't to be out trampling shrubbery anyhow."

"Right," said the other woman.

Emily opened the door for her. Outside, the night was without wind, the oak tree perfectly still. She looked along the quiet street, the pale blue windows in which TVs flickered, the parked cars gleaming in a dull way under street lamps. Mrs. DeSantis turned her collar up again.

She stared at Emily for a time, then she said, "Good night. And thanks."

"Don't mention it," Emily said, closing the door, sliding the bolt back in place. Killers of shrubbery, she thought. Assassins of front yards. She went inside the TV room and stared at the TV a moment. *You didn't hold the mayo, Mel,* somebody was saying. She clapped her hands together for attention. The kids didn't look at her. Mesmerized, she thought. Hypnotized and paralyzed by a world in which Bugs Bunny, deodorants, mouthwashes, Walter Cronkite, Mork and Mindy all had equal time. What did that do to their brains? What did it do to their sense of reality?

She clapped her hands again and said, "Bedtime, kids."

Charlotte was curled on the rug. Frankie ate potato chips from a bag. They looked at her simultaneously, ready to complain.

"School tomorrow," she said. "And if you don't go to bed now I intend to interrogate you both in the matter of running through Mrs. DeSantis's shrubbery. OK?"

Charlotte said, "Why do I have to go to bed when Frankie does? I'm older. I should be able to stay up longer."

"No way," Frankie mumbled through the potato chips.

"Don't talk with your mouth full," Charlotte said.

Frankie got up, blew air into the empty bag, then smacked it with the palm of his hand. There was a short explosion. Frankie laughed.

"I've asked you not to do that, Frankie," Charlotte said.

Emily sighed, the explosion ringing in her ears. "Bedtime," she said again. "Both of you."

They went reluctantly out of the room. Absently, she looked at the TV, at the flood of colors that fell into the darkened room. Something cracked beneath her feet. A potato chip. She bent down and gathered the broken pieces, then dropped them into the wastebasket. On the TV four apparent housewives were giggling like maniacs over the merits of Fruit of the Loom detergent. They must have been imbibing the stuff, Emily thought. You couldn't explain that euphoria in terms of soap powder alone. The picture changed. Somebody said, *Can I ask you a really personal question, Fran?*

Sure. Go ahead.

What do you really think about disposable douches?

"They're wonderful," Emily said aloud. "They just changed my whole life." She killed the picture: blessed silence. She left the TV room and stood at the bottom of the stairs, looking up. She could hear the kids, the sound of running water, the faint noise of a brush moving quickly over teeth. Then she went into the kitchen and drew the bolt on the back door. Secure, she thought. Everything shipshape.

The telephone on the counter was ringing.

The sound startled her. She picked up the receiver.

Ted said, "Were you asleep?"

"Not yet," she said. "How are you? Good trip?"

"Well, I made it to Bangor in one piece. It's damned cold up here."

His voice faded in and out and there was a lot of crackling across the line. She twisted the telephone cord around her wrist and leaned against the counter.

"Everything OK?" he said.

"I just put the kids to bed."

"Kiss them for me," Ted said. "I'll be in this motel for two days. Let me give you the number."

He always gave her a telephone number when he was away, in the event of what he had once called "a real emergency." It was a circumstance that had never arisen. She had all kinds of numbers scrawled in the margins of old bills, the backs of envelopes, on scraps of paper. Sometimes she wondered what would constitute a real emergency for Ted. She found the stub of a pencil and wrote the number down on the back of a drugstore bag. The motel was called the Brewer Lodge, part of the chain Ted worked for. She tried to imagine his room—the statutory double bed, a TV, a bad painting of some brokenhearted clown. She tried to imagine him alone in this room. Stupid—this petty recurring fear. He *was* alone.

Ted said, "When I leave here I'll be two more days at a place called Lincoln. The Penobscot Motor Inn. You got that?"

She bit on the end of the pencil. "I got it."

"Call, OK? If there's anything . . ." He didn't finish his sentence.

"I'll call if I need to," she said.

"OK."

Silence on a bad line. For a moment she thought the connection had been cut. Tell me, Ted. Just say you love me. Just say it. She uncurled the cord from her wrist. "Are you still there?" she said.

"Sure," he answered. "Don't forget. Kiss the kids."

"I won't," she said.

"Love you."

"Love you too," she said.

She put the receiver down. The Brewer Lodge, she thought. Why couldn't he have a normal nine-to-five job anyhow? Why couldn't it be something simple where he caught a train at 8:20 and came back on the 5:36? *Love you. Love you.* It had sounded so shallow somehow without the "I." It had sounded meaningless. But then he'd never been much good at intimacies over telephones anyhow.

She turned off the kitchen light. She checked the bolt on the front door. Then she climbed the stairs. The kids were already asleep in their own rooms. She kissed them both quietly, marveling at the depths of their sleep, at the peaceful expressions on their faces. When they slept they seemed angelic—and what she remembered all at once was how, when Charlotte had been a baby, her most terrible fear was that she'd die in her crib; how, if Charlotte overslept, she'd go to the crib and listen for the sound of the child's breathing. And always there was the same light-headed, ridiculous feeling of relief when she heard the faint noise of the baby quietly taking in air and just as quietly expelling it.

She went into her own bedroom where she drew the curtains. The light from the bedside lamp was thin, throwing a huge misty shadow of her upon the wall. She undressed, watching the shadow. She lay down and closed her eyes but she wasn't sleepy. She listened to the night sounds of the house—inexplicable, unless you were Ted and understood joists and beams and the concept of things *settling*. A sound on the stairs, as if a foot were pressing down on the step. A slight movement in the attic, a creak of some kind.

Childish, ridiculous.

Yet somehow it was easier to personify these things than to think of them in Ted's terms. Somehow it was simpler to imagine a figure frozen halfway up the stairs, or some indeterminate shape in the attic, something moving in the dust, than to rationalize everything away in terms of *the house settling*. Christ, the house was more than ten years old anyhow—and how long did it need before it settled once and for all?

Go on, Emily. Spook yourself out. Work yourself up into a state. She turned over onto her side and gazed at the bedside lamp. The bed was a wasteland: she stretched her arm across the vast empty space, thinking of absences. Ted's uncrumpled pillow. The Brewer Lodge, she thought. What did he do anyway? Northeast Area Manager for VacationEase Industries. (VacationEase: marketing directors and advertising men must have burned the midnight oil to come up with that clinker.) And what did that entail? He made spot checks on the motels and resorts that were part of the great VacationEase complex; he turned up, like some knight of the highways, and looked over the accounts, analyzed personnel needs, solved problems, and presumably saw to it that there were bars of soap and a sufficient number of towels in every unit.

She tossed the sheet aside and turned her face towards the window. Outside, the street lamp forced a single unchanging pattern out of the oak branches. Still. Very still. Nothing lived in those branches, not even a goddam squirrel. Zero. She looked at the closed door and heard from somewhere the faint sound of something liquid, like a faucet leaking slowly or a tank finally filling. She clenched her hands together and thought that she could be the character in some awful gothic fiction. *Emily lay motionless, conscious only of her own heartbeat. Something moved restlessly back and forth in the flagstoned corridor. She swallowed hard. It could only be the dark-featured Sir Guthrie, the owner of Allbright Hall, come to claim what he thought was rightfully his.*

She hoped Sir Guthrie would kick the door down and have his way with her, which was what happened in gothic fictions after all.

Damn. Sometimes you irritated yourself beyond belief.

She got up from the bed and went into the bathroom. She splashed cold water on her face and thought: Be realistic, Em. The house is tight and locked. Nothing can get in. All is well. Ten-thirty, Sunday night in the suburb of West Pastorville, and all is well. Oyez, oyez.

She looked at her face in the mirror and smiled: Nothing reduced you so quickly to sheer absurdity as the sight of your own reflection. She ran her fingers through her reddish hair and studied the surface of her skin in the glass. Only one new wrinkle, and that beneath the eye: but the circles were darker, deeper.

She opened the cabinet and took out a bottle and spilled a sleeping tablet into her hand. She looked at the little red and yellow capsule a moment: a dead sleep guaranteed. Dead and dreamless. She stuck it into her mouth and drank some water from the toothbrush glass. A real neat suburban salve. She imagined the medicine cabinets of West Pastorville filled with all kinds of uppers and downers, a cornucopia of drugs in all sizes and colors.

She went back and lay down on the bed. She heard Frankie coughing in his sleep. The house, slowly, became silent. The Dalmane hit her gently, a hammer muffled in a thick velvet glove, and she shut her eyes.

Dreamless.

Maybe not.

Maybe there was a dream, maybe it was the dream that forced her awake, her throat dry, her body cold, her knees clenched, like something had disturbed her: a memory of the telephone ringing down in the kitchen, the bell intruding on her sleep.

She sat up, crouched. It wasn't ringing now. She listened a moment but the flavor of the dream, if there had been one, was lost to her. She lay back down and closed her eyes.

She overslept and when she woke the kids had already gone to school and the kitchen was filled with their messy attempts at making their own breakfasts—eggshells, spilled Rice Krispies, puddles of milk on the Formica surface. Her head was vaguely sore; the aftermath of the sleeping pill. She surveyed the debris, guilty at not having risen to see the kids off, mildly relieved that she'd slept through their morning clamor, and stared at the pale gray sky of morning from the kitchen window. Rain clouds, driven by wind, flew like misshapen galleons. Coffee, nicotine, she thought: and the heart is started for the day. Then she would drive over to old Pastorville and fill in her registration forms at the community college. She poured water into the Mr. Coffee and plugged it into the wall. She heard it begin to thrust hot water through the coffee basket—but she couldn't wait; she lit the first cigarette of the day.

Then the telephone rang.

She picked up the receiver and a friendly voice said, "I saw your ad in the supermarket."

The fourth call, Emily thought. She felt good about it.

"Can you give me some more information?" the voice said.

"Our first meeting is scheduled for tomorrow night, my house," Emily said. "Eight o'clock. Can you come?"

There was a moment of hesitation. Then: "I'd like to. I'd like to very much."

"Let me give you the details about how to get here," Emily said.

"I've got a pencil," the woman said. "Go ahead."

As she spoke, Emily watched the clouds break and a slow rain start to fall, drizzling at first and then growing, filling the sky, streaming across the back yard and over the slats of Ted's unfinished trellis.

Chapter Two

1.

The freeway separated West Pastorville from the old town, a kind of apartheid keeping the new suburb from Pastorville itself, which was a clutter of narrow streets, graceful houses in various states of dying—rusted eaves, bricked-up windows in high turrets, cupolas stained with the excrement of birds. When she came to Pastorville Emily always felt some passing regret, both for the way the old town had been left to deteriorate and for the fact that she herself lived in the anemic suburb, with its gridlike streets of tract housing, lack of atmosphere, its sense of concrete isolation. Once, Pastorville had been a farm produce center with a dairy that employed several hundred people—but the company had moved twenty years ago to Binghamton, taking with it the essence of the community. There were ghosts here, Emily thought: you could imagine the place as it had been, sixty or seventy years ago, whole families leaving their large houses on Sunday mornings to walk in a somber fashion to St. Jude's church. But St. Jude's was now a warehouse of secondhand furniture and tatty old items passed off as antiques; and most of the big houses had been carved up into tiny apartments.

The community college, which had once been called Pastorville Normal School—a name Emily found amusing, half-suspecting that something called Pastorville *Abnormal* School had been buried deep in the countryside—was located at the edge of town, at the place where Market Street ended near the canal. It was a Victorian building, dark and weathered red brick, and it reminded her of some penal institution. Narrow windows, bare corridors, heavy doors. She parked in the student parking lot and rushed through the rain to the main entrance, pushing the door, passing inside to the entranceway. Here and there a few students stood around, smoking, looking at schedules, talking. Strange, she thought: to be a student after so many years—oddly dislocating. She moved along the corridor, looking for the registration office. She passed under signs that said Financial Aids Office, Dean of Night School, VA Office. At the far end of the corridor she found the room she was looking for. A windowless place filled with women busy at desks, telephones ringing, fluorescent light flickering mildly. She approached the main desk, taking her papers from her purse, spreading them out on the counter. The woman behind the desk was flipping through papers with a rubber thimble over her thumb. She raised her face and smiled at Emily.

"I've come to register," Emily said.

"Night class?" the woman asked.

Emily nodded and thought: I'm categorized already, another married woman looking for something to do for an evening. Broaden your horizons, Em. Have a new outlook on life. She suddenly wondered if the night class was such a good idea after all. What the hell. What can you lose?

"I sent in my deposit," Emily said. "My name is Allbright. Emily."

The woman, momentarily touching her frizzy hair, opened a drawer and flipped through some index cards. She found what she was looking for and took it out, a small white card with Emily's name typed on it.

"One class," the woman said. "Mr. Hamilton's Creative Writing. Poetry." The woman sniffed, as though she didn't approve of the idea of such a class. Emily felt a moment of guilt and wanted to say, It's OK, really it is, somebody will be looking after my kids. The woman put the card down.

"Did you fill out the forms?" she asked.

Emily shook her head. "I thought I'd do it here while I pay for the course—"

"Fine fine fine," the woman said.

Emily took out her checkbook and wrote a check for forty-seven dollars. She gave the check to the woman, who stared at it glumly for a time before sticking it in a drawer.

"Now just do the forms," she said.

Emily spread her papers on the surface of the desk and quickly filled in the various blanks. Name and age and marital status and education. When she'd finished she slid the papers across the desk to the woman.

"Fine fine fine," the woman said, humming absently as she checked the registration. "The class is Wednesday night, seven o'clock, room eighty-three."

Emily waited for her receipt. The woman wrote very slowly, laboriously, like the completion of a receipt were an enormous effort. Emily stared across the large room, listening to the clack of electric typewriters, wondering how these women survived in this stale room with no windows.

And then somebody was standing beside her, his large square hands splayed on the counter, his face turned towards her.

"A poetry student," the man said. "Good to know you."

Emily looked at the man—conscious at first of the eyes, which were light and mocking, as if there were some private joke being played out.

"James Hamilton," the man said.

"Oh." Emily was flustered.

"I heard you signing up for my class," he said.

Emily took the receipt from the woman, tucked it into her purse, and turned away from the desk.

Hamilton said, "Have you written poetry before?"

"I wouldn't exactly call it poetry," Emily said.

"Self-effacing," Hamilton said. "Let me see if I can get it. High school. Notebooks with blue covers."

"They were red actually—"

"Red, blue, what's the difference?" Hamilton took out a pack of cigarettes, Camels, and lit one, coughing slightly over the flame of the match. "You wrote a handful of poems. You were seventeen and it seemed wildly romantic to write poetry. You didn't show them to very many people. Secret things. Right so far?"

"Close," Emily said. She smiled as Hamilton, looking like a medium in a trance—eyes closed, lips tight, brow lined—became silent for a moment.

"Nature was your favorite topic for poetry," he said. "Then you wondered about love, so you did some love poems."

"You get a prize for clairvoyance," Emily said. "What's your secret?"

"Ah." Hamilton put a finger to his lips. Emily watched him a moment, aware now of his height, of how he dwarfed her. He had a thick dark moustache; his skull was covered with strands of thinning hair. A corduroy suit of navy blue—weren't poets supposed to wear such suits anyway? A matter of image. He said, "There's no secret. We all go through those stages. Most of us anyhow. Did you bring some poetry along with you?"

Emily shook her head. "I don't know if I still have the stuff I did. Besides, I don't know if I want you to look at it."

"You still have it," Hamilton said. "Somewhere. You only need to look hard for it."

"You sound pretty certain," Emily said.

"Ninety-nine percent." He placed his hand on her shoulder and walked with her to the door. The touch felt strange to her, a moment of contact, an unexpected warmth. "Promise me you'll look for it and bring it with you Wednesday night."

"I'll try," she said.

They were in the corridor now. Somewhere a bell was ringing and there was the clatter of feet on stairways. She turned to look at him. He had taken his hand away from her shoulder. He touched his moustache with his index finger.

She said, "What happens in the class?"

"We read our work, criticize it. You haven't been in a class like that before?"

She shook her head. "We read our *own* work?"

"Sure. Does it alarm you?"

"A bit."

"Don't let it. Everybody feels the same. You'll get over it."

"That's a comfort," she said.

"Seriously." He dropped his cigarette and crushed it under his foot. "Once you get used to it you'll wonder why it troubled you in the first place. In any case, when you hear some of the shit that gets written you'll be encouraged."

"What if my own stuff is shit?"

"I'll tell you so."

"I don't know if I like the idea—"

"It doesn't matter what I say, though. I can tell somebody that their poetry stinks, but they'll go on writing it anyway because they don't believe they're bad. They think they're good because they can't see how bad they really are. Like being tone-deaf."

She gazed along the corridor. Hamilton, extending his arm, looked at his watch. "I must be off and running," he said. "See you Wednesday. Bring your poems. Don't forget."

The bell stopped ringing. She watched Hamilton, moving in long strides, blue jacket flapping in his own wake, rush towards the staircase. He turned, then he was gone. She remained still for a moment, suddenly awed by the prospect of the class. How could she drag out the specter of her adolescent self for the scrutiny of Hamilton and a room filled with strangers? The notion was quite ridiculous. What are you, Emily? A housewife, a mother—where did this poetic conceit come from anyhow? Hamilton would take one look at the poems and laugh and say: *Get back to your kitchen, lady. Your muse is out of order.*

She walked slowly out of the building and down the steps. The rain had let up a little, softening to a cold drizzle, a faint wind dragging wet leaves across the yard, the parking lot. She went in the direction of the college bookstore where she bought *An Introduction to Poetry, The Book of Forms,* and James Hamilton's collection, *Apples Without Seeds.* It had a photograph of him inside the back flap—presumably an old picture, because his hair was thicker and there wasn't a moustache. A real live poet, she thought. And what have I got but lost notebooks stuffed with kid nonsense? Dear Christ.

Inside her car she opened Hamilton's book and glanced quickly through the poems. Love poems, but not very cheerful ones, each filled with a vague sense of loss. The collection was dedicated to somebody called Deirdre. An old love affair maybe, something that didn't turn out right for Hamilton. She closed the book and sat thinking for a time. I don't have to go Wednesday. I don't have to show up. It would be easy just to let it slide. After all, what have *I* got to offer? Sweet zeros. Sweet sweet nothings. And, besides, it wouldn't matter in the long run.

Would it?

Courage, Emily, she thought. A little courage, that's all. You've been housebound so long you feel like the prisoner coming out of solitary, blinking his eyes against a sun he hasn't seen in months. You'll go, she told herself. Wednesday night, you'll go.

She started the station wagon and drove out of the parking lot, down through the narrow streets of Pastorville, then over the freeway bridge to the suburb. From the bridge she could see it spread out below her, red tiles shining in the rain, the specks of blue that were swimming pools, the geometrical patterns of the streets. Lovely West Pastorville, created from the vision of some fastidious builder, a haven of refuge for those who—like Ted and Emily—had fled the nightmare of urban life to find the kind of real peace in which you could raise your kids and build your trellises. She drove past the Northside Shopping Mall where a Sears sign was lit in the rain, past the Hospitality Cocktail Bar, skirted the edge of the new high school, then the McDonald's outlet, where the Golden Arches looked tarnished in the drizzle. When she turned into her own street, Larue Drive, she felt suddenly weary, numbed, disoriented, as if she had come to a house that was only faintly recognizable—and not her own home, not her own home at all.

She parked the wagon in the driveway and sat for a time looking at the windows. Nothing moved the whole length of the street. A shimmering dream; a street of props. What did they do here? *What did people do here?*

She got out of the wagon, taking the house keys from her purse. They lead their quiet lives, she thought.

That's what they do. That's what we all do here.

She unlocked the front door and stepped inside the living room where she stood for a long time without moving. She stared in the direction of the staircase, the steps that led upwards into shadow. And then she took off her jacket, threw it across the back of the sofa, and she opened James Hamilton's book of poems.

The clock sounded the hour; Westminster chimes.

She began to read.

2.

Shortly before the kids came home from school she went upstairs to her bedroom and took old boxes from the high shelf in the closet, looking for the folder of poems and hoping she wouldn't find it. There were all kinds of things, souvenirs she hadn't got around to throwing away—old wedding invitations (ah, the passage of time: *the marriage of Edward Allbright to Miss Emily Hart*), a menu pilfered from the Falls Hotel, Niagara, where they'd honeymooned (what the hell did I eat? she wondered), photographs of herself and Ted in their first apartment together in Brooklyn, pictures of the kids as babies, matchbook covers from various restaurants, theaters, bars; Charlotte's first handwriting, a creased piece of paper with the words Dog Can Run. Then there were letters from Ted from before the marriage. Spooky now, written in a language he no longer used. Call it love. The words were high corn but they must have meant something once: . . . *all I think about is you, and spending my life with you, for the rest of time*. The rest of time, she thought. The envelope was postmarked Atlantic City. She couldn't remember Ted ever

going there. Amnesia. She folded the letter and stuck it away, smiling. Things change. Love gives way to living together. Passion be-
comes convenience. You hit your mid-thirties and realized you'd
been married for thirteen years, then you thought of all the other
years lying ahead in the dark future, inscrutable moments of time
still to come. That first passion—when? When was that? Then she
remembered being with Ted in the loft of his parents' house in Ma-
maroneck, the parents gone somewhere for the day—a game of
bridge, that was it—she remembered Ted taking her by the hand and
leading her up the narrow stairway to the loft, she recalled the small
window with the view of water, the musty smell of the enclosed space;
then how he'd put his arms around her, how he'd undressed her
in a way she found touchingly clumsy, all fingers, hapless, inexpe-
rienced, how she'd raised her own hand slowly to him, feeling how
hard he was, how he strained for her. And what she remembered was
the way she'd trembled, going down on her knees, aware of the disarray of her own clothes, going down on her knees and opening the zipper and putting her face against him, a moment of loss and strangeness and some odd anxiety, as if she'd known then that whatever
pleasure they might have later it couldn't compete with this time in
the loft. She'd lain down with her legs parted, watching him hover
above her, seeing him come closer like some massive pale shadow
descending, covering her, entering her; and the surprised sound of
her voice, not her own voice but coming from someplace else, some
other source, a sound she'd never heard before. He'd come in one
painful shudder, his body pressed tightly against her—and what she
couldn't remember now was her own coming, or whether she'd come
at all. Funny. Funny and sad. Fucking Ted in the loft of his parents'
house.

Ted had wanted to know how many others there had been.

She told him, listing them on the fingers of one hand. Four in
all.

He wanted to know who they were. If they were any good. If she
cared about any of them. Solicitous, touched by envy, a look of hurt
and fear in his eyes: she thought she had never loved him so much as
she did then. Neither before nor since. That vulnerability, like some
transparent thing held up to a bright window.

They had all happened in her senior year at high school. Except
for one, an accountant in the office where she worked as a secretary.

A married man called Richard. The clichéd unfolding of a banal drama—an office party, too many drinks, then finding Richard driving her home, coming up into her apartment, removing her clothes, screwing her on the rug by the unlit fireplace. Then he had to catch his train back to Bridgeport in time for Christmas Eve dinner with his family. Ted had found the narrative sordid. She wished she hadn't told him, then and now. What the hell. Things like that happened, didn't they? They happened all the time. And she'd been drunk and lonely, which made it seem like nothing in retrospect.

She found the folder of poems, an old manila folder with a couple of school notebooks tucked inside. She hesitated a moment before she opened the books, staring at their dull red covers, her own handwritten name—Emily Hart—done in a romantic, elaborate scrawl, woven around by fanciful flowers inscribed in ballpoint ink. She opened the top notebook and read:

> The dark is lonely
> And I yearn for something
> The night is starless
> And I am cold for something.

Was it possible? Had she written that junk? That morbid, masochistic crap? She shut the notebook and opened the other one, flipping the pages in a quick embarrassed way. *For William,* she had written. William—but she couldn't remember his second name, only the fact that she'd lain down beside him in a field after some sporting event, a football game maybe, and the way he'd shoved her dress up and climbed up on her and come before she'd completely understood what the hell was going on. Why had she written a poem to him? She stared at the lines, conscious of her own history, of the lack of *event* in her life. A narrow life, when you considered it. An unexciting one.

> The sky is black above
> And you speak to me of love—

She squirmed, shutting the notebook.

How could she have written this? This *dreck?*

She lay on the floor, staring at the ceiling, laughing at herself. It wasn't the rhyme at the end of the lines that made her laugh, it was the sheer stupidity of remembering how she'd struggled with these idiot verses, chewing the ends of pens, tearing up drafts, laboring—as if they amounted to something. *The sky is black above/And you speak to me of love:* she rolled over onto her side, covering her mouth with her hand.

"Mom?"

Charlotte was standing in the doorway, holding a schoolbook under her arm.

"Mom? Are you OK?"

"Sure," Emily said. "Sure I am."

"What's so funny?" Charlotte smoothed fair hair from her forehead.

"Sometimes you run into things you'd forgotten and they're hilarious, that's all."

"What kinda things?"

"Just things, kid. Where's my kiss?"

The girl came across the room and Emily sat up, crosslegged. She put her arms around her daughter, squeezed her, kissed her loudly on the cheek.

"How was your day?" she asked.

"Uh." Charlotte shrugged. "Our PE teacher is a saddist."

Big words, Emily thought. "You pronounce it sadist. Not like *sad.* How come you call her that?"

"She drives us real hard," Charlotte said. "I think she gets her kicks like that. I mean, you could be laying there and sweating your brains out and she'd pull you up so you could jump over that rotten wooden horse one last time. Know what I mean?"

"Yep," Emily said. She got to her feet, staring at her daughter. "Some people, my dear, take their work very seriously."

"I suppose." Charlotte sat on the edge of the bed and was silent for a time.

"Where's your brother?" Emily said.

"He's coming," the girl said. "He wasn't exactly rushing when I saw him."

"You want some milk, cookies maybe?"

Charlotte nodded. "The school lunch was yucky. I don't believe their mashed potatoes are for real."

"Probably powdered."

"I bet they are."

Emily went to the door and stood looking down the stairs. She could hear the clock chime the half-hour. A door was closed below, something clattered on the floor, then she heard Frankie calling, "Hey! I'm home!"

Emily shouted, "You and how many others?"

"Just me." He appeared at the foot of the stairs, looking up. One sock was folded down to his ankle, the other beneath his knee.

"Sounded like the U.S. Cavalry," Emily said. She began to descend. Frankie followed her inside the kitchen, where she opened the refrigerator. She poured two glasses of milk, then laid some chocolate-chip cookies on a plate. She sat at the kitchen table, watching Frankie slide onto the seat facing her.

"Did Dad call?" Frankie said.

"Oh, yeah, last night. He said he loves you."

"Good." Frankie bit into a cookie and rotated his jaw slowly. "How is he?"

"Cold, I think," she said.

Frankie concentrated on his cookie now, washing it down with milk. Charlotte came into the kitchen, having changed from her school clothes into a pair of faded blue jeans. Emily watched her cross the floor to the table: a graceful child, even at ten, smart as a goddam whip, a real heartbreaker in the cocoon of childhood. She sat at the table, staring at her brother as he chewed.

"Some people make a lotta noise when they eat," she said. "I'm not naming names, though."

Frankie opened his mouth, which was stuffed with crumbs. "Yeah? Well, *excuse me*. Sorry for even breathing."

"Kids," Emily said. "Quit sniping."

"What's sniping?" Frankie said.

"Shooting at each other," Emily said.

"She started it," Frankie said.

"You're right." Emily turned to her daughter. "How do you answer the charges, Charlotte?"

Charlotte hung her head in an exaggerated way, holding one hand above her neck as if the palm contained a noose; she stuck her tongue out and crossed her eyes, like somebody strangled. Frankie laughed.

"You look better than usual," he said.

Emily lit a cigarette, saying, "Cookies. Milk. But no arguments. Truce, OK?"

"Truce," Frankie said.

"OK." Charlotte sipped her milk.

There was a long silence, broken only by the sound of a school bus passing along the street. When it stopped on the corner the brakes groaned; the sound reminded Emily of chalk screaming on a blackboard. She puffed on her cigarette, then stubbed it out and poured some of that morning's coffee, which tasted stewed, grim.

"Why can't we see a movie tonight?" Frankie said.

"Who said we can't?" Emily looked at her son. The face, only now beginning to lose the shapelessness of early childhood, was becoming set, the jaw firm like Ted's, the small expressions of determination like mirror images of his father.

"They're showing *Bad News Bears Go to Japan*," Frankie said.

Charlotte groaned. "Count me out," she said.

"What else is showing?" Emily said.

Frankie thought a moment. "Something called Phant something—"

"*Phantasm*," Charlotte said. "A horror movie."

"Ugh." Emily folded her hands on the Formica surface.

"Don't you like horror movies?" Charlotte asked.

"Only when your father is home."

Charlotte made a pattern with her index finger in the cookie crumbs. "I guess," she said.

"Can we see *Bad News Bears* then?" Frankie asked. He was hopping up and down on one foot, excited.

"Sure," Emily said. "If Charlotte agrees to come."

"Do I *have* to?"

"I don't want you staying here alone," Emily said.

"Why? I could read. Watch TV. Something."

"Nope," Emily said. "We go together or we don't go at all."

Charlotte made a face. "I hate those baseball things," she said.

"They're fun," Frankie said.

"Oh, sure—"

"They *are*. You'll love it. Really."

Charlotte got up from the table. "OK. OK. I'll go. I'll suffer, little brother, but I'll go."

"I think your sister deserves a kiss for her wonderful sacrifice, Frankie. Don't you think so?"

"Yuck," Frankie said.

"Double yuck," Charlotte remarked.

They stared at one another, smiling. Emily got up and put the empty dish and the two glasses in the sink. Kisses were rare, she thought. Instead of touching they had devised the routine of Yuck and Double yuck, a substitute form of affection. It was something. It was better than nothing.

She heard the back door open and she turned to see the two kids moving outside, circling Ted's unfinished trellis as if it were an alien thing that had landed from some far galaxy. As well it might be, she thought.

She watched them through the rain for a while, then she drew the door shut.

3.

She couldn't get her eyes used to the dark, blinded by the bright flickering images that fell into black spaces, slivers and oblongs and sparks of light; and then the pain was gnawing in her head like some small sharp-toothed animal. She stretched her hand out in front of herself, stumbling forward until she encountered something hard. She bent, inclined her head, found the nearest vacant seat, shut her eyes— an old trick, because when you opened them again you could see in the darkness. The sound coming from the screen was a jumble of irritating noises, people shouting at each other and their voices scratching back and forth like buzzsaws over hard wood. She opened her eyes.

That actor's name, what was it?

Curtis. Tony Curtis. Except he wasn't dark-haired and beautiful anymore. She sat forward on the edge of her seat, straining through the dark, wondering why she'd come here in the first place—not for the picture, not for that, it didn't make the least sense to her. But then, she'd been sitting in her car, watching the house, just looking at it, wondering whether she'd go inside when the time came—and the door had opened and several figures passed under the yellow light to the station wagon. A woman—it had to be Mrs. Allbright, the one she'd spoken with on the telephone—followed by two kids; then the wagon had been backed out of the driveway and she'd followed it, followed it in a mindless kind of way to the parking lot outside the cinema. After that she'd come inside, bought a ticket, and now she sat in this cold half-empty theater, puzzled by lights, by sounds. She sat in the cold darkness, her eyes used to the place now, and she saw them sitting several rows in front of her. Three of them.

Three. Intact. Sharing—

Tony Curtis was saying: *Leave the arrangements to me, kids. You'll be rich. Rich!* She leaned back, satisfied that she had located them, and she stared at the screen. The pain knocked against the inside of her skull, like something hard pressing upon the soft part of the brain, finding a hole in the bone and boring through. She put her fingers to the sides of her neck and massaged herself lightly, as if this might do something to help. She hadn't brought her pills, but they didn't help anyway. Nothing helped. Nothing. She sat forward again restlessly. She remembered the first time she'd ever brought Charlie to a movie, how the three of them—herself and Nick and the kid—had shared popcorn and soda and laughed all the way through the picture and how she'd turned sometimes to watch the bright reflected light in Charlie's eyes. . . . Gone. Gone. All that warmth. Just gone.

She stared at the three people farther down.

She felt something hot begin in her neck and spread upwards until it had crossed the scalp, the rush of blood maybe, a violent thrust of her own blood. An attendant came by, flashing his light past her face briefly. She stood up to let other people come into the row, then she sat again. She couldn't stand the picture. She couldn't take the noise.

She moved her moist palms together nervously, then rubbed them against the side of her coat. Now somebody was getting up, and instead of three there were only two, one of them had risen and was walking up the dark aisle. She sank into her seat, watching.

The feeling of intense heat grew stronger. Sweat, so much damn perspiration: why? The figure was approaching, tiny against the light of the large screen. She turned her head as the figure went past and then she got up from her seat and went along the aisle, keeping some distance from the other person, following her out through the door and into the foyer.

A girl.

A child.

Yellowy hair hanging from under a dark beret.

She was faint for a second, leaning against the wall, absently pushing her foot down on the pedal that sent an arc of water rising from the drinking fountain. And then it seemed to her that everything stopped suddenly, everything came to a dead halt, movement and sound and light—everything frozen in some monstrous tableau, actors silenced and stilled on some vast stage. Herself too, her pulses, her heart, the working of her lungs. Nothing moved. It was as if everything that suggested life had just spilled away. She saw the child motionless in the doorway of the room that said Ladies. Her small hand was pressed against the wood. Nothing happened.

Then the door swung shut, there was the noise of popcorn popping in the foyer, the laughter of somebody taking tickets, a cash register ringing. She felt a constriction at the back of her throat but she went forward anyway, her mouth dry, her muscles stiff—she went forward, passing through the same door as the child had done. It closed behind her and she was in a room of stunning white tiles, cubicles, sinks. An air purifier made a shrill electric noise high on the wall.

She saw herself in the mirror. In the artificial light she looked ghostly, dreadful, black circles beneath the eyes, the mouth a tight terrible line, a slash. She passed the reflection and stood looking at the cubicle doors.

The child had gone inside one of them.

Then in the space between the door and the floor she saw the girl's feet dangle. She heard something—recognizing it after a moment as the sound of the girl singing quietly to herself, her voice tuneful, lyrical. *Everybody's gone surfin', surfin' USA. . . .* The tune stopped, the toilet was flushed, and she turned away and began to run cold water over her hands, closing her eyes, opening them again—watching the girl in the reflection of the mirror as she came out of the cubicle, wiped her fingers on the towel, and then went towards the door.

The door opened, swung shut.

The toilet was suddenly silent, chill.

She caught the edge of the sink to steady herself.

And then she couldn't help herself, she was crying, twisting her mouth, watching her own image break up in the mirror, she was crying and the pain was hurting worse than ever before and the echoes were stronger, sharper, more accusing than they'd ever been. It was more than grief, more than that lonely emptiness, more than the agonizing sense of reaching out for something no longer there and closing your fist over thin space, feeling the flimsy texture of nothing, of nothingness.

She held a tissue to her face, fighting for control.

But when she dried her eyes and checked her face in the mirror all she could see was the girl floating past, again and again, a ghost in glass.

She rushed out of the toilet, crossed the foyer, and pushed the glass front doors open, and then she was quickly moving over the parking lot to where she'd left her car. She got inside, fumbled with the keys, started the car and backed it up out of the lot and on to the street.

She didn't know how long she drove, couldn't remember stopping the car or getting out of it again, but the next thing she knew she was sitting in an empty all-night doughnut shop with a cup of coffee in front of her, a cigarette burning in an ashtray, a book of matches lying open on the table. She clenched her hands together to try and stop the shaking. For God's sake, calm, calm yourself. She looked at a dark reflection of herself in the window of the doughnut shop, aware of the girl leaning with her elbows on the counter at her back. The door swung open and a man came in, a fat man in a plaid jacket and a cap with earflaps.

She raised the coffee to her lips.

She sipped, set the cup down, looked briefly in the direction of the man who was balancing coffee and several doughnuts as he made his way to the table next to her. He was going to say something to her; she sensed it. He was going to lean across and ask for the sugar or something, and she wished he wouldn't.

Think.

Just think.

You're a wreck. You look ruined. You feel wasted deep inside.

Take some deep breaths, relax, let it all go.

Just relax.

She ran the tip of a finger round the rim of the cup.

A girl in the toilet of a cinema. A girl with yellow hair.

Lots of girls had hair that color. There were always resemblances. You couldn't help seeing correspondences. It was perfectly natural. Wherever you went, you couldn't help likenesses. Don't think about it, forget it, let your mind drift elsewhere, anywhere.

She stared at the surface of the coffee where some oleaginous matter floated, a tiny rainbow of colors. And what she remembered all at once was something she hadn't thought about in years, what she remembered was the day, three years after Charlie's birth, when she'd lost the baby in her womb. A normal day in the beginning, an ordinary day in the third month of a pregnancy, and then without warning the attack of stomach cramps, the hot and cold flashes that traveled the surface of her skin, the sudden contractions—and then warm liquid slithering down the insides of her legs and Nick saying, *It's blood, it's blood, I've got to get you to a doctor,* but a doctor was pointless then because it was too late, nobody could have restored the fetus that dropped from her body like some misshapen intruder, a trespasser, and she remembered looking at it, a lump of bloody clay, of soft wax, membranous and scummy, not human, not even remotely human, nothing she could love or feel sorry for, she remembered looking at it with disgust, aware of her own body's inadequacy to carry this thing the full term. And then Nick had covered it with a newspaper, crying as he did so, his hands covered with blood and mucus like the hands of a butcher. And later there was the physician saying, *Another one would be too much of a risk, frankly.*

Frankly.

She hadn't thought of that in a long time. She hadn't let that crawl into her mind for a long, long time. That kid would have been six or seven by this time. If it had lived.

She moved towards the door. She stepped out, turning up the collar of her coat against the chill of the autumn night. Then she went towards her car. Forget, she thought, unlocking the door, getting in behind the wheel. Forget Mrs. Allbright, her kids, her home, her Tuesday night meeting: you wouldn't belong there, you would be a counterfeit, something false, and everybody would be able to tell just by looking.

They'd know just from the look on your face.

Everybody would.

She rolled her window down, driving home by way of the old canal road, a blacktop that was pitted and pockholed and collapsed in places, like a road that had been captured in a war. She could smell the stench of stagnant water and sometimes hear the motion of the reeds or the sound of water breaking as some night animal disturbed the placidity.

4.

Frankie stood in the open door of Charlotte's bedroom, scratching his left calf with the toes of his right foot. He was balanced like an agitated stork. Charlotte, already in bed, was flicking the pages of a book, an illustrated edition of *Treasure Island*. She didn't look up at Frankie.

Frankie said, "Good movie, huh?"

"Oh, yeah. Terrific." She turned to look at her younger brother with an exaggerated expression of distaste.

"I like the times they played ball best," he said.

"Surprise, surprise."

Frankie stopped scratching and took a stick of chewing gum from the pocket of his orange pyjamas. The cotton was covered with little pictures of racing cars. He stared at his sister while he chewed, listening to the sound of his mother doing something downstairs in the kitchen. Water running. It seemed to him that she was always in the kitchen. When he came home after school, she was there. When he was getting ready for bed, she was still there. Most times, when he got up in the morning, she was *still* in the kitchen. He wondered if it was her favorite room.

Charlotte closed her book now.

"What's that called?" Frankie asked.

"*Treasure Island.*"

"Yeah? Mrs. Rosenblum was reading some of that to us. A coupla days ago."

Charlotte lay down with her eyes closed. What she was thinking about was her beauty sleep. She'd read in one of her mother's magazines, maybe it was *Ladies' Home Journal,* about the benefits of beauty sleep. "Did you understand any of it?" she said.

"Sure I did," Frankie said. "I like Jim whatsisname."

"Hawkins. Jim Hawkins."

"Right." The boy blew a bubble and popped it and Charlotte opened one eye in disapproval.

"You brush your teeth?" she said.

"Soon's I finish the gum, I will."

"She likes you to brush them before bed," Charlotte said. "It's one of her health things, you know. If you don't brush them you know what happens?"

Frankie shook his head.

Charlotte sat up on one elbow, and looked at her brother. "Bacteria grow in your mouth while you sleep, that's what happens."

"Bacteeree. What's that?"

"Little crawling things—"

"Yeah? Then how come if I don't brush my teeth at night I don't see anything crawling round my mouth in the mornings, huh?"

Charlotte sighed with impatience. "You can't see them unless you've got a really strong microscope, dummy. They're invisible to the naked eye. OK? Too small to see."

Frankie smiled with a look of disbelief. "*Sure,* Charles. *Sure.*"

"And don't call me Charles, Frank Hart Allbright. I hate that name."

"I never knew you hated it, Charles. Oops. Sorry Charlotte."

Charlotte closed her eyes and turned over onto her side and said, "Switch off the light on your way out, will you?"

"You think I'm a slave?"

The girl groaned. "I asked nicely, Frankie. I didn't *order* you to do it, did I?"

The boy leaned against the doorjamb, blowing still another bubble. He could hear water running below. Maybe she was filling up the dishwasher or something like that. Then he thought of his dad and how much he missed him, hoping the next time he came home he'd let him help with the trellis out back. He wasn't sure what a trellis was anyway. He just wanted to get the feel of the tools. But the shed out back was locked with a padlock and he didn't know the combination.

"The light, s'il vous plait," Charlotte said.

"How's that?"

"It's French for please. Please turn out the light. And quit with the bubbles."

But Frankie didn't leave. He stepped farther into the room, looking around. It was a crummy room, he thought, a real girl's room. And it was so neat and tidy it made you sick. There were all these dolls on a shelf, dolls from all over the world. There was one with a kilt, and a black one with bananas on her head. He thought that one was specially funny. He blew another bubble and this time the thing popped too quickly and strands of moist gum adhered to his lips and nostrils. He clawed it off. Charlotte was watching him again.

"There's a word for that," she said.

"For what?"

"I'd call it disgusting, Frankie."

Frankie stuck the gum back in his mouth. He had to moisten it all over again to get the different pieces to stick together in a small ball. "Listen," he said. "What are these women coming here for?"

"What women?"

"You know."

Charlotte yawned. "It's got something to do with baby-sitting."

"Baby-sitting?" Frankie didn't like the idea much. He had been raised with repeated warnings about strangers and he thought of the world as somehow menacing, unknown people passing out apples at Halloween with razor blades hidden in the flesh of the fruit, or candies that had been dipped in poisons.

"It comes down to this," Charlotte said, indulging him. "It's like people in a club kinda helping one another out. OK? And Mom doesn't like Mrs. DeSantis to baby-sit because she's a snooper. And she doesn't like any of the girls from the junior high because last time whatsername, Helena, drank some of Dad's scotch. So she's started something like a club."

"Is she going away?" Frankie asked, the gum suddenly hot and still in his mouth.

"'Course she isn't *going* away. But she's got to get out sometimes. I mean, she can't be stuck in the house night after night. Anyway, she's going back to school."

School, Frankie thought. His own mother at school. It just seemed silly somehow. "Whose class will she be in?" he said.

Charlotte moaned, pulling the blanket over her head. "She isn't going to *our* school, Frankie. She's going to this night school thing. OK? I read the literature on it. Some kind of poetry class on Wednesday nights over in Pastorville."

"Oh," Frankie said. He hated poetry. Something about it didn't appeal to him and sometimes, when he thought about it, he couldn't find a single good use for it. His second grade teacher, Mrs. Rosenblum, read poems to the class occasionally—and she looked pretty silly doing it, stretching a hand out like she was in a play, or whispering certain words as if they were supposed to be scary. Frankie found it funny more than anything else, but after a while it stopped being funny and then it became boring. "Why's she going to do poetry?"

"Switch out my light, Frankie. Please."

"Yeah. OK." He did so, and stood for a moment in the dark and thought about his sister. It seemed to him that she knew a whole lot of things he couldn't even begin to learn. She knew about poems, and she knew what French was, and she could read *Treasure Island* without somebody having to explain it all. One time he'd overheard his grandmother say, *Charlotte has the brains in this household*—and the way she said it made him feel low. He liked to build things, to make things, like the windmill he'd created with his Erector set: didn't anybody realize that that took brains as well?

He stepped out of Charlotte's bedroom and stood for a time on the landing, looking down the flight of stairs. The living room was in darkness except for a band of light that fell through the open kitchen door. She was still running water down there. He went towards his own bedroom, which was a wonderful mess, a terrific place—nobody really knew where anything could be found except himself. He liked it that way. He stepped into the room, raising one foot so he wouldn't walk on the microscope he'd been given last Christmas.

He got into bed, stuck his gum against the bedpost, then decided he wasn't going to brush his teeth because he didn't believe in bacteria anyway. Charlotte was always making things up to tease him.

He lay with his eyes open, staring at the lampshade on the bookshelf. There were pictures of nursery-rhyme characters on the shade and Frankie looked for a time at Little Red Riding Hood with her basket in her hand. You better stay away from that cottage, kid, he thought. It isn't your grandmother that's in there.

Emily drew the bolt on the kitchen door, turned out the light, and then went to the front door, slipping the bolt, pressing her eye momentarily to the viewer—and seeing nothing out there but the yellow house light and the oak tree. She thought for a moment of the wretched movie she'd been obliged to sit through. Still, it had pleased Frankie, even if it hadn't exactly delighted Charlotte.

Now she climbed the stairs, stopping halfway up, listening to the sound of a child's voice. Frankie saying his prayers. She paused a moment, eavesdropping, feeling awkward as she did so. *And please bring my dad back home safe and bless my mother and I guess my sister too if you think she deserves it. . . .* Emily smiled and went into her own bedroom, closing the door.

She undressed and lay on top of the bed. She folded her hands between her legs, waiting for the night sounds to begin. Frankie's bed creaked; then she heard him cough. The wind soughed through the tree out front, but she didn't turn to look at it. For a time she thought of William and the loss of her virginity in that field but it was funny how she couldn't see his face, funny how time had masked his features. William Whatever. She heard the wind again, making a sound like that of a garment being trailed along a wall, a hem touching a smooth surface.

She tried but she couldn't sleep. She opened James Hamilton's volume of poems and read the first two or three slowly. He was very fond of colors, she noticed—whites and reds and tangerines—but the images in which he placed the colors were somehow depressing. She shut the book, turned over onto her side, and closed her eyes. *A tangerine sun brings it back again/And I have no memory for it. . . .* When she slept she dreamed she was sitting on the floor in a room somewhere, her legs crossed, and James Hamilton was reading his poems to her—and then she asked him who Deirdre was and he looked puzzled, and somehow in the dream the dedication page, where her name had been written before, was inexplicably blank.

Then Ted came into the room, pushing the door hard, and speaking angrily in a foreign language.

5.

The blind man listened, his head slightly tilted in concentration. Sounds were like acquaintances, reliable old friends—he could set his clock mornings by the movement of the mailman, or by the guy next door laboring to get his car started, and after that there was the school bus with the squealing brakes and the hiss of automatic doors closing after the kids had boarded, then there was the laundry delivery van that stopped twice a week three doors down. Diapers, maybe. He recognized the sound of the motor because it was poorly tuned and skipped a beat. He timed his life by these sounds. He knew, too, when night came, because it arrived with the silences of children, a fall of temperature, the sound of his daughter preparing something in the kitchen.

He moved his legs, swinging his feet from the floor back into bed, then feeling for the sheet and drawing it up over his body. There was a numbness in his legs, something that always happened whenever he tried to get out of bed. He couldn't carry his weight anymore and somehow that was worse even than the blindness—the idea of his muscles wasting in a way that couldn't be retarded.

When he heard her car turn into the driveway and the sound of the front door being opened and closed he shut his eyes and pretended to be asleep. You're scared, he thought. She scares you. Your own daughter. He listened, feeling a slight pulse move under one eye. He could hear her in the living room below and he wondered where she'd been until this time of night. She crossed the room, she went into the kitchen—he could hear running water, the click of a plate on the table—and then the back door was opened and he could hear the sound of her feet crunching on the gravel that surrounded the swimming pool. Silence, silence now.

Why did she go to the fucking pool like that?

He wished he could see, he wished he could look and see the expression on her face: what the hell did she do? Did she just stand there and stare into the dark water? Was that it?

He kept his eyes shut tight and what he wished now was that Nick was still in the house because he'd liked Nick. Nick sometimes would read Erle Stanley Gardner or Agatha Christie to him—his own daughter wouldn't ever do anything like that. Christ, how could you blame Nick for leaving her? You couldn't blame a man for walking out on a wife who didn't do a goddam thing but whine and mope—

And that other stuff.

That crazy stuff.

In the depth of night sometimes he could hear her go into Charlie's room and he would listen to the way she spoke in soft tones, like she was hushing the kid to sleep. *It's OK, Charlie. Momma's here. Was it a nightmare, honey? Was it a bad dream?*

Shit, he said to himself. Don't fucking think about Charlie. Goddamit. He tried to think of Nick now, wondering where he was and why he didn't even visit. Maybe he didn't want to come back: you couldn't hold that against him. I'd leave too, he thought, if I could just move. If I could just get my goddam limbs to work.

He listened to the noise of gravel again, then he heard the back door closing. She was inside the kitchen once more. And then there was silence: what is she doing now? he wondered. Just sitting at the kitchen table? Looking out the window? Just what exactly is she doing?

This blindness. This useless world of noises. This lack of color and

shadow and light. He was frightened all over again, thinking the kind
of thoughts he didn't like.

*I couldn't do a goddam thing. She could put something poisonous
in my food and I couldn't stop her. She could come into the room
when I'm asleep and press a pillow over my face and I wouldn't have
the strength to fight back—*

You can't defend yourself.

Where the fuck is Nick?

Nick would see she didn't harm me.

Nick would see to that.

Then he thought, She blames me and Nick, she hasn't stopped
blaming us for what happened. Christ, it was too goddam bad, but it
wasn't *his* fault they'd bought a house with a fucking pool. It wasn't
his fault, for God's sake!

He turned his head and thought: A Saturday afternoon and she'd
been out somewhere, maybe at a store—he wasn't sure—and Nick had
come to the room with a six-pack of cold beer and they'd drunk it.
He remembered that, feeling good about that part of it. Then Nick
had been sleepy and had gone to his own bedroom to nap. He even
remembered Nick yawning as he went out of the room. He'd sat
clutching a half-empty can of beer and listening to Charlie playing
downstairs, playing with her dolls like they were real people, talking
to them, scolding them. *I told you to sit still! Didn't I tell you that,
Belinda?* Then Charlie was singing something, a lullaby perhaps, like
she was trying to get the dolls to sleep. And then what?

He felt cold now. He could hear her moving on the stairs. She
climbed slowly, stealthily, as if she didn't want him to hear her. A
thief, a shadow in the night—that's what she was like.

And then what?

Then the house had been silent, maybe he'd dropped off, snoozed,
he couldn't remember the details except for the noise of Nick snoring
through the wall. What made him try to get up then? Something: call
it an instinct, maybe. He'd risen, leaning against the wall, his legs
hurting, his muscles weak: and what he remembered was the way
he'd called to the child over and over again.

Charlie? Charlie? Charlie!

Nothing.

Nothing at all.

No sounds.

He tried to forget that memory. He tried to block it from his mind. He heard his daughter pause outside his bedroom door now. He wasn't sure if the door was open or shut. It worried him, not knowing, because if it was open she'd be standing there staring at him and he wouldn't know the look in her eyes. She could kill me now. *She could easily kill me now.*

He held his breath until he thought his lungs would explode. Then he could feel her staring at him, as tangible as tiny waves in water. He could *feel* the look.

She hates, he thought. And she hates in a way she can't forget, can't forgive.

Then she was inside the room, saying, "You're not asleep."

"I was," he answered. "You woke me."

"I didn't wake you," she said. "You weren't sleeping."

He wondered if she could hear the vague panic in his voice. She was moving towards the bed, touching something on the bedside table.

"You didn't eat your supper," she said. He heard the sound of a tray being lifted, the rattle of glasses, bottles. His pain pills, his sleeping tablets.

"It's a terrible waste," she said.

"I wasn't hungry."

"No?"

"Sometimes I'm not hungry," he said. "Is that a crime?"

She didn't say anything. He could smell cigarette smoke now—and then he heard a faint sizzling sound that lasted only a moment. The scent of something burning, briefly and then gone. She'd stubbed her cigarette in the tapioca or whatever it was she'd brought up earlier for his supper. Don't blame me, he thought. Don't take it out on my life.

She picked up the tray and turned away from him and he heard her go towards the door.

"Good night," she said. "Sweet dreams."

He didn't answer. The door closed quietly—and for a disorienting moment he had the feeling she was still in the room, that she was playing a trick on him, trying to make him believe she had gone out. He turned his face in the direction of the door, waiting.

Just waiting.

Sweet dreams. Sweet deadly dreams. He wondered if his heartbeat was audible.

Then he heard her going down the stairs and he breathed more easily. He lay flat on his back now, his eyes open. He thought, I can't let her kill me. I can't let her kill me without a fight. I didn't do anything wrong. How can she blame me?

There was another sound from outside now, a car moving slowly along the edge of the sidewalk, stopping, and then backing up to the driveway entrance. The motor was silenced and for a time all he could hear was the sound of his daughter in the kitchen. Then two doors slammed and he thought. Visitors? Visitors at this time of night?

Who?

He sat upright, straining to listen. The front door opened and closed and there were voices all at once but they were too goddam quiet for him to hear. He tried, inclining his head, but it was impossible: she had shut his bedroom door on her way out. A sense of his own dark isolation came back to him again, like a swarm of colorless birds.

6.

There were two of them, one a small man with hair the color of sand; the other was tall and said very little, just stood looking at the titles of the books on the shelf. She smiled at them, invited them to sit—but they remained standing, as if they were in a hurry to go elsewhere. It was strange, she thought, how they crowded the living room, how the twin lamps on the end tables threw their shadows on the ceiling like inflated balloons.

"His landlady hasn't seen him in four days," the small one said. He shrugged and put his hands in the pockets of his raincoat. "He didn't say he was going anywhere, that's the thing. All his stuff is still in the apartment."

She rubbed her bottom lip with her index finger. "We are separated," she said.

"Yeah. I understand that," the small one said. "You haven't seen him recently?"

She shook her head and said, "Our marriage is over."

She glanced at the taller man, who was slipping a volume from the shelf and flipping through the pages. She wondered why he was doing that. She tried to see what the book was—one of those book club condensed things.

The one with the sandy hair said, "He hasn't been at work. He hasn't called in sick. He hasn't been in his apartment since Thursday morning. So far as his landlady can tell."

She sat on the arm of the sofa. She watched the other man put the volume back; now he was picking up a framed picture of Charlie, one taken when she was about eight, and he was holding it at an angle to the lamp and staring at it. "Pretty girl," he said. "Your daughter?"

She said, "Yes. That's right."

There was a silence in the room now. She shouldn't feel nervous, she shouldn't—all he was doing was looking at a photograph, but it seemed to her that in some way he was touching Charlie herself.

"Pretty girl," the cop said again. He put the picture back but he didn't stop looking at it and she wondered if it reminded him of anything.

"Very pretty," she said. She laughed quietly. "A mother shouldn't boast about her own daughter, I guess."

"Sure she should," he said. "You've got every right to be proud."

The smaller man cleared his throat and rubbed his mouth with a handkerchief. "When did you last see your husband?"

"When he left," she said. She felt calm suddenly. "The marriage was finished. He packed his stuff. He left."

"He ever call? You ever call him?"

She shook her head.

"Was there another woman?"

"I don't know," she said. "I don't care."

"Yeah. Well." The cop folded his handkerchief. "And you've no idea where he might have gone?"

"None," she answered.

"He didn't take his car wherever he went," the cop said. "It's still parked behind the apartment. I don't know. People."

The taller one was moving around the room. What is he looking for? she wondered. A sign, a trace, of Nick? A clue? A stain of blood or something? She realized that if she closed her eyes she could make them go away but somehow it was important to deal with them, to answer their questions, to be helpful.

"Can I make you some coffee?" she said.

They both refused. The taller one was looking at his watch.

He asked, "Does he have parents?"

"His mother died two years ago," she said. "I don't know about his father. Sorry."

"Were they divorced or something?"

"Nick never mentioned him," she said. "I guess they were divorced when he was a baby."

"People," the smaller man said. "They just get up and go and they don't care if they forget to tell somebody where they're going. It's a pain in the ass."

She nodded her head and said, "I guess."

"Yeah, yeah," the man said, and stroked his hair flat with the palm of a hand. "I'm going to leave you a card with my number on it. If he gets in touch, let me know. Better still, get him to call me. OK?"

She stood up now. She glanced through the open door that led to the kitchen; on the table was the tray of uneaten food. She saw her cigarette butt sticking up from the bowl of oatmeal and she wondered if either of the cops had noticed that the oatmeal was dark blue in color because she'd added a food dye to it. A whole bottle of food dye. She moved to the kitchen door and stood there, blocking their view. The two men were leaving now.

"Thanks for your time," the taller one said. "Get in touch if you hear from him. Appreciate it."

The smaller man nodded.

Then they were gone. For a while she didn't move. She stared at the small card that had been left beneath the lamp on the end table. She turned off the kitchen light, then the two lamps, and she went upstairs to her bedroom. She closed her door. She could hear their car going down the street. Her diary lay open on the desk, the page blank. She put her hand inside the center drawer, feeling Nick's old revolver, then the other thing, the folded card—which she took out and spread flat on the surface of the desk. She read the words over and over, a sense of hatred seeming to grow with each reading, and then she remembered how, only a few minutes ago, she'd gone out and stood looking at the surface of the dark pool. A fractured memory: except what she remembered was sunlight and blue water, not the moonless dark and the still, unreflecting surface.

She sat down with the card in her hand and she thought, They'll never find Nick. How could they? *Why do we have to talk here, baby? There's nothing to talk about now anyhow. I'm happier, I think I'm a better person than I was before, and I finally got rid of that shit, that guilt.* . . . Leaving me to carry it, she thought. Deserting me. Abandoning me.

She shut her eyes, opened them again, stared at the card:

> Have you noticed how the price of baby-sitting
> continues to rise? There's a practical way for
> parents to obtain baby-sitting services free on
> a cooperative basis. Anybody seriously interested
> in such a cooperative should call 532-6708.
>
> Emily Allbright.

What was it about this message that irritated her? she wondered. What was it in the tone? She couldn't think. She couldn't quite put her finger on it.

She folded the card over once more and tore it in two pieces, then in four, then again, dropping the scraps carelessly on the rug.

She thought of the yellow-haired girl in the cinema.

Chapter Three

1.

The day was a rush, a blur, a series of preparations plagued by small domestic disasters. The downstairs toilet plugged, spilling brown water across the tiles: Emily had to attack with the plunger, a task that took twenty or so minutes before the water flushed clear again. The garbage disposal gave out and she tried to resuscitate it with a broom handle but a piece of bent metal—a crushed dime, a bottle top —had become jammed between the blades, and the reset button wouldn't help either. Then the brownies she was making turned black and inedible, acrid smoke filling the kitchen. Screw it, screw it all, she thought—and in the middle of the afternoon she went outside to the back yard and sat on a folding chair and stared at Ted's trellis. Maybe good old Ted was right after all, she thought: maybe I should never have dreamed up this—what had he called it?—this *project*. You could build fences with projects, she realized. You could make your whole life one unfinished sequence of projects. She blew tobacco smoke lazily, shut her eyes, and wondered if it wasn't too late to get out of it. How had the idea started anyhow?

How did any idea take fire?

Answer: She'd been bored and watching an early morning talk show and a group of fervent women were extolling the merits of a baby-sitting cooperative and the talk-show host was nodding his head, weaving with his microphone through the studio audience, beaming and generally giving his approval to what seemed a sound economic proposal. But I'm not the type, she thought. I'm not an organizer, I can't make plans, set up schemes. And then Ted had been gone for almost ten days and somewhere in that time she'd thought: You gotta do something, Em, or before you know it you'll be taken away with a profound case of the willies. Okay, she'd thought, I'll write out my little card and pin it up in a supermarket and see if anybody bites—

And there was something else behind the project, there was Ted, an end to Ted's lame excuses about not going out because of the shortage of decent sitters—no more, Ted. No more thin pretexts, my love. When you're home we're going to start going out together—restaurants, movies, and maybe even a weekend in the city. *Put a little romance back in your life, Mr. and Mrs. Allbright!*

She stuck her hands into the pockets of her jeans and wandered around the yard for a time. She paused by the toolshed, opened the door, switched on the light, and went inside. Windowless, it smelled of damp metal. All Ted's tools hung neatly on small hooks. Even the hammers were apparently arranged by size, so that the smallest was on the first hook, the largest on the last. Just so, she thought. Everything in Ted's life, just so. She idly fingered the tools, feeling she was intruding on something intensely private. She sat down at the workbench, looking at the various plans and blueprints that were stacked on the surface. From the pocket of her white jeans she took a slip of paper and she spread it out on the workbench. The names of strangers, soon perhaps to be friends. She looked down the list of all the women who'd called about the cooperative:

> Adrienne Bullion
> Carole Kirkham
> Susan Gallo
> Marylou Fretz

Then she thought, Maybe they won't all show up for the meeting. Maybe none of them would. Project Baby-sit down the tubes. She folded the paper over and stuck it into her hip pocket, then she locked the door of the shed when she left. Strangers and friends. Whoever finally turned up tonight, she'd have to provide something, she'd have to be the dutiful hostess, passing out coffee and cakes.

She locked the house and got in the station wagon and drove to the Twin City Mall, a new construction that had gone up only a few months ago. It lay in the shadow of the freeway, a slab of characterless concrete with discreet neon signs burning pale in the orange afternoon. *Montgomery Ward. Carvel Ice Cream. Thom McAn. The Baby Box. Stag Tobacco.* She parked and crossed the lot and entered the mall, which was air-conditioned and empty—and for a moment she wondered if perhaps it were closed and she'd missed the Closed sign; but the little stores inside were lit and she could see sales clerks sitting at desks, a customer leafing through a book of wallpaper samples in the Design Center, someone carrying a small pup from the pet shop in whose window a nasty-looking parrot preened itself. She stared at the huge bird for a while, reaching some mutual understanding with it that neither would ever like the other.

She walked to the center of the mall where a fountain was located, sending up a jet of water that fell in broken sprays over garishly colored pebbles. She watched it for a time, wondering whose bright idea it had been to paint the pebbles in such dreadful pastel colors. Tacky, she thought. Across the way from the fountain there was a bakery store, and she headed in that direction. Inside, assailed by the kinds of smells that would add pounds to the body simply by inhalation, she bought a box of cakes and a bag of cookies; then, with time to kill before the kids would get home from school, she windowshopped. You could lose yourself in a color supplement dream, she thought. You could imagine your home filled with white low-slung sofas, aluminum lamps that twisted whichever way you wanted them to, rugs that could never be walked on, silver-framed wall prints that shimmered even as you looked at them. Razzle dazzle, mazelike black lines on white, reds dancing against greens to the point where you either had to shut your eyes or suffer a migraine. She returned to the fountain and sat on the surrounding bench, smoking a cigarette, gazing absently along the empty corridors of shops. What was it she found spooky about places like this?

The height of the ceilings?

The artificial light?

A weird underlying sense of nothingness?

Smoke your cigarette, Em, and go home. But there was something faintly hypnotic about the place—the gleaming passageways, the lights in store windows, the rattle of water over the pebbles. You could let yourself drift just sitting here, thinking of nothing. Forgetting yourself. Spending imaginary money. Suburban Woman Found Amnesiac in Shopping Mall. Says She Can't Remember Her Name.

She stubbed her cigarette underfoot, feeling just a little guilty at the smear of dark tobacco on the pale yellow tiles. Then she stood up (a bone cracked in her leg: you grow old, baby) and moved in the direction of the exit. Halfway there, she stopped.

It was one of those feelings you can't explain, neither at the time nor long afterwards: it was a sensation of certitude, but it somehow filtered through none of the normal avenues of sense. You just knew. You just somehow knew that somebody was watching you. She didn't turn to look at first. She held the box of cakes and the bag of cookies against her side, waiting, waiting as if something were about to happen. I won't turn, goddammit. I won't. You heard of men in raincoats wandering the malls and the plazas and staring at women in the afternoons, following them, walking a few yards behind with their hands clenched in their pockets. Loonies on day-release programs or something like that. The quiet faces of perverts. Sex maniacs. She moved a few paces forward, reached the glass door that led to the parking lot, and then as she pushed it and started to go outside she glanced back quickly. The door swung shut with a flash of cold light. Along the main corridor the fountain continued to send up a stream of water. But that was all. Nothing else moved. The mall was empty. Nobody, nothing. Nobody had been looking at her. Sheer fancy, she thought. Sheer goddam fancy. You've got some imagination there, sister. Next thing you'll be driving along the street when suddenly you'll have the intuition that somebody is lying on the floor of the car behind the driver's seat. A shrink might tell you any number of fancy things, but what it would come down to was the fact that the inactive mind creates its own demonology. Sheer goddam ridiculous fancy.

She went to the station wagon, unlocked it, checked the space behind the front seat, slung her shopping in back, and drove out of the parking lot.

Home, James, and don't spare the horsepower.

But even when she had turned into her own street, even when she had the wagon back in her own driveway, the ludicrous feeling persisted: Somebody had been watching her. Somebody. She got out of the wagon and looked the length of the street. Nothing moved. Nothing was different. A patrol car of the Pastorville police department went slowly past and the cop looked at her a moment, but after that there was nothing else. She unlocked the front door and stepped into the living room. She put her shopping on the table beside the philodendron and looked around the room—and in one quick burst of activity she stacked the magazines in a neat pile on the coffee table, sprayed every wooden surface she could find with Pledge, and ran the vacuum cleaner over the rust-colored rug. There, she thought. There. Nobody could say she wasn't a responsible *hausfrau*.

She sat down on the sofa, fatigued after the rage of cleaning, and she sighed. After a time she picked up James Hamilton's book of poetry and she read the one entitled "Beyond Mars." It didn't make a whole lot of sense to her, she had to admit. She was still pondering it when the doorbell rang and she found a man on the doorstep trying to sell her dead moths pinned to pieces of cork and mounted inside glass cubes.

"They'd make great paperweights," he said.

"I don't really need one," Emily said.

"Or a conversation piece," the man, squinting behind his glasses, added. He had a stubbled growth on his chin, which he scratched.

"I really don't think so. Sorry."

"Well, OK. Maybe next time."

She shut the door and listened to him move away. A conversation piece, she thought.

It's a dead moth, Ted.

I can see that.

We're supposed to converse about it, Ted.

Yeah.

Lovely wings, don't you think?

I've never seen anything so beautiful, Emily.

A conversation piece. She put the book of poems back on the shelf, turned on the radio, heard a voice tell her that there was a place in the heavenly kingdom for her even if she was a sinner, and then she went into the kitchen and stood for a while, conscious of her own muted reflection in the waxed floor. Then there was some country music, a man singing: *Kick off your shoes, turn out the light, and love me tonight.*

I wish, she thought. I wish you were here, Ted.

2.

She fed the kids hot dogs and French fries for their supper, thinking as she served them at the kitchen table that it was a nutritional horror show: but they ate it anyhow, asking for more when they were through. She cleaned the surface of the table quickly, ushered the kids through to the TV room, and thought: I am some kind of mother —hot dogs and fries and TV, pacifiers of a preteen generation. They seemed oddly acquiescent though, as if they understood that the house would soon have guests and that their behavior had to be exemplary. They sat in front of the TV and stared at the vicissitudes of fortune in a quiz show called *Family Feud*. Feeling a little guilty that she'd packed them off like this, Emily lingered a moment in the room and gazed blankly at the screen. A bunch of people were hugging one another to the roar of studio applause.

Frankie said, "You ought to get on a money show, mom."

"You think so?"

"Sure. You could win something good. Like maybe a reclining chair or something."

"A reclining chair. Far out," Charlotte said.

"Well," Frankie said, meaninglessly. He gave his sister a quick sullen look.

"I'm sure it would be nice to have, ah, a reclining chair," Emily said. "Every family needs one."

"It kind of slides back," Frankie said. "Or it can stay up like a normal chair."

I love you, Emily thought; sometimes I even love your small talk, and the serious look on your face when you make it. She shifted the weight of her feet, placing her arms in a folded position under her breasts. She stared at Frankie a moment. He had his face turned once more towards the TV where the same sickening display of video happiness was taking place—and what she suddenly wondered about were all those cereal commercials in which well-regulated families sat down every morning to a nifty table of breakfast goodies, everybody dressed and ready for work or school, sunshine sparkling out of cornflake bowls, stupid grins all round. Did the kids get their concept of family from such sources? Was she supposed to rise in the dawn and set this lavish table? Snap crackle pop.

Charlotte said, "Maryanne Turner had her thing today."

"Her thing?" Emily said.

"You know. You told me to expect it one day soon."

Emily hesitated a moment before she recalled a conversation she'd had with Charlotte on menstruation, explaining it in strictly clinical terms—a prospect Charlotte hadn't found the least upsetting. But something stirred in Emily a moment, some vague sadness at the notion of her own daughter passing soon into puberty, as if it were a region where the child would be lost to her: a dark place. She watched Charlotte for a time, but the girl didn't say any more on the subject of Maryanne Turner.

Emily said, "Well, it happens. I told you."

"Yeah," Charlotte said absently.

"It's natural. It's nothing to get upset about."

"Mom, I'm not going to get upset about it." A tiny edge of impatience in the voice there, Emily thought: do I worry too much? Do I brood over my kids too avidly?

"Upset about what?" Frankie said. "Doesn't anybody in this room care I'm trying to watch TV?"

"A hundred apologies," Emily said, moving towards the door. There was a commercial on the screen now. The Jolly Green Giant. At the door she paused, one hand on the knob. "Don't forget I'm expecting company," she said. "So keep the noise down and no running around shouting, et cetera, et cetera. OK?"

Neither of the kids answered.

Emily shrugged and closed the door as she left the room.

After a time Frankie said, "I think it's dumb."

"What's dumb?" Charlotte was pulling long strands of hair in front of her face and squinting at them.

"A house filled with women," the boy said.

"What do *you* know? She thinks it's important. And that's fine with me. In any case, you can see she's a bit nervous about it all." Charlotte watched her brother a moment.

"How do you mean nervous?" Frankie said.

"Nervous, that's all."

Frankie lay on the floor, head propped up against his hands. He belched briefly.

"That's disgusting," Charlotte said.

Frankie swallowed air and belched again.

"Pity they don't have burping in school," Charlotte said. "Then your report cards would be just terrific."

Frankie reached up and changed the channel. Finding nothing that appeared to please him, he flipped the changer quickly, round and round, filling the darkening room with rapid colors and shadows. Charlotte turned on the lamp and opened a book that had been lying on the sofa. She dropped it in disgust when she saw it was her father's bible, *The Complete Home Repair Manual*. She sat with her eyes closed, trying to block out the noise of the TV. Now and then she could hear the doorbell ringing, then the sound of voices. Later, when it was appropriate, she would find some pretext for going into the kitchen, passing the room where the women sat—and then she'd have a good look at them, she'd have a *good* look. After all, there would be times when they'd baby-sit: and she had every right to see the faces of the prospective candidates.

Emily laid cakes and coffee on the table and watched as the three women who had so far come helped themselves—tentatively, coyly, as if they were wondering about their real purpose in coming to her house. It's too late to back out, she thought, and yet she wanted nothing more than to say: *OK, this is a mistake, I changed my mind, ha ha.* They looked at her with some kind of muted expectation, and she hated the messianic feeling she got. How could she ever have dreamed this notion up in the first place? A leader of women, she said to herself, after the various introductions had been made and coffee poured and cakes lay in crumbs on plates. Three out of four had turned up: why couldn't it have been none out of four? She found herself standing in the center of the room, watching the other women as they sipped coffee or dissected the cakes in their laps with the small forks she'd put out. A leader of women, like hell. Uneasily, she heard herself talking about her kids while the women watched her, nodding their heads, chewing, lifting cups—she heard herself laugh with a small anxiety, wondering why nobody seemed ready to respond to what she was saying. An icebreaker, that's what we need, she thought. A whoopee cushion. A party favor that farted. Then she could turn it around into a joke of some weird kind, saying: *I only put the card in the market for laughs. . . .*

My front room is filled with silent strangers. Maybe Ted was right after all; you pin a card up in a supermarket, and what can you expect? Fruitcakes. The lonely. The deprived. Those in need of free coffee and cakes. There was a silence now in the room and she made an idle gesture in the direction of the coffee pot, but nobody took her up on a second cup. Sweet sweet Christ, why didn't somebody say *something?*

"I hope the cakes are OK," she said. "I got them at that new place over in the Twin City Mall."

She nodded her head, as if she needed to underline her own statement. Cakes, let us talk of cakes. Let us consider, for the sake of argument, a cake-sitting cooperative, or how we might hang around waiting for soufflés to implode. Better still, we could hire ourselves out to fill up the empty seats during a wake.

Then the doorbell rang and she was glad of the interruption. She opened the door and a woman in a short fur jacket, her red hair piled up in an old-fashioned beehive and sprinkled with some glittering matter, swept into the room—swept into the room in a way that suggested she meant to change people's lives, a sparkling motion of quick energy.

"I'm late," she said. "My apologies to all. Hope you haven't been waiting for me to arrive. Have you? Damn car wouldn't start. I had to come in a cab and you know what it's like trying to get a taxi around here—"

She paused, breathless, and looked at the faces.

"Which one is Emily?" she asked.

"Me—" Emily moved forward.

"Terrific idea, terrific. I'm Adrienne." And she took off the fur jacket and slung it, like it was a dead thing, over the back of a chair. She sat down, crossed her legs, lit a cigarette which she took from a slim gold case, and tilted her head back, blowing smoke upwards. "Did I miss anything, Emily? I usually do. I never get anyplace on time. I have a natural dislike of clocks and timepieces. Well."

Emily said, "We hadn't actually talked about the cooperative, Adrienne—"

"Great. Then I haven't missed a thing." She flipped her cigarette ash absent-mindedly on the rug and leaned forward to look at the other women, who sat in a row, awkwardly, like people awaiting a tetanus shot, or something equally unpleasant. Adrienne smiled at them and Emily, trying to get names matched with faces, made an attempt at introductions.

"Let me see if I can get it right," she said, feeling nervous, rubbing her palms together. "Adrienne, this is Susan."

Adrienne made a little humming sound, still smiling.

"I got that one right anyway," Emily said, and laughed, and wondered why she had this nervous urge to fill the silences with such a meaningless sound. "And this is Carole. And then Marylou. Right?"

The women nodded, watching Adrienne in a kind of communal silence that suggested conspiracy. Adrienne stopped humming and smiling and said, "I love to guess about people. It's one of my little hobbies. I take somebody's face and try to imagine what their life is like. Ever try that? No?"

Emily laughed. "I can't say I—"

"Take Carole there," Adrienne said.

Carole seemed embarrassed, blushing as she smiled. She picked at the remains of her cake, avoiding Adrienne's stare. She was a slightly plump woman of about thirty, dressed in a shapeless navy blue pants suit and high-heeled shoes through which her fat toes could be seen.

Adrienne said, "Let me guess. Three kids. Your husband drives—what do you call them—a big rig? You work part-time in Woolworth's. Right?"

Carole didn't speak for a time. Emily, pouring herself a cup of fresh coffee, saw that her own hand trembled slightly.

Carole said, "You're way off. One kid. Divorced. And I work fulltime at Sears in the credit office."

Adrienne threw her head back and laughed. "Well. Can't be right all the time, can I?"

Carole put her empty cup on the coffee table. Something in the gesture, something in the way she hunched her shoulders and inclined her head to one side, made Emily feel sorry for her. One kid, divorced, overweight, self-conscious: she had a flash into a life of drabness, harshness. She turned to look at Adrienne, who was searching for an ashtray. She found one, crushing her half-smoked cigarette. Then she immediately lit a second, fishing it out of a purse stitched with multicolored beads.

"And you're Marylou," she said, looking at the thin pretty girl who sat facing her.

Marylou, who wore dark-framed glasses, took them off and snapped them shut in her fingers and stared at Adrienne: "Can you guess about me?"

Adrienne was silent for a time, then said, "Married. Two kids. You're separated. You work in a public library."

Marylou sat back in her chair and smoothed long strands of dark hair away from her face The hair was worn with a center parting, reminding Emily of a style you used to associate with what was once quaintly known as the counterculture.

Marylou said, "Not bad. Not bad at all. Married, right. Separated, right again. Two kids, right again. You got the library part wrong. I'm on welfare, in fact."

"Welfare?" Adrienne said.

"It's part of the system," Marylou said. "Uncle Sam's handouts when your old man skips and nobody can find him and he doesn't send child support."

Adrienne looked glum for a second: "Some men," she said, shaking her head. "I mean, some men are scum."

Marylou didn't answer. She placed the palms of her hands flat on her blue jeans and glanced at Emily—and there was something in that glance, Emily thought: but what? Some tiny jealousy? Some form of scorn? Emily looked away, wondering if Marylou resented her because of the obvious comfort of the house, because it was obvious from her surroundings that *she* didn't know the meaning of welfare. There was a space now in the conversation, a crying silence, and Emily mumbled something about there still being coffee in the pot. Only Adrienne went to help herself. As she poured, Emily turned to look at Susan—Susan who sat with her knees jammed together in a manner Emily found somehow virginal: shyness, maybe, the fact of finding herself in a room of strangers—and who could be stranger than this Adrienne? Susan had the slightly faded good looks of an old cheerleader, the kind of face you see in yearbooks that go back ten years. . . . It was easy to imagine Susan striding on the sidelines, baton in the air, knees raised high.

Adrienne said, "Law of averages. I must get one right. Married. Two kids. You don't work. You run an efficient household. OK? Right?"

Susan smiled in a thin way. "More or less. My husband teaches over in Hunter. I try to run an efficient household."

"And the two kids?" Adrienne asked, smiling.

Susan nodded. "Right on the button."

Emily asked, "What about you, Adrienne?"

Adrienne carried her coffee back to her chair, pausing to look at the tray of cakes and shaking her head: "Mustn't be tempted. Calories are the very devil. They look delicious, though." She sat down, holding her cigarette high in one hand, the coffee balanced on the arm of her chair. "Me? Well. Married twelve years to the same man. Nice man, but Dullsville, if you know what I mean. Three kids, eleven, ten, and nine—I worked very hard for those three years, flat on my goddam back. And I work very hard now as well, but not in giving birth to more kids."

"What kind of work?" Marylou asked.

"I have my own agency in New York City," Adrienne said.

Marylou stuck her glasses on and said, "What kind of agency?"

"Modeling. I supply girls for advertising assignments."

"Ah. The cheesecake market," Marylou said.

Emily shut her eyes a moment, feeling the edge of an argument begin to sharpen—the women's libber against the peddler of flesh. But Adrienne skipped over the remark, saying, "Those girls earn a lot of money, don't forget that."

Marylou sighed. She turned her face and looked around the room, staring at things as if she didn't approve of anything she saw. I could do without this, Emily thought. I should never have stepped into the breach. She heard Adrienne laugh, although the laugh seemed directed at nothing in particular. Then there was silence again and Adrienne, who seemingly found all silences contrary to the laws of nature, said, "Well. Do we get started on business now? I have an appointment later, so . . ."

"Sure," Emily said. "I guess you all know the principles behind a baby-sitting cooperative?"

Silence. Some heads nodding. Why did she feel she was a teacher in front of a class on its first day?

"Well, basically, the idea is we enter into a mutual agreement concerning free baby-sitting services. That's it. It's not the most original notion in the world, I guess. But it works. And it doesn't cost anything." She paused, staring at Marylou, as if she intended her last sentence to mean something only Marylou could understand.

Marylou said, "I already belong to the Pastorville Food Co-op, so I guess the basic concept is the same with regard to baby-sitting. It comes down to my baby-sitting for you, free of charge, and you baby-sitting for me in return."

Emily thought of the Pastorville Food Co-op, which she had passed a number of times in her car—a small brightly painted storefront with a sidewalk always piled high with empty wooden crates and boxes. She wondered why she'd never gone inside.

"We have a points system," Emily said. "I figure that's the simplest way."

"Points?" Adrienne said. "Like how?"

"OK. Take a hypothetical situation. Maybe Carole there wants Susan to sit for her one night. Susan agrees. Susan gets a point, and Carole gets a negative point."

"So far, so good," Adrienne said.

"OK. Then maybe Carole baby-sits for, say, Marylou—well, her negative point is canceled and Marylou gets a negative point. That way, it's easy to keep track of who does what."

Marylou leaned forward, a look of intensity on her face: "Keeping track is what makes it work. A cooperative only succeeds if everybody does their share."

Carole said, "It means somebody has to keep a book of points."

Emily nodded, folding her arms. "We do that on a revolving basis as well, you see. I'll keep the book for the first month, recording points. Then somebody else can take it over, then somebody else for the month after that. And so on."

"OK, I got you," Carole said.

Marylou turned her face slightly, so that her glasses glinted in the lamplight. Dear Christ, Emily thought, how serious, how goddam serious, she looks: a convert to the cooperative way of life. "We need to agree on a maximum number of negative points, though. Like, if one of us uses the service and doesn't return it, then it doesn't work. I figure five negative points maximum, huh?"

Emily said, "Sure. Sounds OK to me. If you've got five points against you—which means you've used the service five times, without taking your turn sitting—then you don't use the service again until you've brought your points under the maximum."

Marylou smoothed the palms of her hands over her tight jeans and said, "Does everybody understand that?"

"Clear as a bell, dear, clear as a bell," Adrienne said. She went back to the coffeepot and drained it.

Susan cleared her throat and said, "What do we do with our own kids on the nights we baby-sit?"

"You've got two choices, basically," Emily said. "You bring your kids with you when you sit—or if there's somebody at home to look after them you can leave them home."

"It all sounds so wonderfully easy," Adrienne said. She was shaking the coffeepot, listening to the rattle of the last drop.

"It *is* easy," Marylou said. "Provided everybody pulls together. That's how the Food Co-op works. Everybody pitches in. Nobody screws around."

Emily picked at the crumbs of a cake and said, "Since I'm going to keep the record for the first month, it's important that you call me if you're going to baby-sit. That way, I can record it in the book. So what we have to do next is exchange telephone numbers. Everybody has to have everyone else's phone number and address."

She went into the kitchen and found a scratch pad and a couple of blunt pencils. As she was about to go back with them, the telephone rang. She picked it up.

Ted said, "Hi there."

"Ted. I didn't expect you."

"No? What's happening?"

"You sound strange. You been drinking?"

"A little tipsy. Just a tad. One of those business ordeals. A pep talk with a motel manager and his assistant. Maybe I downed too much wine."

"Where are you?"

"In my motel room. What are you doing? I hear voices."

She paused. Then she said, "It's the meeting."

"What meeting?"

"The cooperative."

"Shit. I thought I made it plain—"

"I don't want to talk about it now, Ted."

"The meeting. The witches' coven. Christ, Emily. I told you what I thought—"

"I haven't forgotten," she said. "They're OK. They're an OK bunch of people."

"Sure. Sure they are. You give everyone of them the Rorschach test? Do a little verbal free association, huh?"

"Yeah. I also examined their federal income tax returns, verified their birth certificates, and personally met their kids." She sighed.

Ted said nothing for a time. "We'll talk about it when I get back."

The Stern Voice. The Lecturer's Tone. She hated it when he put that voice on. Then she was aware of a woman's voice in the background and for a moment she thought it was somebody in Ted's room, but it wasn't, it was Adrienne, it was Adrienne talking in the front room. . . . *Some of the girls I employ haven't got the brains of an anteater, honest. All they know is how to smile, how to walk, and how to cash checks.*

"I might be home Thursday night," Ted said. "It depends."

"OK. I better get back. I think they're about to throw a live toad into the old cauldron," she said.

But Ted didn't laugh. "Kiss the kids, will you?"

"Sure—"

"Love you."

"Likewise," she answered.

When she'd hung up she went back inside the front room with the scratch pad and the pencils. Adrienne was strutting across the rug, one hand on her hip, imitating the walk of a model in an exaggerated way. Emily watched her for a second: a perfect figure, perfect balance, tiny waist and firm breasts.

"I found some paper," Emily said. She began to tear sheets from the pad, passing them out.

"I was talking about my agency," Adrienne said. "About some of the girls."

"She was giving us a terrific impersonation," Marylou said. "It was tough you missed it."

Sarcasm too, Emily thought. She felt suddenly very tired, even though it was still early. She watched the women silently write numbers down on their papers, watched the papers passing from hand to hand. She realized she wanted them to leave now, and yet in some other way she didn't—thinking of herself and the two kids alone in the house: whatever else these women brought with them, they filled a huge space. But the tiredness was inside her head, like a slow labored pulse. She listened to the scratch of pencils, the crinkling of paper. And the sound, a constant thing, an irritant, of Adrienne's voice. Now she was talking about how she had just risen one day with the resolve to start her own model agency, all the hard work she'd put into it, the tough struggle it had been, and then the rewards. Her speech was punctuated by Marylou's impatient sighs—sounds Adrienne either didn't hear or chose instead to ignore. Carole, sometimes looking up from her paper, was watching the talkative woman with a glazed look that might have been admiration. Secret dreams, Emily thought. Your very own face on the front of *Cosmo*. Draped in satins somewhere in *Vogue*. Stripped down to the nitty-gritty in a *Playboy* centerfold—pinned up on dorm walls all across the land, or masturbated over in rooms of silent desperation. The papers were being passed round. Then it seemed everybody had one another's number. List complete.

Emily thought, Wednesday night. James Hamilton's class.

The idea of raising the fact she would need a sitter the following night seemed uncomfortably self-serving, impertinent almost. What the hell. What was this co-op for anyhow?

Adrienne said, "One thing. One thing I simply have to mention. I can't do Thursday nights. I stay over in town Thursdays because I have an early meeting every Friday morning."

"It figures," Marylou said, almost inaudibly. "Does anybody else have nights they can't do?"

Susan said, "Sundays for me. Sunday nights are just hopeless. My husband and I have a kind of standing date Sundays." She laughed in a slightly embarrassed way.

"Nothing beats romance," Adrienne said.

"Except living on welfare," Marylou said. She stood up, brushing cake crumbs from her jeans. "I have to be boogying. I think it's settled, Emily. Don't you? Have we left anything out?"

"I don't think so," Emily said.

She went with Marylou to the front door. Marylou had a small beige VW parked outside the house.

"I'm glad we met, Emily," she said, and rattled her keys. "Hope this thing works."

"Me too," Emily said.

She watched Marylou go towards the car, then she shut the door.

Adrienne said, "I'm glad *she's* gone."

Please, Emily thought. No fights, no gossip, no divisions, please.

"I like her," Susan said.

"Oh, I'm sure she's OK," Adrienne said. "But she ought to smarten herself up a bit. She doesn't look—hell, feminine or something."

Emily began to clear the cups and plates away. Then Carole, followed shortly by Susan, left: only Adrienne showed no apparent desire to go. She tracked Emily into the kitchen and watched her stack the cups and plates in the sink. Adrienne wore a particularly heavy cologne that hung thickly in the air, trailing a cloying wake behind her wherever she moved.

"I like your wood paneling," she said to Emily. "Real wood?"

"My husband put it up," Emily said.

"Nice. Very nice. Gives the place a rustic feel. Like a cabin."

"He does things around the house," Emily said.

"Wish I could say the same for mine," Adrienne said. "He doesn't know a nail from his ass. When something needs doing, I have to hire a man."

Emily turned at the sink, looking at the woman: "That must be expensive—"

"Sometimes," Adrienne said. She was quiet for a moment. "Is your husband around?"

"No, he's away. Business."

"Does he go away often?"

"More often than I like. . . ."

"Ah."

Ah, Emily thought. What exactly was *ah* supposed to signify? What kind of meaning was she supposed to discover in the sound? She watched Adrienne, who was smiling now.

"You must come visit with me one Sunday afternoon. We live on Arbor Road. You know it?"

Arbor Road. The Park Avenue of West Pastorville. The few homes that had gone up before the rest of the suburb, at a time when the builder had had delusions of grandeur wrecked eventually by rising costs.

"Sure. One Sunday we'll drop over," Emily said.

"I think we'll be friends, good friends, don't you?"

Emily sighed inwardly. "I'm certain of it," she answered.

"It's hard to make friends in a place like West Pastorville," Adrienne said. "I don't know why. There's some kind of isolation, don't you think?"

There. The crux of the matter, Emily thought. Husband has fallen into soporific slumber. Kids growing up, becoming secretive. A singular lack of passion. And what have you got—a lonely talkative woman with too much makeup and overdressed into the bargain. Poor thing, Emily thought, she tries too hard. Way too hard. And maybe she doesn't see that the way she looks and the way she talks—they didn't fit in a place like good old West Pastorville. A fur jacket, Jesus. Glitter in her hair. Dark blue eye shadow around the eyes and a smattering of rouge on the cheeks and pink lipstick that was glossy, reflective as a tinted mirror. She gets caught in the rain, Emily thought, there's gonna be nothing left of her.

They went back inside the front room. Adrienne looked at her wristwatch and then, to Emily's relief, picked up her fur jacket.

"It's such a lovely idea, this baby-sitting thing. You're very clever to have thought it up," Adrienne said.

Emily smiled. "I can't take all the credit."

Adrienne looked round the room. "Don't hide your light under a bushel, dear. Never, *ever,* do that. Believe me. If you don't blow your own horn, there's not another goddam soul who will do it for you. Numero uno, in the long run. I had to scratch to get my agency where it is today. And I've still got some more scratching to do."

There was a short silence. Emily pretended a yawn, covering her mouth with her hand. Adrienne looked once more at her watch. Then, from outside, there was the sound of a car horn, and Emily suddenly realized that the woman must have been killing time until the return of her cab. That was it, just killing dull time.

Adrienne opened the door, stared out into the darkness. "Well, dear, I guess we'll be seeing one another before too long."

"I'm sure of it," Emily said. She stood in the door and watched Adrienne cross the lawn, passing under the shadow of the oak tree where she was momentarily lost in darkness. Then she reached the cab and got inside the back, waving once from the window as the taxi —sleek and yellow in the streetlamp—pulled away. There was something altogether regal in that wave, Emily thought: it reminded her of newsreel pictures of the Queen of England raising her hand in the back of a limousine. Emily shut the door and drew the bolt and looked for a while around the empty room.

Then she went into the TV room where Charlotte was reading a book and Frankie playing with a toy, a plastic figure of Evel Knievel that ran up a small ramp and landed invariably on its head. The TV was on. Merv Griffin was singing "I Love You Just the Way You Are." She had rarely seen an expression that so suggested someone in bad need of a laxative. She crossed the room and killed the sound, then she sat down on the sofa beside Charlotte and lightly stroked a strand of hair from her forehead.

"Have they gone?" Charlotte asked.

"Into the night," Emily said.

"I peeked, you know."

"Me too," Frankie said.

"Did you now?"

Charlotte said, "It's only fair. Me and Frankie have a right to look at people who might baby-sit—right?"

"Right," Emily said.

"Weird," Frankie said. "The one with the hair like a Christmas tree."

"Yeah," Charlotte said. "She kinda reminded me of a clown."

Emily shrugged. "She's OK, I guess."

"The others looked all right," Charlotte said. "The fattish one had a kind face. The one with the big glasses, though—she reminded me of a schoolteacher."

"Yeah," Frankie said. "Like Mrs. Rosenblum."

"The other one looked nice too," Charlotte said. "The one who was wearing the red dress."

"Susan?"

"She looked almost pretty."

"Hey, you're pretty free with your compliments tonight, kid."

Charlotte closed her book. She sat closer to her mother and was silent for a time. Frankie, putting his toy down, was quiet too—lying flat on his back on the rug and looking at the ceiling. A moment of peace, Emily thought, understanding how much she enjoyed these silent times with the kids, like a privacy they all shared without having to describe it or spell it out, like making their own small universe in a house that was locked against the dark outside.

She listened to this silence, almost feeling it as you might the vague strand of a web linking her to the two kids. She sat back, one arm around Charlotte, one foot resting lightly against Frankie's leg—and she was puzzled, as she had been so many times before, by the stealth of love, by the surprise of loving. It crept up on you, covering you, and when it had you covered you felt some profound inner peace; and nothing else mattered, not Ted's absence, not the oak tree and its phantasms, not the night that pressed upon the walls of the house. For a single moment you knew who you were; you saw yourself clearly and liked what you saw.

And then something broke the moment gently, in this case Charlotte's sudden question: "Did you like them?"

"Who?"

"The women."

"Sure, they're fine."

"Do you trust them?"

Emily looked into her daughter's eyes. "That sounds like one of your father's questions, kid."

"Do you, though?"

"I think I do."

"OK," Charlotte said. "If you trust them, then that's fine with me."

"Me too," Frankie said. He turned over onto his side and looked at his mother, then at his sister.

"I have to trust them, don't I? I'm not going to leave two very important people in their care otherwise, am I?"

Silence again.

Then she remembered.

She'd forgotten to arrange for a sitter for tomorrow night. Damn— she'd let the moment slip past and now she would have to make a call. But which one? She wondered. Which one to call? She got up from the sofa and went inside the kitchen, where the air was still heavy with Adrienne's scent, and she looked at her list of numbers. Carole, maybe. Why not? She dialed Carole's number, but there was no answer. Maybe she hadn't made it back home yet. She tried Susan's number. No reply. And when she called Marylou a man answered in a gruff voice, as if he'd been awakened from sleep, saying that Marylou wasn't home. (A man, she thought. Hadn't Marylou said her husband had skipped? Well, maybe if she was into the cooperative thing all the way she probably shared a house as well: a commune.) All of which left Adrienne. She wasn't sure why she didn't want to ask Adrienne.

It could wait.

She would try Carole's number again later.

3.

It was an all-night diner close to the freeway ramp. It had a pink neon sign, the word Diner enclosed in an oval, that flashed off and on and on and off almost at random, like the timing device had short-circuited. She went inside, aware of the rows of empty tables, of glistening chrome, a jukebox in a corner playing some maudlin country tune, a guy who looked like a trucker sitting alone near the window, glancing occasionally at her and at other times through the glass to where his rig was parked. What was she doing here? Why had she come here now? She didn't know. She went up to the counter and quietly asked for coffee and she carried the cup to a table near the Jukebox, listening, half-listening, to the words of the song. . . . *Saturday night, gonna make myself a name. Take a month of Sundays to try and explain* . . . She stirred the spoon round and round in the dark coffee, round and round so that she made a small whirlpool in the liquid, then she dropped the spoon on the surface of the table and the trucker turned to look at her and smiled, rubbing his jaw with the palm of his hand. She stared down at the surface of her table. Grease marks. Small granules of spilled sugar. Idly, she made a pattern. Then she sipped the coffee and could barely swallow it. She took the pain pills from her purse and spilled two into the palm of her hand and threw them back quickly, washing them down with the coffee. *Losing somebody you love so dearly, well, there's no telling how much you blame yourself, how much you blame others, how much guilt you'll feel or even how it will manifest itself.* . . .

Spassky, she thought. Why did Spassky's words always come back to her? She made a diamond pattern with the sugar, conscious of the trucker still watching her, and she thought: They were looking at me tonight, they knew, somehow they knew about me, they knew I wasn't for real. Oh, Christ, why did they have to keep looking at me the way they did?

And Emily Allbright.

Emily motherfucking Allbright with her tidy house and her coffee and her cakes and the smug way she looked with her arms folded under her breasts and how she talked, how she ordered things, how she took charge, with her book of records and her endless talk of points, negative points, like it was some huge fucking game.

Some monstrous fucking game—

Shutting her eyes, she heard the record change, she heard the scrape of the trucker's shoe on the floor, the sizzle of an egg slithering on a griddle. My pain, she thought. Maybe they were looking at me because they could feel *my* pain.

No, nobody could do that.

Only you could feel your own pain.

But they were looking, staring openly sometimes.

She wouldn't be surprised if they were holding a second meeting now, holding it without her, if Emily Allbright had waited until she'd gone and then telephoned round and called everybody back and said: *We don't want her, we don't want her in our outfit, do we?*

The pain turned inside her skull like a worm.

No, she thought. Be calm. Be in control.

She looked at the trucker. He was still smiling at her, still rubbing his jaw. She stared at him for a time, then she looked back down at the surface of her coffee where a slick of oil floated. The tune on the jukebox changed. She heard the whir of the electric mechanism.

The trucker was lighting a cigarette. She could see it from the corner of her eye, the flare of a match. She raised her face and looked at him again and she knew what he was thinking, she knew he was thinking of going inside the cabin of the rig with her—but she didn't want to think about that. Not now. Instead, she was remembering Nick and the pain was harder inside her skull, a fist beating on the taut surface of a drum.

You let our child die, she thought.

And then you let our marriage die.

And you died.

It formed a circle, a certain circle of justice.

But then she was confused, because she still heard Charlie in the night—a small distant cry: but it changed, it became less than human, and then it wasn't Charlie at all but it was ice-blue water that was rising up and screaming at her, forming a small wave that grew larger, grew tidal, screaming and screaming. And then she became the scream herself, her whole being turned from flesh and blood and bone to endless noise.

You let my baby die.

You let her die.

You left her with a stupid blind old man who can hardly move. You left her to die. And then even grief wasn't a bond anymore. There wasn't a glue to hold things together. Whatever existed fell apart. In pieces. Small pieces. Fragments.

And she tried not to remember, thinking instead of Emily Allbright and how she'd seen her in that shopping mall and how funny she'd looked when she'd turned around in the doorway, staring back, seeing nothing. How funny and how stupid.

She clenched her hands. Pain became cold anger. Blood rage.

She shut her eyes, and what she remembered was how, for a brief second in time, a door in the hallway had opened a crack, a mere slit, and how the girl with the yellow hair had peered out. The girl with the yellow hair. And Emily Allbright had gone on yakking and yakking and saying her kids were called Frankie and—

And Charlotte.

Charlotte.

The girl with the yellow hair.

Do you ever call her Charlie for short, Emily Allbright?

Do you ever do that?

My baby was called Caroline and that became Carly and that changed to Charlie, and after that it was always Charlie. It was never anything else.

She looked up. The trucker was standing at her table, watching her. He had a kind face somehow, but she didn't need his conversation now, or anybody else's for that matter. In Emily Allbright's house they were still talking about her.

"Can I sit? Or is this table reserved?"

She said nothing. She watched him slide into the chair across the table.

"What's your name?" he asked. When she didn't answer, he said, "I guess some days are mighty bleak."

Bleak, she thought. What was he talking about? Bleak.

"It's the look on your face," he said. "I get the idea you're down."

She stared at the tabletop, picking up her spoon, passing it back and forth from one hand to the other.

"You don't want company, you just say the word," he said.

What word? she wondered. He wants me to go into his truck with him, that's what it comes down to. He wants me to spread my legs for him.

"Hey. You OK?"

"I'm fine," she said. "Really. Just headache."

"You want aspirin? I got some. Out in the truck."

Where else would you have them, she thought. "I took a pill. It's fine," she said.

"Sure?"

Goddam sure, she thought. "Positive," she said. She looked at him and smiled faintly.

"You've got nice hair," he said. He raised his hands to touch it and she snapped her head away quickly. She heard him sigh. "Sorry, no offense meant. I'm just after some company, that's the name of the game. I hauled ass all day long, lady. This morning I woke up in Newport News, right? This time tomorrow night I gotta be in Montreal. I don't know why I'm telling you this anyhow."

"What do you want?" she said. "You want to go inside your truck with me? Is that it? Is that what you expect?"

"Hold it," he said. "I never mentioned anything like that, did I? I don't remember suggesting anything like that."

She stared at his face. He had weary green eyes, deep circles under them, deep lines etched from the corners of his mouth to his nostrils: a tired face. What did he expect: that she'd feel sorry for him or something? Then she was thinking of Nick again, she was remembering that amazing moment when all her senses were suddenly sharper than they had ever been, when her whole awareness was heightened to a clarity she'd never experienced before—when she could smell everything, the mustiness of the canvas sacks and the creeping scent of the canal and the oiliness of the old tarpaulin, even the smell of Nick's fear; when she was conscious of everything, the crushed white shirt he wore, the motion of his larynx above the open collar, the dull metal teeth of the zipper on his windcheater, the expression on his face and the way he'd said: *Hey, this is a joke, baby. Come on, you're taking it too far. . . .* All of this had come in at her with the speed of thought, a whole bombardment of sensations, a totality of perceptions that splintered and blew apart like so much stained glass when she'd pulled the trigger and shot him directly through the chest and watched as he fell backwards, groaning a moment, then yielding to that final silence of all.

She'd never felt like that, before or since.

Only pain, only the dull edge of grief.

Now she got up from the table and walked quickly towards the door. Outside, the night air was cold. Winter hung in the darkness, the smell of winter. She turned and saw the trucker staring through the window after her, his pose motionless. What had he wanted but some simple human warmth? But there wasn't any, there wasn't any to be had. Only the perfect chill of death.

She crossed the parking lot. She thought of the girl with the yellow hair.

Not Charlotte.

Charlie.

She had to be Charlie.

And nobody deserved Charlie except for her.

4.

Emily put the kids to bed, then tried Carole on the telephone again, but again there was no answer. She stacked plates and cups in the dishwasher and filled the container with soap powder. At the touch of a button, she thought: one small domestic miracle. She listened to the hum of the machine, the spray of water, and she reflected on the first meeting of the cooperative. Okay, it hadn't exactly started well, but by the end it had turned out fine—easier, really, than she'd anticipated, the arrangements, the points system, the quick acquiescence of the other women in the scheme. She leaned against the kitchen counter, seeing the subdued light burning in Ted's paneled walls, and she mentally considered the women one by one. In general, she liked them. She might not have chosen quite that group, but for a lottery it hadn't gone too badly. Carole seemed kind and reliable and—terrible word—homely. (Was that called damning with faint praise? she wondered. A slight act of condescension?) Susan was perhaps a little shy, but that was understandable in the circumstances—and maybe the fading of her looks had something to do with it anyhow. What would it be like, she asked herself, to watch the years ruin your beauty, seeing your reflection change gradually from the unblemished bloom of cheerleader to the jaded complexion of suburban housewife?

I have had *that* problem, she thought. She hadn't been beautiful to begin with, going through her teen-age years with the kind of looks which at best could be described as "having character"; the kind of face that, with the passage of time, might be called handsome. Handsome was another terrible word, she thought. A boring word. It was the kind of description somebody might use to fill an embarrassing silence, a void.

So what's Emily look like, Ted?

And he might say: *She's a handsome woman.*

Handsome. Like how you might describe a pair of gloves, or a piece of furniture. Or a trellis, maybe.

She turned her thoughts to Marylou. The sharp one. You could imagine somehow getting on the wrong side of Marylou and cutting yourself on an abrasive edge. Her prettiness was something she seemed determined to react against, to mask behind heavy glasses and androgynous clothes. One of the New Women, Emily thought.

Call me a person before you call me a woman. She was organized and obviously dedicated to the idea of a cooperative and you needed somebody like her to look to for a decision when nobody else could make one. Brisk and businesslike, sure: and what Emily could imagine was Marylou taking over the running of the thing, perhaps even hogging the book of points and keeping it entirely to herself. A pleasing prospect. Already the Book of Points had the significance of a Dead Sea Scroll. All she would have to do would be to find an exercise book and inscribe *Book of Points* on the cover. And voilà, one baby-sitting cooperative is set in motion, noted and recorded.

She drew the curtain slightly on the window of the kitchen door and looked out into the black back yard. The night was moonless, indifferent. Adrienne, she thought.

Ah, Adrienne.

She was reminded of those girls in high school who'd been class clowns or who, according to the prophecies in yearbooks, would succeed as dramatic actresses, the kind who were amongst the first to audition for school plays, dreaming of stardom, emoting on the boards of local repertory theaters, and finally vanishing out of sight. Swallowed by humdrum invisibility. Is this what happened to them—they turned up years later with their ambitions tarnished but their enthusiasms nevertheless undimmed? Did they take up occupations where they could live their fantasies vicariously? Like Adrienne and her model agency, perhaps. Whatever else you could say about her, it was only her entrance, her appearance, that had melted the ice and started things going.

Generally, Emily thought, they could have been worse.

She turned out the kitchen light and walked to the foot of the stairs. She stared up at the dim light on the landing. It wasn't the coven of witches Ted had talked about—at least you could say that of the group.

She climbed the stairs. Inside her own bedroom she stepped towards the bathroom door, seeing her own image in the dressing-table mirror. She paused, turned to look at herself, then swept her hair up from the back of her neck to the top of her scalp and pouted at herself in the mirror. *Cosmo,* she thought. You don't know what you're missing.

5.

A door closed and there was the sound of a lock turning and then a single footfall, a pause, a period of waiting. Then he could hear her feet crossing the rug, but after that some time passed before there was the sound of her footsteps on the stairs. A creak, as of a loose floorboard, on the landing outside his bedroom door.

His open bedroom door.

He had his eyes shut, listening. He heard how she breathed in the open doorway, a heavy uneven sound like she'd been running or crying. He thought: Leave me in peace, for Christ's sake, just leave me in peace. You live your long blind life and you win no victories along the way and what you deserve near the end of it is peace. Plain and simple. Hearing her, he thought of his wife. He hadn't thought much about her in years. When he did he was touched by a sadness that he didn't want to admit to; it would be like opening a door and letting a stranger into your most private room. Maria. Maria. She had been his sight, his life, his world. Always Maria, always there, waiting on him, tending to him, even when the muscles began to waste and he could hardly walk without pain she'd pushed him miles in a wheelchair every day. And then she got sick suddenly. Just like that. No goddam word of warning. She got sick in the night and died and he became dizzy and confused, doctors telling him this and that about heart failure, bandying words around like "aorta" and "occlusion". . . . Now he even remembered her voice, the sweet considerate way she'd talked to him, never raising the voice above a whisper.

The damnedest thing was how he'd never known what she looked like. Hours he'd spent touching the contours of her face or her body —feeling the way she was shaped. But not knowing, not *really* knowing. It was like some joke of God. Blind love.

He heard his daughter move in the doorway. She caught her breath. It was a broken sound, like a sob. For a moment he felt some form of pity for her, but pity was a bird that soon flew away. She didn't deserve pity, not any longer. Pity was like a checking account you could keep drawing on until one day there just wasn't any more left. That's what she had done. Used it all up. All of it.

He turned his face towards her, opening his eyes now. She was still standing there and he wondered: *why didn't she speak?*

"I hear you," he said. "I know you're there. You can't fool me."

She said nothing.

He crossed his hands over his belly, trying to contain the feeling of emptiness. "You haven't brought me a goddam thing to eat. All day. You've been gone all day. I get hungry, you know? I'm like other people. I get hungry as well."

She said nothing.

He could feel it in the air, terrible vibrations, like a sign that flashed the word Danger over and over. He took one hand from under the blanket and, holding the headboard of the bed, drew himself upright. He felt the warmth of the bedside lamp against his cheek. The room wasn't dark, then. She could see him plainly. He hated the idea of her watching him struggle like this, pulling himself so he could sit up.

"Is that your idea then?" he said. "You're gonna starve me? Is that it? Punish me."

Nothing. She said nothing.

"You think that'll work, huh? You think you can starve me? Huh? Well, you got another think coming. You surely do."

He leaned forward slightly so that his head hung over the side of the mattress. There was the smell of excrement from the bedpan that lay on the rug. She hadn't come to empty that either. Damn her. Damn her to hell. Was he supposed to lie here like some zoo animal? Shit and piss all around him and no food unless she had a sudden whim to bring him something. Like a keeper, he thought.

She's my keeper.

"It won't work," he said. "You can't make it work. You can't do a thing like this."

She didn't speak.

He could detect her in the doorway again. In silence, he waited. It was like waiting for something to strike you, something you couldn't see coming, a bolt from the blue.

"You can't blame me," he said. "You can't punish me."

When she spoke her voice was controlled and slow now: "I can do what I like. Anything I like. *Anything.*"

Then he heard the door close quietly. A click of metal. He listened. She had gone into her own bedroom and she was slamming drawers, as if she were looking for something, opening drawers and just banging them shut again. He called her name several times, but she didn't come back, and after a time he felt weak anyway. He tried not to think of his hunger, which had begun to make him feel hollow inside, a little nauseous. His stomach churned. He pressed the tips of his fingers against his belly and there was an empty liquid sound.

She's going to starve me, he thought.

Maybe that was her plan. Her punishment.

Well, he'd find something to do about that. He wasn't going to let that happen. Dammit, he wasn't going to lie here like a helpless old fool and take it.

He didn't move for a long time, then the hunger vanished and all he felt afterwards—before he fell into a dreamless sleep—was weakness.

Chapter Four

1.

"I know it was short notice," Emily said. She watched Carole step into the front room and take off her plastic rain hat.

Carole folded the wet hat and stuck it in her purse: "I wasn't doing anything anyhow," she said. She smiled at Emily, almost in an apologetic way, and her neck seemed to disappear into her shoulders. "I don't mind. Seriously. That's what it's all about anyway."

Emily glanced at the sweep of rain through the oak tree as she shut the door. She saw Carole stand uneasily in the middle of the room, her hands hanging at her sides. Emily said, "Make yourself at home, OK? I got some Coke and some beer in the refrigerator. There's potato chips. The kids will show you where everything is."

Carole looked around the room, then sat down on the edge of the sofa, hands bunched. Emily looked at her a moment, trying to get the other woman's biography straight: what was it? Divorced? One kid? She asked, "I don't know whether you mentioned a son or a daughter, did you?"

"I have a little girl," Carole said.

"Yeah." Emily was silent for a time. From the upstairs part of the house she could hear the kids. Charlotte was singing something. Frankie was playing a wretched electronic game Ted had got him last Christmas: *beep beep beep*. She wondered why it hadn't broken yet. "I thought maybe you'd bring your daughter with you."

Carole made an awkward gesture with her hand. "She spends alternate months with her father. That's the agreement we worked out. I don't know if it's good or bad. She's with her father now."

"You must miss her," Emily said.

"It's a pain," Carole said. She shrugged and stared into her hands and for a time Emily thought she was about to cry.

"Does he live nearby?"

"He's over in Pastorville," Carole said. "So she can keep going to the same school at least. I guess that's something."

Emily turned to the stairs and watched the kids come down, both of them strangely shy, descending slowly. "Carole. Meet Charlotte. And Frankie."

"Hi," Carole said. She got up from the sofa.

Frankie said, "You wanna watch TV or play something?"

Carole smiled. "Whatever you like."

Charlotte, saying nothing, slid into a chair and looked at the baby-sitter like she was trying to figure something out. There was a silence and then Carole said, "I like checkers. You got a set of checkers?"

"Sure. I'll play you checkers," Frankie said. He turned and ran upstairs and Emily could hear him rummaging through the junk in his bedroom closet.

"I don't think you should have any trouble," Emily said. "I'll be over at the community college. I figure to be back around ten."

"Sure," Carole said.

Emily hesitated, even after she'd put on her raincoat. What was it—this strange reluctance to leave the kids for a couple of hours? She looked at Carole and thought: What are you so damn worried about? She looks okay, solid maternal type: even Charlotte had said she had a kind face, right? So you go with the kid's own instincts? Don't you?

Carole said, "I've baby-sat before."

It must be obvious, Emily thought. Some look of profound concern on my face. Betrayed by an expression. She tried to relax, sighing, smiling at the other woman, then glancing at Charlotte.

The girl said, "You'll be late for your class, mom."

"Yeah, you're right." Emily looked at her wristwatch and then went to the door. Outside, she turned as she crossed the lawn to the driveway. Charlotte and Carole were watching her. They waved simultaneously, then the door was shut. Emily got inside the station wagon, turning the key in the ignition and half-hoping the damned thing wouldn't start, but it came to life immediately and she reversed out of the driveway and on to the street. You'll be late for your class, mom. Role reversal. Okay, she thought, admit it, admit it even to yourself—you're the worst kind of overprotective mother, you brood over your kids, you stifle them. But that wasn't strictly true. Find a better word for your attitude. Caution? The simple caution of love? Maybe. Then she was crossing the freeway bridge and over into the old town, listening to the meter of the wipers as they swept slicks of rain from the glass. Say this to yourself, she thought: The kids are all right. Say it over. A simple principle of repetition bringing belief.

She parked in the student lot at the community college and she thought: I don't know anything about the woman. I don't know a thing about her background. I don't even know if she's telling the truth about a kid, a divorce, a job at Sears or wherever she said she worked. That's an extreme, she thought: you need to hire a private detective every time you want to get a baby-sitter? Anyway, it was a contradicting, because you'd hired high-school girls in the past without really knowing much about them or their background—

And she remembered a time, when the kids had been younger, and she had gone out with Ted—an anniversary supper, a treat from Ted —and left a girl called Melody in charge of the house. When they'd come home Melody had two sullen boys in the living room and the air was filled with marijuana smoke: Ted, losing his cool, a rare moment, had been livid. Then the last time they'd gone out, to some social function connected with Ted's work, Ted was certain that the baby-sitter, a junior-high-school girl called Lilian, had siphoned off some of his scotch. (What did Ted have? A mark on the bottle?) And Mrs. DeSantis one time had been seen by Charlotte going through the kitchen cupboards and sifting old correspondence.

After all this, you still worry about Carole? she thought.

Relax. It's going to be okay.

She crossed the parking lot quickly against the rain and she went inside the building, where the corridors were filled with students rushing to classes and somewhere a bell was ringing. A bell, Emily thought. A bell, a smell of chalk and dampness and pine disinfectant: it takes you back to those unforgettable sounds and perfumes of high school. What had the night-school brochure promised? *Enrich Your Future by Enriching Your Mind . . .*

She went up the stairs, looking for the room number. When she found it, she took a deep breath, stepped inside, and thought: Right, let's be enriched, Emily. Let's see what that feels like.

It was, Emily thought, an odd group of people that came to James Hamilton's class. At first she couldn't figure out why they seemed strange to her, and then she realized that it was a sense of their incongruity: in a setting she had naturally associated with young people, those who sat in Hamilton's class were mainly middle-aged or elderly and they had a kind of youthful eagerness about them—something about the way they sat listening to Hamilton, the almost embarrassingly conscientious fashion in which they took notes, as if they were afraid of missing something, a hushed sense of being in this room to *learn* whatever Hamilton might have to teach them. Emily sat at the back of the room: it hadn't occurred to her to bring a notebook so she scribbled meaninglessly on whatever scraps of paper she could find in her purse, her mind drifting away from Hamilton, away from the classroom, into some state of absence. He had a poor classroom manner, she thought—droning, mumbling, his sentences broken by long silences. Maybe the silences are an important part of it, she thought; the moments of crystal rumination, poetic enlightenment, whatever. She found that whenever she looked up from what she'd been doodling Hamilton caught her eye across the heads in the room and she thought she saw some tiny light of warning in the way he looked at her. So she kept her head down much of the time, listening to Hamilton who had stopped droning and was answering questions from the class. What's wrong with me? Emily wondered. Why can't I get into this? Why can't I think of a question to ask? She leaned forward in her seat with a look of concentration, forehead lined, but her mind remained empty.

Hamilton explained that every Wednesday night members of the class would bring their work and read it aloud, after which it would be discussed, analyzed, critiqued. "It's pretty common to take criticism personally," he was saying. "Like it's aimed directly at you as a human being. But it's not. It's aimed at the heart of the poem, not at the heart of the person." He walked back and forth along the raised platform as he spoke, his hands stuck deep in his pants pockets. He had the curious habit of taking coins from one pocket, staring at them, passing them into the other hand and then into the other pocket; then, a little later, he would reverse the process. Back and forth like this several times; and he was seemingly unaware of it.

"Does anybody have anything to read tonight?" he asked quite suddenly. Silence. "Mrs. Allbright—weren't you going to bring some things for us to read?"

Me, Emily thought. He has to single me out. She felt a rush of blood to her face and wondered if she was blushing. A number of heads turned to look at her.

"I couldn't find anything," she said.

"Feeble, feeble," Hamilton said, smiling a little. "Maybe next week?"

Emily mumbled maybe, and then some nice old lady at the front of the room volunteered to stand up and read sections from her epic

narrative poem, which had something to do with the great philosophers—and each section of the narrative explained how one of the
philosophers had achieved his moment of enlightenment. The old
woman chose to read a part about Paul on the road to Damascus.
Emily wondered what it was all about. The lady stood up on the
platform and rambled on in a shrill voice for almost half an hour,
while Hamilton sat staring at the floor and passing his coins back and
forth. There were a great many exclamation points in the poem, or
so it seemed from the shriek of the woman's voice.

When she'd finished she went back to her seat. Hamilton rose to
the platform again and asked the class if there were any opinions.
Some disagreement followed that apparently had nothing to do with
poetry, more to do with this or that aspect of Christianity. Emily,
amused, watched Hamilton try to steer the class towards the poem itself. He said, "We're not really here to discuss Jesus, people. We're
here to discuss this poem. The fact that it has something to do with
Christianity isn't what should concern us. It's whether the poem
worked. Whether it did what it set out to do."

A long silence followed.

Hamilton said, "Was it a good poem? If so, why?"

A middle-aged man at the front of the room said, "I think some of
the rhymes were forced."

"How?" Hamilton asked.

"Well, it's kind of funny to hear Damascus rhyme with 'ask us.'"

The poet herself said, "I'd like to see *you* find something to rhyme
with Damascus. The two lines read: *Where are we going you ask us?
I'll tell you we're going to Damascus.* What's wrong with that?"

The critic shrugged and said, "Dunno. Just sounds comical."

"Comical?" The old lady was offended.

"If it's comical to you," Hamilton said patiently, "I think you
have to try and explain why."

The middle-aged man said, "I can't pinpoint it."

"It's perfectly serious," the lady remarked.

"Sometimes," Hamilton said, "I think a rhyme can sound a little
funny if it's forced. Maybe all this gentleman is saying is that yours is
forced—"

"Oh, no," the lady said. "It came naturally."

"I didn't exactly mean it like that," Hamilton said. Emily looked
at him: he was gazing at her and his expression was saying: *Help me.*

Help me out. She looked down at her scraps of paper. What was she meant to do? Stand up and put it all into perspective with a well-rounded phrase? She couldn't say why she was amused to see Hamilton look so uneasy. But she was. She drew tiny interlocking triangles on her paper and thought about the kids again. Then she glanced at her wristwatch. It was just before nine. She tuned the argument back in again, but it seemed pointless somehow, emotional statements that circled back on themselves again—and she wondered what she was supposed to learn here on Wednesday nights. Enrichment, the brochure said. Could she sue the college on the grounds of false advertising?

Hamilton, seemingly fatigued, was bringing the class to a close. He raised his hands in the air and said, "I think what we see here is something of the subjectivity of poetry, and how we judge it. People disagree on whether something is good or bad, especially with a thing like a poem—"

A small birdlike lady sitting along the row from Emily asked: "Why haven't *you* said if you liked it, Mr. Hamilton?"

James Hamilton smiled. His somewhat angular face appeared more gaunt with the expression. "Frankly, I think it's a poor poem."

Murmurs in the room.

Then suddenly Hamilton was a fury of words, a torrent of criticism, going through the poem seemingly from memory and listing bad point by bad point, and what could be done to improve the work, and why it didn't reach the objectives the poet had in mind. He was animated all at once, intense, and Emily found herself drawn into the way he moved, how he gestured with his hands, the concentration on the face: it was almost as if nothing else in the world existed, for those few moments, except for the old lady's terrible poem. He sweated, shut his eyes and there was something of the preacher's fervor in the way he spoke, in the cadences of his voice.

When he was finished there was a long silence.

Then he said, "Next week. Same time. Same room." And he began to gather up his papers and before anybody could detain him with a question he was gone from the room. Emily watched the door swing closed behind him, and then the class was beginning to disperse in a series of closed notebooks and whispers and people glancing at one another—as if a prophet had appeared and then dematerialized before their eyes. An impressive display, Emily thought. Memory and concentration. How could he have remembered so much of that poem from just one reading—unless he'd really been listening to the exclusion of everything else? She picked up her purse and made her way towards the door, then out to the stairs.

When she reached the front door she paused to do up the buttons of her raincoat. Outside, Hamilton was standing bareheaded in the rain, smoking a cigarette he held cupped in his hand. He moved towards her across the steps and she wondered if he'd been waiting for her (and if so, why?).

"Have fun?" he said.

"Only at the end," she answered.

"I warned you, Emily Allbright. I told you what the poetry was like," he said.

She stopped on the bottom step. "I thought your criticism was constructive."

"Sure, sure it was," he said. "I work on that end of things. The funny part is, it doesn't ever make much difference. That nice old dear will go home, all grim determination, all grit, and sit down to write the next bit of her alleged epic and she won't have retained a solitary word of my criticism."

"Why do you seem so sure?"

"It happens all the time, Emily. They don't have the talent for listening. Do you have that talent?" He threw his cigarette into the rain.

"Sometimes, I guess."

"Only sometimes?"

She said nothing. She began to walk in the direction of her car. He walked alongside her. In step, too, she noticed—not really knowing why this perception amused her.

"Want a glass of wine?" he said.

She paused, turning to him. "Not really. But thanks."

"There's a nice little bar near here," he said.

Didn't he hear me? she wondered. "Thanks, but I don't have the time. Really I don't."

His hand was on her arm lightly. "Five, ten minutes."

"But why? Why me?"

"Why not you? You look sane. You look normal. Why not you?"

She looked at his hand against her sleeve. "I mean, it's nice of you to ask, it really is. But I'm an old married lady. Two kids and a house and a trellis. The whole bit. You see where I'm leading?"

"I'm cut to the quick," he said, smiling.

"Sure you are. And I'm flattered. But I have to get home."

"I didn't mean to flatter you. I need a glass of wine and I hate drinking alone. That's all. When you sit in a bar and you're drinking solo, it's like having some social disease. People *stare*." He looked at her and she was suddenly embarrassed, understanding that she wanted to accept the invitation, realizing that she shouldn't—a stupid set of contradictions in the rain.

"Some other night maybe," she said. She looked across the parking lot. Rain made shimmering webs in the lamps.

"Some other night depresses me. It really depresses me." He spread his hands, a ham actor's gesture of despair.

"If I accepted it would depress my *husband*," she said, feeling priggish all at once, and then wondering if Ted would be troubled at all. If he knew. If he found out. She paused, watching Hamilton's face. He looked sadly intense, like her acceptance was of some real importance to him. What does he want with *me?* she wondered. When she was younger, and the language had been different, she might have thought: He's making a pass. But that kind of thought echoed like some useless old ghost. Making a pass, forsooth.

"One glass," he said, and he began to drum his fingers on the roof of her car, keeping time to the rain. "One glass. No strings."

She sighed. "You keep up the pressure, don't you?"

"Only when I really want something. In this case your company."

She took her car keys from her raincoat and rattled them in the palm of her hand. "I can't," she said. "Honestly. I can't do it."

He was smiling again. "It's no big deal. A glass of wine. A couple of minutes. It's nothing."

She closed her fingers over the keys, silencing them. "You don't have kids, do you?"

He shook his head. "I couldn't take that kind of claim on my life."

"It's not like that—"

"What *is* it like?"

"If you don't have them, I can't explain." She rubbed a slick of rain from an eyelid. "I left them with a baby-sitter. I don't really know the person. I don't know if she's good, bad, or indifferent. I have to go home." She wondered if she somehow sounded neurotic, tethered to her children by invisible strings, strings that were being pulled ever tighter and tighter. What difference did it make how she *sounded?* If Hamilton didn't have kids of his own, he would never know anyhow.

"You're worried about them," he said.

Bravo, she thought. "Not worried," she answered. "It's not really that."

"What then?"

"I just can't explain it," she said. She looked at her wristwatch. The kids, she thought. But the kids are all right. They're all right. "It's stupid, I guess, but sometimes you imagine all kinds of things. You imagine the worst."

Hamilton said nothing. He had turned his face to the side and was staring across the parking lot as if, having drawn a blank, he might find another prospect of company elsewhere. But the lot was silent and motionless now. Emily stuck the key in the door of her car, watching the interior light come on as the door opened slightly.

"Maybe next week," she said. Why did I have to go and say that? Make some moronic promise?

Hamilton said, "I'll hold you to that."

She smiled at him and, saying nothing, finding nothing adequate to say, she got inside the car and pulled the door shut. As she drove away she saw him turn and go back towards the college building— where, she imagined, he would shut himself in his office and begin a new poem, something called "Elegy to the Housewife," something with the lines: *Your pantyhose bag at the knees, lady. Haven't you learned any better?*

She wished she'd accepted his offer. It wasn't anything, after all, to make a Supreme Court issue out of, was it? A simple glass of wine and then home. It was no big deal. But even as she thought about it she felt a mild and delicious sensation of guilt, as if what she'd turned down were not a glass of wine with a poet but some inscrutable adventure.

An adventure.

Was that what she needed in her life?

Through the blur of rain she saw the small storefronts on Market Street—an old-fashioned ice-cream parlor, Suzanne's Garments (Specialists in Clothes for the Full-Figured Woman), a furniture shop in whose illuminated window four wax figures sat around a breakfast table, frozen in attitudes of happiness that you could attain if only

you bought Ethan Allen furniture, a small haberdashery with a window display of ribbons and buttons on cards.

Making a pass, she thought.

That was absurd.

He was lonely, that was all. A solitary man. She turned the car towards the freeway ramp.

2.

Charlotte had watched a documentary about whales and how they
needed to be saved—a threatened species, that was the phrase used:
there had been a series of gross pictures, huge bloody whales being
dragged through the sea, people prodding a giant carcass dumped on
a beach. It was all sickeningly compelling somehow. She wondered
what part she could play herself in saving the whales, but even as she
did so she was struck by a familiar sense of impotence—you were a
kid and you couldn't do very much until you were a grown-up: yet
that was curious, because she had the feeling that when you were an
adult you stopped being interested in such things as saving whales,
you changed into someone else altogether, someone with less interest
in what was going on in the world outside. When she really thought
about it she realized that, given a choice, she'd remain at her present
age—but that was pretty stupid because there wasn't anything you
could do to change the passage of time. You were born, grew up,
grew old, died. It wasn't the best plan she'd ever heard of, but it was
apparently the only one.

She watched Carole and Frankie on the rug, the checkerboard between them. They were playing their hundredth game, it seemed,
moving the circular pieces back and forth loudly. From time to time
Carole would get up and go into the kitchen and come back with a
can of beer. Sometimes she'd disappear into the bathroom and be
gone for a long time. Charlotte couldn't figure what she did in there
that took so long. Maybe it had something to do with the mystery of
menstruation, something that took Carole ages to fix, whatever it
was. She was on her fourth can of beer now and she drank it in a
sloppy way, foam spilling down her chin to her blouse. Drink made
grown-ups weird, Charlotte thought. Her own father hardly ever
drank anything except a glass of scotch at Christmas, and she'd never
seen her mother drink *anything* alcoholic, but Erika Strassman's

mother always had a martini in her hand, a strange smile on her face, and a faraway look in her eye—like she was someplace else. And when she talked her words ran together the way colors sometimes ran in a washing machine.

Click click click. Carole moved a black checker across the board and Frankie groaned. "I didn't see that," he said.

Carole laughed and set her beer down on the rug, glancing now at Charlotte. The girl thought the baby-sitter had a sad face. She felt a little sorry for her, like the way she felt sorry for Bea Cunningham who was the fattest girl in class. People laughed at Bea because of her size and shape and the way she plodded around—fat shaking on her legs like colorless jello—but Charlotte found it hard to think of Bea as being funny. She wasn't funny at all, just sad and lonely. Bea was one of life's underdogs and Charlotte had an instinctive feeling about underdogs. Maybe Carole was one too, although you couldn't really say that she was fat. Plump, sure. But not fat.

Carole said, "I don't think I can play any more checkers."

"One more. One more, please?" Frankie urged.

"All right. One more. The last one."

Frankie was beginning to set up the board again, carefully replacing the pieces. Carole was getting up now, crushing the empty beer can in one hand and heading towards the door.

"I'll be back," she said. "Don't go away."

The door swung shut behind her. Charlotte watched her brother as he studied the checker pieces.

"Do you like her?" she asked.

"She's all right."

"She drinks a lot of beer," Charlotte said.

"I guess." Frankie shrugged, still staring at the board.

Charlotte picked up a book and flipped the pages. The thing about Frankie was how, sometimes, it was hard to get him to talk. He had all these silences he used. But even when he did speak it was often worse than the silences. *I guess,* he would say. Or *Yeah, sure.* Or, *All right.* There were times when Frankie was a mystery to her, something locked away just beyond view. Other times, she found herself thinking of how much she loved him—even if she'd die before admitting such a thing to anybody. It was a strange kind of love, naturally, because it crept up on her in a quiet way, taking her quite by surprise. She didn't entirely understand it. Brotherly love. Part of it, maybe, was something to do with her being the older of the two; she had to look out for Frankie. In one of the dark fantasies she created for herself, both her parents were wiped out—not by something so mundane as an auto accident or a plane crash but by plague or rabies or something unusual, and she was alone in the world with Frankie. It was a forlorn kind of thing; she could see herself holding Frankie's hand as they went through the night (and the rain, because it was always raining in this place she invented) looking for shelter. It was, she supposed, a responsibility as much as a sense of love. Without their parents what did they really have but one another?

She watched him in silence now. He had such a serious little face that you sometimes wanted to laugh. The way he gazed at the checkers—like nothing else mattered. Right now she caught herself wishing she could get up and hug him, but she never did that kind of thing, and even if she did Frankie wouldn't like it. At his age, she thought, you don't like sloppy stuff. She shut her eyes and laid her head against the back of the sofa, thinking briefly of her mother. It was strange her going out at night. But Charlotte, who had vaguely eavesdropped on conversations between her parents, thought she understood it. You couldn't be trapped at home all the time with your kids. That wasn't any kind of life, really. Then she opened her eyes and looked at Frankie again, remembering her worst fantasy about her brother, the one she couldn't stand, the one that made her so angry that she felt water forming in her eyes. It was the one in which people were cruel to him. It wasn't always the same. Sometimes it was a gang of big kids who made him do the most unspeakable things. Sometimes it was a spooky hooded figure who chained him to a cellar wall and beat him. Charlotte couldn't bear these images, but sometimes they just popped into her mind from out of nowhere. It was the cruelty, the sense of Frankie suffering hurt, that brought a pain to the inside of her chest. Whenever they came to her now what she did was to laugh them away.

She got up from the sofa and yawned, stretching her arms. Carole still hadn't come back. Maybe she was in the bathroom again. She went to the door, opened it, and turned the corner to the kitchen. She was suddenly thirsty.

She found Carole sitting at the kitchen table.

It was weird. She was sitting at the table, both arms held in front of her, her hands clasped around a new beer can. She was gazing at the can but you could see she wasn't really looking at it, she was thinking something else, seeing something else. Charlotte paused, unable to stop looking at the woman but disturbed by the feeling that she was intruding on a private thing.

"Carole?" she said.

The woman didn't seem to hear her.

Charlotte opened the refrigerator. "Carole?" she said again.

The baby-sitter turned her face and smiled thinly, quickly. It was strange how, in the kitchen light, the face looked sunken somehow, shapeless.

"Are you OK?"

"Why wouldn't I be?"

Charlotte shrugged. "I don't know. I mean . . ."

Carole got up and moved towards the open refrigerator. "Lost in thought," she said. "That ever happen to you?"

"Oh, sure," Charlotte answered. "All the time."

Carole laughed. There was something off-tune in the sound, a wrong note. Charlotte thought it had to do with the beer she'd drunk because she'd seen Erika Strassman's mother behave in the same way at times—just drifting off to an unknown place and then snapping back again, laughing at something you could never understand, saying things that didn't always make good sense.

Charlotte poured herself a glass of milk.

"You've got lovely hair," Carole said. "Real nice."

"Thanks." Charlotte didn't move for a moment. She had the unsettling feeling that the woman was about to lift a hand and *feel* her hair—but what she couldn't really explain to herself was why this caused her a moment of unease. She was lucky to have nice hair and people were always telling her that and sometimes they even went so far as to touch it. But now, thinking of Carole feeling it, she just froze.

Carole didn't touch it, though. The moment passed and Charlotte, turning round with the milk in her hand, felt easy again.

"I don't have good hair," the baby-sitter said.

"There's nothing wrong with your hair. I think it's nice the way you have it like that."

Carole smiled. "Flatterer."

"I wasn't trying to be."

"Thanks. Thinks," Carole said. She looked sad and glum again and Charlotte suddenly experienced one of those small insights that delighted her when they happened. It was like in a comic book of Frankie's when an electric lightbulb lit up in somebody's head. There was always the word *Eureka* attached to it. It was as if a door had opened into somebody else's room and Charlotte could see for a moment through Carole's eyes—and she *knew* that Carole saw herself as being *massive,* that if she was asked to draw a picture of herself she would draw a great blimp. It was strange to have these moments of recognition, stranger still to think that people saw themselves so wrongly at times.

"You have really good hair," Charlotte said and sipped her milk.

Carole put a hand up to her forehead. The look of sadness made her appear attractive in some way; a melancholy kind of prettiness. But then she smiled and the sadness was broken. She raised her can to her lips and drank. A noisy action. Charlotte watched her for a time. *Chugging.* That was the word for how Carole drank the beer. *Chugging it down.*

"You're a good kid," Carole said. "Your mother's very lucky."

Charlotte laughed. "Tell *her* that, will you?"

"Oh, I'm sure she already knows."

They went back to the TV room. Frankie was rattling checkers in the palm of his hand, impatiently. He looked up as they opened the door. Charlotte glanced at the TV. A man and a woman were embracing each other, sighing heavily; it was quite sickening. The man said, *Don't let the ghost of the past interfere with our love.*

Carole said, "Roger Moore and Carroll Baker. What's the name of that movie?"

"I don't know," Charlotte said. "It looks *bad.*"

"You don't like romance?" Carole said.

Charlotte sat on the edge of the sofa and drank her milk. She looked at Carole. Her eyes were shining in the reflected light of the TV; it was as if *she* were in Roger Moore's arms, and not the actress. Funny, Charlotte thought, how grown-ups can behave so strangely. Like Erika Strassman's mother with her endless afternoon soap operas and how she would sit, martini in hand, and watch people mope tragically about life. Why did they inflict such misery on themselves anyhow? Didn't they *want* to be happy? Why did they sit around and watch such sad stuff?

There was a commercial interruption.

"Ready to play?" Frankie said.

Carole sat down cross-legged on the rug beside the boy. "This is the last game," she said.

"OK."

Charlotte watched them for a time while they moved the pieces back and forth. Poor Frankie—you could tell from his determined expression how badly he wanted to win. He struggled with a yawn, fighting sleep. She thought about her mother again. She didn't think, as her father did, that the poetry thing was a waste of time. Quite the opposite; in fact, it would be terrific if her mother could write some poems. It was a better hobby, anyhow, than carpentry. She turned her face to the screen where the man Carole had called Roger Moore was going off to fight at a place named Waterloo. She stifled a yawn.

"Got you," Carole said.

"Hell." Frankie, looking dejected, was staring at the board.

"Next time we play you'll get even." The baby-sitter raised her beer can and drank.

Tired, Charlotte rose from the sofa. "Bedtime, little brother."

"I don't wanna go until Mom gets home."

"It's nine-thirty."

"I don't care."

"You're supposed to be in bed by nine."

"I don't care."

Charlotte sighed. "Be it on your own head."

"What's that mean?"

"It means it's your funeral, kid," she said.

"My funeral?" Frankie looked puzzled.

Carole crumpled the empty can in her hand and laughed. "You should both go to bed," she said.

"Right," Frankie said.

Charlotte resisted the suggestion. "I'm older than he is. It entitles me to stay up longer."

Carole got up from the rug, unsteady on her feet now. She was still laughing. "Both of you," she said again.

For a time Charlotte didn't say anything. She was tired, but it was a matter of principle for her. She *deserved* to stay up later. Still, why make Carole's life difficult for her?

"OK," Charlotte said. "I'll go."

The baby-sitter went with them to the bottom of the stairs and watched as they climbed up to the landing. At the top, Charlotte turned round and looked down. The light that fell from the landing seemed to obscure Carole's face, making it smooth and without feature. She was looking up, intently, in a way that made Charlotte feel self-conscious. My hair again, she thought. She's looking at my hair. Sometimes it was more a curse than a blessing.

"Good night," the girl said.

"Good night, kids."

Inside her own room Charlotte undressed and put on her nightgown and got into bed. She lay with the lamp on and stared for a time at the ceiling. She could hear Carole moving around below, going into the kitchen, opening the refrigerator, popping a can of beer. That made it a total of six, she thought. Six beers. After that there was silence except for the distant echo of the TV. Charlotte felt sleepy, her mind drifting, mixed images coming and going—her father going away, the scrambled eggs in the railroad station, Carole's flattened beer cans. Then she heard the sound of the baby-sitter's feet on the stairs. She opened her eyes. Maybe it wasn't Carole coming up, maybe it was her mother who'd come home—but no, it was a different sound. She knew the noise her mother made when she climbed the stairs. This one was heavier, slower—then it had to be Carole coming up to check if they were in bed. She listened. The footsteps reached the landing, then she heard Carole pause outside the door of her bedroom. But nothing happened. The door didn't open. She didn't come in.

Instead—

But that couldn't be. Why would she go in there? She didn't have any need to go in there, any right.

Charlotte looked at the surface of the closed door. She could hear the sliding glass of the medicine cabinet in her mother's bathroom—the faint screech of glass on metal. Why had Carole gone in there?

Snooping? Like Mrs. DeSantis?

Carole wasn't a snooper, was she?

Charlotte turned on her side and stared at the printed shapes on the cotton curtains. Dorothy and the other figures from Oz. What would Carole look inside the medicine cabinet for? Charlotte listened closely for a time, but she didn't hear anything else. Eventually, even though she struggled against it, she fell asleep.

3.

An empty freeway—why was there something so unsettling about night driving on an empty freeway? The absence of things, of traffic, of movement. A curious perversion of a norm, that was it. The highway without traffic had no purpose—a needless stretch of concrete. Emily came off the freeway at the West Pastorville bridge, realizing that she was driving a little too fast, perhaps even a little carelessly. Worn rubber on the wipers made a scratching noise on the windshield: it was the sound nerves might have made. There's no great rush, she told herself. No great hurry. She stopped at the red light on the bridge and tapped her fingers on the rim of the steering wheel. Sometimes this was a long light. You were tempted to glide slowly through regardless. She looked down through the rain at the lights of the suburb, seeing the deep blue glow of a distant shopping plaza and the red lights atop the antenna of the local radio station WPAS. The stop light burned in the dark, unchanging, seeming to signify something other than the mere cessation of traffic—like a warning of some kind.

You could panic, she thought. Sitting here like this, waiting for change, you could panic. She looked at her watch. 9:32. The little digital display lit up as she pressed the button. Ted's Christmas gift last year, highly imaginative. She stared at the light again. Come on, she thought. Hurry, for God's sake. A truck went past, hurtling through the darkness like a monster. Change. *Change.*

But the light didn't turn to green. A malfunction, she thought. A breakdown of some kind. What would it be like to sit here forever in the dark and stare at that red signal? Spiders would spin, your flesh flake and peel off, and one day you might be found in a rusted-out station wagon—unidentifiable bones. A dentist could identify you from his charts. She rolled her window down, feeling the chill of the night air against her face. If the light were broken, then sooner or later a cop would come along and direct traffic. Later rather than sooner, she thought. She let her hand dangle outside the car, as if the touch of rain and cold might calm her. She stared at the spread of suburb beneath her, searching vainly for her own street, thinking: What was panic but some breakdown of control valves? Needless worry? Undue concern? Ah, but you're prone to it, aren't you? It comes in when you don't expect it and what you live with are those moments of profound dizziness when your mind is nervous as a starling. Then you imagine your house is on fire or the roof has collapsed or some prowler of the dark suburb has smashed a window and is inside the house, terrorizing the kids. . . . *Dear Abby, I am prone to panic attacks. Do you have any suggestions? Nervous, West Pastorville. New York.*

She breathed deeply, drummed her fingers against the side of the car, watched the red light. Ted had once told her she ought to learn to relax more, take things in her stride. *Take things in one's stride,* she thought. That was meaningless. When she thought about that image she always imagined herself taking extremely long steps wherever she went, snatching things up as she hurried briskly along. Ted, dear Ted—well, he didn't worry like her. Worry wasn't part of Ted's psychological makeup. She shut her eyes a moment, thinking of Ted in distant Maine, imagining all over again his motel room. . . . The trouble with panic, even a small panic, was how it began to flood through you, how it started in a tiny way and picked things up in its tidal rush as it coursed along. The house. The kids. Ted away. Wholesale disaster. Your whole life collapsed.

She opened her eyes.

Green! At last. Thank God. She edged the car through the light and then over the bridge and down into the streets of the suburb. There was a speed limit of thirty miles per hour which she ignored, passing parked cars and dark trees and rooms in which TVs threw colored lights upon windows, passing all of it quickly. It was a disorienting place in the dark, so many streets that resembled each other, so many houses that, drawn from the same blueprint, looked alike. You could easily park your car in the wrong driveway and go inside a house that wasn't your own and see a bunch of strangers seated around a kitchen table, all of them staring at you in wonderment. Even in daylight, she thought, it wasn't always easy to remember where you lived. Once or twice, despite the ten years they had lived there, she had driven straight past her own home. When you were gone from the main thoroughfares, there was an absence of landmarks. An absence of signs. When they'd lived in the city the visible marks of decay had always told her where she could find their apartment. But nothing was decaying here yet. If there was rot and disintegration they were slow things, hidden, subterranean.

She drove across the corner of St. Catherine Drive and St. Paul Street. The lamps, spaced as they were, threw only the thinnest of lights. Trees caught and muted the lights, trapping them in shadows. She turned on St. Mark's, suddenly remembering that this was a cul-de-sac. Why had she forgotten that? She braked, reversed, and swung around. I'm late, she thought. Later than I said, later than I wanted to be. She went quickly along Albany Street, suddenly beset by the feeling that she'd never been this way before. It was that part of the nightmare in which you realized all your friends were strangers, in which you knew everybody but nobody recognized you.

And then there was Larue Drive and home, the house where the street curved slightly, where the huge oak stood alone in the front yard and dripped in the night rain like a miserable animal. She turned the station wagon into the driveway, parking and getting out and slamming the door behind her in what was almost one continuous movement. Then she was inside the living room, she was inside the living room—expecting what? The kids to come running towards her?

But not this.

Not these silences. This emptiness.

This emptiness.

She gazed round the room, then at the lamp, at the globe of light making a bright circle on the ceiling. There's nobody here, she thought. There's nobody here. *They've gone.*

OK. OK, she thought. Don't panic. The kids. First of all, the kids. That's what you check before anything else. Dreamlike, feeling a weird sense of dislocation, she moved towards the stairs and began to climb, slowly at first, then faster as she reached the landing. *Something's happened to them, to my kids.* Her mouth was dry, her tongue adhered to the roof of her mouth. *Someone's hurt my kids. . . .* On the landing, she tried to still the feeling she had of melting, dissolving, yielding to some panic as shapeless as hot wax. The kids. First of all, the kids. She pushed open the door of Charlotte's room.

The child was asleep, tangled in bedsheet and blanket, breathing regularly, slightly. She crossed the floor and leaned down over the girl, putting out her hand to touch the strand of hair that had slipped across the forehead. Frankie, she thought. Frankie now. She crossed the landing, went inside the boy's room, moved through the darkness

—her feet clumsily knocking over some toys, making a sound of wood clattering. Lincoln Logs, something he'd been building on the rug. Frankie was asleep, his small mouth open and oval, his hands clasped under his head. She bent over him, kissing him lightly so as not to disturb him. Then she stood up and left the room, closing the door behind her. On the landing again she hesitated. Carole—was it possible she'd put the kids to bed and left? Was it conceivable she'd gone home, leaving them asleep in an unlocked house? How? How could *anybody* do that? She felt a strange mixture of anger and relief.

"Carole," she called out. "Carole?"

She moved to the top of the stairs and looked down into the empty room below. How still it seemed in the lamplight. She reached out to touch the handrail, as if what she needed now was support. But the sense of panic had dissipated itself, gone as fast as it had come, and now she felt oddly empty, confused. Everything was all right. No, she thought, it's not all right. It's not all right. Something is wrong.

She pushed the door of her own bedroom open with her foot. The room was in darkness—and yet she knew, silent as it seemed, that the room wasn't empty. She stepped inside and turned on the lamp and saw the baby-sitter sprawled across the bed, *her* bed, she saw Carole lying at a strange angle that suggested nothing so much as death. . . . And then that illusion was wrecked by the turning motion of the woman, hands rising and falling, body twisting over on its side. My bed, Emily thought. On my goddam bed. Fast asleep. And on the bedside table a can of beer, a small pool of liquid lying on polished wood. Christ, how could she? How could she?

"Carole," she said. She stood over the plump shape of the sitter. "Carole. Wake up. Come on, wake up."

The woman opened her eyes in a fluttering way, hauled out of God knows what dream. Slowly, she struggled into an upright position. Then she looked at Emily in a dazed way, as if she didn't know where she was, her moonlike face puzzled, her hair mussed out of shape. She swung her legs over the edge of the mattress and Emily saw the flesh tremble on her kneecaps.

"I guess I felt sleepy," she said.

"I guess," Emily said. She looked a moment at the beer can. What was she supposed to say? How angry was she supposed to be? You've been sleeping in *my* bed. She licked her dry lips and watched Carole gaze at her, the eyes dark and stupid and apologetic. She didn't mean any harm, Emily thought. She's a harmless kind of person. How could she be otherwise? And this—this intrusion on her privacy, this act, this minor violation, it was just some kind of carelessness, thoughtlessness. That was all. What was important here anyhow? The kids, right? And the kids were fine and sound asleep and that was all that mattered.

"I'm sorry," Carole said.

"It doesn't matter—"

"No. It does. I shouldn't have crashed here."

Emily stared at the rug. I just don't have the capacity for anger, she thought. It was a gift I never had, an energy I don't possess.

Carole was standing now, straightening out her clothes. "Emily, really, I'm sorry. I guess I came upstairs to check the kids, then I felt tired. I don't know. Too many beers. I lay down. After that . . ."

"It's OK," Emily said. Nice: that was the word to describe her. A nice person. Sometimes she didn't want to be a nice person. Sometimes she wished she could turn mean and show her irritation. But it was a gap she couldn't quite close. And then she thought: *I don't know this woman. I don't know any of these women.* But that was a re-creation of Ted's argument, and she didn't want to yield to him, to give him any sense of victory.

"I'm sorry," Carole said. "It won't happen again. I mean, if you ask me again. I don't deserve it."

Emily smiled at the other woman. "Of course I'll ask you again, Carole. It's no big deal."

The sitter shrugged. Emily had the feeling, like she'd had before, that Carole was about to weep. What she saw again was an aura of loneliness about the other woman—and maybe, just maybe, this was what had motivated her to reply to the advertisement in the first place. To join something. To belong to *something.* Emily Freud, why not?

"You won't ask me again," Carole said.

"I will," Emily said. "I promise I will."

"You sure?"

"You want me to cross my heart, Carole?"

The other woman smiled now. She reached down and smoothed out the impression she'd made on the bed cover. Then, still embarrassed, she started to move towards the door. Emily followed her across the landing and down the stairs The silence had begun to irritate her; even the way the other woman moved, lumbering, clumsy, with an awkwardness that suggested extreme self-consciousness. In the kitchen Carole picked up her coat from the back of a chair. She fought her way into it, saying nothing.

"Carole," Emily said. "Forget it. OK? Just forget it. It really doesn't bother me."

Carole was fastening the buttons slowly. "You've got nice kids. You know that? I really had a good time. I like them."

"Thanks," Emily said.

"That's why I'd like to come again."

"Next time I need somebody, I'll call you first." It sounded unconvincing somehow, like a false promise. Emily didn't like the way her own voice came out—a phony quality. But Carole, turning up her coat collar, seemed not to notice.

They went together to the front door.

"Good night," Carole said.

"Good night."

Emily shut the door and leaned against it. Her breathing was tense, tight. She heard the sound of Carole's car, the way the engine spluttered several times before it finally turned over. And, then there was silence. She checked the bolt in the kitchen, then she drew the one on the front door. At the foot of the stairs she stopped, her hand on the handrail. After the panic there was a sense of exhaustion, of nerves running down to their limits. What the hell did it matter, though? The woman fell asleep on my bed, that's all. Weigh that against the fact that the kids are OK and what have you got? Nothing. Nothing else mattered so long as the kids were OK.

And they were. They were just fine.

She reached the landing and turned out the light, then stepped inside her own bedroom. As she undressed, she thought: There are times when you behave in a perfectly stupid manner, when you just give way to fears, phantasms, vague dreams. A tree in the front yard filled with wind, the sound of something creaking in the attic, a baby-sitter asleep on your bed—the sum of these things was zero, sweet zero.

She folded her clothes untidily on the back of the armchair and then rolled back the sheet. She lay naked on top of the bed, gazing at the lamplight. Tomorrow, she thought, Ted might be home. And she was glad she hadn't accepted James Hamilton's offer. Even guilt ceased to be new and delicious after a time.

4.

The small man with the sand-colored hair was called Steadman. His partner, known in the department as the Undertaker, was called Quayle. They had a relationship constructed around a series of grudges and old complaints concerning such things as promotion, seniority, and a general difference in temperament. Quayle was inclined to be cold and indifferent, while Steadman was impulsive and sometimes indiscreet in a garrulous way. Loose talk, gossip, a tendency to aggressive drunkenness: or so Quayle perceived him. What it boiled down to was the fact that Quayle preferred to work alone; the concept of sharing did not come naturally to him. And yet here they were, together again, in this large drafty apartment. Too many nights, Quayle thought often—too many nights spent in wasted pursuits, sifting through people's lives as if what might be discovered at bottom would crystallize in some conclusive pattern, some definitive shape; but that was sheer dreaming. You ended up with bits and pieces and nothing that dovetailed so smoothly as you wanted or needed. He watched Steadman light a cigarette and pause in his rifling of a drawer. The floor beneath Steadman's feet was littered with handkerchiefs and socks and shirts. That was it, Quayle thought —you dug through the laundry of strangers. He turned away from his partner and opened the closet door, although he knew he would find nothing inside of any interest; he understood this intuitively, because he had the strange ability to enter a room in which he'd never been before and get the feeling that something would be turned up or, conversely, that it wouldn't be. The inside of the closet was dark. He made out a bag of old golf clubs (unmatched), a couple of jackets on hangers, a super-eight movie camera still in its original box.

"The guy didn't keep a diary," Steadman said from across the room.

"He didn't keep much of anything," said Quayle. He closed the door of the closet and stared for a time at his partner. Steadman was stuffing articles of clothing back inside the drawer. He shut the drawer and drew on his cigarette until Quayle was sure his lungs would burst open. On the top of the chest of drawers there lay the pile of letters they'd found earlier.

Steadman gestured towards the letters now. "He kept them," he said. "God knows why."

Quayle picked up the pile and shuffled through them. What he'd felt before when he'd glanced inside the envelopes was a sensation of pain—someone else's pain. He wondered if a time might come when there wouldn't have to be this distasteful eavesdropping on another's private suffering. He listened to Steadman sighing, a weary kind of sound. The real difference, he thought, between himself and his partner was that he had a sense of humanity, an awareness of compassion, whereas Steadman lacked something in these departments. The pain in the letters, for one thing; when Steadman had looked at the letters he'd laughed and said something about a broad carrying a goddam heavy torch, as if this assigned everything to a manageable category. It was more than a heavy torch, as far as Quayle was concerned: it was a burdensome weight of an immeasurable kind. Torches went out eventually, but some weights you couldn't ever put down. He felt sorry for the woman. Steadman felt nothing.

Quayle took out one of the letters now and read it slowly. *I sometimes know this is the end of my world,* she had written. *I sometimes know I can't go on. Why can't we be together, even without Charlie?* He folded the letter and wondered who Charlie was and what he was remembering now was the time they'd gone to see the woman and he'd picked up a picture of a young girl and said: *Your daughter?* And he recalled how pleased the woman had been. A simple compliment and she'd looked as if the sun might never set in her life. Then who the hell was Charlie, who was this Charlie referred to throughout the letters? He slipped the letter back in its envelope and drew one hand in a tired manner across his forehead.

"It's not much of a place," Steadman said. "It doesn't feel lived-in."

It isn't lived-in, Quayle thought. He's gone. Vanished. Off the face of the goddam earth. People made their lives untidy and messy. It was thoughtless most of the time. Then at other times, rarely, it was calculated. He sat on the arm of a chair and stifled a yawn and stared around the room. There was a bedroom with nothing more than a mattress in a corner and a small portable radio. A bathroom in which the tiles glistened and the porcelain toilet shone like it had never been used. And then this room, a combined living room and kitchen. It was Spartan, Quayle thought. Once, maybe, this had been a grand house—but now it had been butchered into a series of boxes for living in. He looked up at the high ceiling and the ornate frieze, yellowing and flaky. He got up and opened the refrigerator. Inside there was a moldy can of beans, its top missing, a couple of slices of ancient bread, curling and hard and somehow grotesque, a couple of eggs, half a carton of milk. The guy hadn't entertained much, for sure.

Steadman, still smoking, was pacing back and forth and sometimes stopping at the window to draw the curtain back and look out into the rainy night. Quayle shut the refrigerator door and stuck his hands in the pockets of his coat.

"So what have we got?" Steadman said. "A guy disappears. Doesn't take his car. Doesn't say a goddam word at his work. Doesn't have any financial worries we know about. He's separated and his wife isn't too happy about the whole deal. A bunch of weepy letters. What else?"

A bunch of weepy letters, Quayle thought. That didn't cut it, really; that didn't exactly embrace the sadness. Maybe Steadman was immune by this time. Maybe experience was a form of inoculation and after a time you didn't admit anything to yourself. Quayle gazed at the letters for a while.

"And a gun license," he said.

"A gun license and no gun," Steadman said, shaking his head. "You want to know how I figure it? The guy gets up one day. He can't hack it anymore. His wife's letters get him down. So he decides, fuck it, and he takes his gun and decides he's going off someplace, Florida maybe, and what he's going to do to alleviate the boredom of living is maybe shoot a few people—"

"Yeah," Quayle said. He hated the way Steadman was grinning; it was lewd, skull-like.

"You got a better idea?"

Quayle said, "Sometimes people want to step outside their skins, you know?"

"Tell me about it."

Quayle tightened the faucet in the sink. "Sometimes it's a sickness you can't explain."

Steadman laughed. "Yeah? Shock me some more."

Quayle shrugged and looked at the discolored porcelain of the sink. "So where's the gun?"

"I told you. It's in Florida. Lying in the drawer of some motel room—"

Quayle shook his head just as there was the sound of someone knocking at the door. The door opened slightly and the landlady stepped into the room, rubbing her hands together in a manner that suggested fear—as if what she worried about most was a corpse hidden in the apartment, death under the floorboards or concealed behind new plaster. She wore small spectacles at the end of her nose; she reminded Quayle of a ferret, or some other small sharp-featured furry thing.

"You want some coffee?" she asked.

The two men looked at her. "We're just about to leave," Quayle said.

"Yeah." The woman looked round the large room. Rain knocked on the loose windowpanes. "I don't know what to do, honestly. I mean, his rent is paid up until the end of the month, so what do I do? Rent it out? I wish I knew."

Quayle took his hands from his pockets, conscious of their rather glacial appearance, a white and icy look. "Did anybody ever come here? Did he ever have a visitor? A woman, maybe?"

The landlady shook her head. It irritated her to have a tenant on the loose. She enjoyed the idea of everybody in the house being in bed and fast asleep by midnight. "Only his wife one time."

"His wife came here?" Quayle said.

"Once. He wasn't home. I let her into the apartment to wait. I guess she waited for a while, then she left."

"You left her alone?"

"Sure." The woman fingered her little glasses. "They were separated I understand. I guess she was pretty upset by the look of her."

"She left before he got back?" Quayle said.

"I think so. I heard her leave."

"Thanks." Quayle glanced a moment at Steadman who had taken a handkerchief from his pocket and was blowing his nose, a rude honking sound. Always with the handkerchief, Quayle thought. He looked at the landlady who was gazing in a worried way around the room; then she withdrew hesitantly, as if she suspected the policemen of some minor crime, some mischief in her absence. Quayle watched the door close.

"File it under Missing Persons," Steadman said. "I'm beat. Beat. I want to go home."

Quayle nodded. Missing Persons: the classification masked a galaxy of sins. But maybe Steadman was right, maybe all you had to do was to relegate the mystery into MPs, and there it might lie unsolved forever. Except there were a couple of loose ends here—a missing gun and someone called Charlie; and Quayle, in his own fastidious way, hated loose ends. They irked him the way lint clinging to a dark suit did, or dandruff on a collar.

Steadman was going to the door. "Ready?" he said.

Quayle had one last look round the room, then he followed Steadman out on to the landing.

"Must've been a nice property at one time," Steadman said.

"Yeah," Quayle said.

"Like everything else, it's gone to the goddam dogs."

"Yeah," Quayle said again.

5.

She thought she shouldn't have gone to the house, she shouldn't have gone there—but she had, and now it didn't matter very much. She was remembering the single oak tree in the front and how, when the rain spilled through it, it was like a hundred different voices all whispering one word constantly, over and over, only she didn't know what that word was. From the side of the pool she looked up at the dark window of her own room, hearing the rain sweep across the stagnant surface. She pressed her hands to the sides of her head as if she might restrict the pain in this way, but she couldn't. She could take one of Spassky's little pills and that might help—but she didn't move to go indoors, because now the surface of the pool had taken her attention and she stared down at it in the darkness, barely seeing the water but hearing it respond to the rain.

She was dizzy then. She shut her eyes very tight and thought how easy it would be to fall into the water, just get too close to the edge and lose your balance and fall. Then behind her eyes she saw the same stark shape of the child floating face down in the pale blue water like a foreign object being drawn towards the pool filter, like a leaf maybe, something tossed onto the surface by wind, she saw the sleeves of the white blouse bloated with water and strands of yellow hair drifting from the face in the manner of tendrils, she heard the merciless hum of the filter and the soft rattle of the pump—all of this locked in behind her eyes in a picture of blinding white sunlight that had lain like ice that day on the surface of the pool. I could pull the child from the water and lay her face upwards on the deck and breathe life back into that dead face, revive her, resuscitate her, put all the clocks back to that moment when she was first stepping to the edge of the water, hypnotized by treacherous blue tiles, then slipping, then falling. . . .

She opened her eyes now. She thought: That's not the way it happened. It didn't happen like that. She dreamed that. She had crossed a borderline somewhere into a dream, and the dream screamed at her. (Nick sleeps off beer. The blind man listens.) She had dreamed all of it, all the way down the line, from the rage of her panic, the wild helplessness, the heartbreak, the whine of an ambulance racing through the streets and the howl of a police car and the men who had tried to save the girl, pressing on her ribs and blowing their own breath into her limp mouth. I dreamed it. Yes. That's what I did.

But then you couldn't explain the empty bedroom, could you?

Could you explain that?

She turned, confused, away from the edge of the pool.

Yes, it could be explained. It could be rationalized easily—

Somebody took Charlie. Somebody stole her.

And I know who it was, she thought.

I know her name and where she lives. And I'll get Charlie back again.

She opened the back door and stepped into the unlit kitchen and stood for a moment listening to the feeble sound of the blind man calling her name from upstairs. I won't go up, she thought. I won't go up to see him. Already he doesn't exist. Not for me. Already he's dead.

The rest was a technicality, that was all.

Chapter Five

1.

"I heard her, I tell you," Charlotte said.

"You're absolutely sure?" Emily laid two plates with toast and overdone sausages on the kitchen table.

"I wouldn't make it up," the girl said. "I mean, what would be the point in just making it up?"

"No, I believe you."

"I can't figure out why," Charlotte said. "Unless she was just kinda snooping. You know the way people are in somebody else's house."

"What would be so fascinating about a medicine cabinet?"

Charlotte smiled at her mother, raising a piece of sausage to her mouth and chewing on it deliberately. "Well. Don't *you* wonder what people keep in their medicine cabinets?"

"Not really," Emily said.

"Plus she drank six beers."

"I noticed the empty cans."

Charlotte shrugged. Frankie, taciturn in the early morning, snapped off a corner of his toast. With his mouth full, he said, "She's nice. I like her. She plays a mean game of checkers."

Emily stared at the boy for a time. When he pushed hair away from his face he did so with fingers to which toast crumbs adhered; his scalp was covered now with tiny flecks of bread.

"I think she's nice too," Emily said. "It's just that I don't like the idea . . ." She let her voice trail off. It was one thing to find the woman in her bed, another to find she'd been through the cabinet. Make allowances, look for justifications. She had a headache, say, and wanted an aspirin. Christ, even so, you didn't just rummage inside somebody else's belongings. She tried to think now of what the cabinet contained, but she couldn't come up with a real inventory. Later, she'd take a look. Still, it irked her to think of Carole on the plunder. She turned to Charlotte and said, "I don't think you should mention it to your father. I'll deal with it."

Charlotte shrugged. She looked at her mother with an almost intolerably knowing expression, as if she understood the feebleness of

Emily's statement. *I'll deal with it*—which meant it would be allowed to lapse into silence, a subject sealed and closed. The girl bit off another piece of sausage and smiled to herself. Emily went to the refrigerator and poured two glasses of orange juice from a carton. Sometimes the kid is impossible, she thought. She understands too much. Sees too much. Eavesdrops a little more than she should. Right at this moment she's listening to Ted's future lectures. . . . *I told you no good would come of putting up a goddam postcard in a goddam supermarket and throwing our house open to loonies, Jesus Christ.* . . . Emily carried the two glasses to the table and set them down. Frankie was already getting up.

"Well, maybe she needed a pill or something," Emily said.

"Sure," Charlotte said.

"She *might,* Charlotte."

"Sure." Charlotte could be infuriating at times in this easy, sarcastic acquiescence.

"I should call the cops in, huh? I should get fingerprint men to come over and take a look, is that what you think?"

"Not exactly," the girl said. She pushed her chair back and rose. "I better run. You ready, Frankie?"

"He's not ready until he cleans that toast out of his hair," Emily said.

"What toast?"

"Go look in the mirror."

Frankie went out of the kitchen, dragging one foot behind him as if he were paralyzed. Charlotte giggled and, as she turned from the table, spilled the orange juice. It slithered in a slow puddle to the center of the table.

"Shit," Emily said. She ripped a paper towel from a kitchen roll and began to sponge the mess.

"Sorry," Charlotte said.

"Forget it." Emily, seeing the orange soak through the paper fibers, thought about the strange fact that she loved her children less in the mornings than at other times. Perhaps it was something she could raise the next time the co-op met in full session, suggesting that baby-sitting could be a more practical prospect if it were done at breakfast time rather than in the evening. Now the radio was blaring in the living room and she could hear Frankie sing over the noise. The Bee Gees. I need the Bee Gees right now, Emily thought. I need to get off on "Stayin' Alive." Why was she so jumpy today anyhow? Maybe it wasn't just the fact that Ted might be coming home, maybe it wasn't even the idea of Carole going through the cabinet like some prowler—maybe it was how, when she had risen, she had found herself thinking about James Hamilton, as if something of a dream remained in her mind, a relic. We go through this, do we? This retarded adolescence? This romantic fantasy? Is this when you know you're lost in the quicksands of the middle years? Sweet Jesus. What would happen next? A glass of wine, a touch of hands, somebody whispering a sonnet in your ear? Grow up, kid, she told herself. You can't be responsible for what you dream. Besides, even if you were drawn and attracted, think of the guilt. Ah, the guilt—there you had it, a whole sense of some indefinable moral order distilled in one piddling little word. Like a teen-age girl, she thought, the brief attention flattered you. And in an age when flattery is not your everyday happening, well, you have to feel a little good about it.

She crushed the sodden towel in her hand and threw it into the wastebasket. Sticky too. She ran her fingers under the cold water faucet. Who needs it? she thought. The morning hassle, the mess, the smell of sausages, sticky fingers, the edginess of recent sleep—screw it, she thought. Today, maybe, Ted will be home. Look forward to that at least. She poured a cup of coffee and lit a cigarette and sat at the kitchen table. She longed for the house to be silent now, the kids to be gone—a weird longing, because as soon as they'd gone you started to miss them. No, not immediately, but after a half hour or so.

Charlotte, dressed for school, came back into the room, followed by Frankie, who had soaked his hair with water and brushed it ridiculously flat with a crooked center parting, so that he looked like some dwarf version of a barbershop singer.

Emily got up and kissed them. Then she watched from the window of the front room as they walked, Frankie trailing his sister the way a duckling would follow its mother, to the corner where they caught the school bus. She continued to watch until they had boarded the muddy yellow vehicle, then she went upstairs to her bedroom and opened the medicine cabinet. Figure it out, she thought. What would Carole be after? There wasn't much really because apart from store-bought items there was only one prescription bottle—the Dalmane. She uncapped the small brown bottle and spilled the capsules onto her hand, but she hadn't kept track of their use so she didn't know how many of the original thirty should be left. Okay. Big deal. Maybe Carole swallowed a sleeping pill. Emily stuffed the pills back inside the bottle. Then she took off her robe and climbed into the shower and let the water bring her awake, thinking of Ted as she stood there, wondering how she could contrive to make Ted's return more of an event, more of a real homecoming. She wanted to please him. But maybe he wouldn't be back today. He hadn't called yet, but then he was given to the annoying habit of telephoning only when he arrived at Pastorville station, summoning her the way you might a taxicab. She got out of the stall and dried herself and then put on a pair of stiff clean blue jeans and a white blouse that knotted at the navel. She looked at herself in the full-length mirror in the bedroom. It wasn't a bad figure, was it? The breasts were still firm, pointed, and the waist still small. Her belly was flat, even if it was no longer taut, hard. After two kids, what would you expect? All right, she thought. You're not so bad looking. But it doesn't alter the fact that the kitchen has to be cleaned. There are dishes to be loaded and surfaces to clean and a supper to be planned. Screw that too, she said to herself. She wondered if instead she might write a poem—but the thought made her apprehensive, in part because she hadn't attempted to write one in so many years, but also because she wasn't sure of her motivation. Was it to please herself? Or Hamilton? But then she had no real reason to please Hamilton, did she? If she sat down to construct a poem it would be on account of her own urges. Then, what did she have to say? You could burn all your fuses out dwelling on that one.

She went downstairs and looked at the mess in the kitchen. She didn't want to touch it. She imagined it as someone else's mess, as if she were perceiving it through glass, or seeing it in terms of a framed photograph. The kitchen could wait. She turned the radio off and the house grew silent, like something turning in on itself, something huddled within its own secrets. But day silences were different from those at night somehow; a day silence was a thing you could relish. She made an entry in the Book of Points, giving herself a negative credit, and Carole a positive one, and then she went into the back yard. Sunlit morning, yesterday's rain nothing more than a smell issuing from damp grass, wet shrubbery. She pottered idly around the yard, hauling a few weeds out of the lawn, circling Ted's trellis a

couple of times as if it bewildered her, and then she went back indoors when she heard the doorbell ringing. Who was selling what this
time? More encyclopedias, free samples of detergent, some stubborn
census taker? She opened the front door.

It was Adrienne.

"Surprise, surprise." And she stepped into the living room, then
plumped herself down in a chair where she crossed her legs. She was
wearing black pants with gilt embroidery stitched into the seams.

"I didn't expect—"

"Took the day off," Adrienne said. "One of the few advantages of
the self-employed. You can play hooky and no repercussions, dear.
How are you? What's new?"

Emily sat down on the sofa that faced the other woman. She
stared at the garish pants with the gold threads, the silver blouse
opened to the cleavage, the heavy pendant around the neck, the short
plaid jacket with the large pockets. Cacophony, she thought. Especially with that purse Adrienne clutched, a small thing stitched with
hundreds of colored beads. She was thinking of an artist's palette at
the end of a hard day's painting.

"Am I intruding?" Adrienne asked.

"Of course not—"

"Had breakfast?"

"Not yet—"

"I know a neat little place. Let me take you out to breakfast."

Emily hesitated a moment. "I'd like to, but I'm waiting for a call
from my husband—"

"What a terrible waste of time, dear." Adrienne, snapping her
purse open, took out a cigarette and lit it. Emily pushed an ashtray
across the coffee table towards her. "Is he still away?"

"Yeah. But I expect him back today."

Adrienne pulled a face, as if surprised by some bitter taste in her
mouth. "I'd *never* wait for my husband to call. I taught him long ago
he couldn't count on me to be servile."

"I don't think I'm being servile," Emily said.

"No? But you're trapped in the house on such a fine day—"

"I'm not exactly *trapped,* Adrienne. You make me sound like a
prisoner or something."

"What would *you* call it?"

"I don't know. But not servile. And not trapped."

"Ah-hah. Then let me treat you to breakfast."

There was an irritatingly fixed smile on Adrienne's face, the look of someone who has divined a truth too subtle for common understanding. Servile and trapped, Emily thought. But that wasn't it. That wasn't exactly correct. Adrienne had it all wrong.

"When I told my husband I was going into business for myself, he had a fit. But I'll tell you—he soon learned to treat me as an equal, dear. Make no mistake. When you start to bring home more bacon than they do, they soon wake up with a shock."

"I'm sure Ted treats me as an equal," Emily said.

"I'm sure," Adrienne said. Now she seemed to be patronizing. Emily stretched her legs and shoved her hands into the pockets of her jeans. The strange thing about Adrienne's appearance was how drab it made Emily feel—anemic and colorless and boring. And plain dull. She looked away from the other woman, and from the corner of her eye Adrienne formed a misshapen rainbow—all bright hues and glitter. Why don't I just accept and go to breakfast? she wondered. What was an hour or so anyhow? Besides, Ted hadn't called yet. And there was no guarantee he'd be home today. Servile and trapped, Christ.

"Where is this neat little place of yours?" she asked.

"That's better, dear," Adrienne said. There was still something smug in her expression, the light of some minor victory. "What else is there but to get out of the house sometimes? Blow the cobwebs away. Let a little light in. Am I right? Am I?"

Emily said nothing. Damn, of course you're right, she thought.

"I was thinking of the Cream Pantry—do you know it?"

"No, I don't."

"It's just outside of Pastorville."

"Do I need to change?"

Adrienne laughed. "Why? There's something to be said for the beachcomber look."

"Is that what I look like?"

Adrienne stood up, shutting her purse. "I was teasing you, dear. Shall we go?"

The beachcomber look. Was that some muted put-down? Some little jibe? She couldn't be sure with Adrienne. She went out into the kitchen and found a pair of sandals in the closet. The telephone was ringing. She picked it up.

"Emily?"

"Speaking—"

"This is Susan."

"Oh."

"I hope you don't mind me calling—"

That terrible hesitancy: Emily tried to picture the woman's shy face. "No. Of course not."

"I was wondering . . ." Susan faltered. There was a long silence. In the background there was the sound of a child singing; after a moment Emily realized it was coming from a TV, that it might have been something from "Sesame Street." "I was wondering if I could keep the Book of Points next. . . ."

"I'm sure you can."

"I'd like to—"

Emily paused, waiting to hear what more Susan had to say. Then she tried to remember if Susan had said her kids were of school age or not; if "Sesame Street" was playing to keep them occupied while Susan did housework or whatever.

"I'd really like to," Susan said.

"I'm pretty certain it can be arranged."

"Thanks."

Thanks for what? Emily wondered. Keeping the Book of Points hadn't turned out to be the most exhausting task in the world. So far it had only one entry.

"Nobody's called me to sit yet," Susan said.

"Well, we've only just begun. . . ."

"I guess."

"Early days," Emily said. "But we'll get going soon enough, I'm sure."

"Absolutely," Susan said. "I think it's going to be a great success. I really do."

"I hope you're right."

Silence. Then: "And thanks again. About the Book of Points, I mean."

"You're welcome," Emily said.

When she put the receiver down she went back to the living room where Adrienne was standing impatiently by the open door.

"Ready?" she said.

"Just about—"

"We'll go in my car," Adrienne said.

Across the front lawn there was a navy blue Oldsmobile parked rather badly at the sidewalk. Emily followed Adrienne out, locking the door behind her, wondering why Susan wanted the Book of Points like that. Maybe the cooperative spirit had taken her over; maybe she just wanted to play her part. Halfway across the lawn she paused under the oak from whose uppermost branches a startled bird flew, its dark shape glistening in the bright sun. Adrienne's right, she thought. It *is* too fine a day to waste waiting for a telephone call in a silent house.

2.

Where is she? he wondered. Where did she go? He moved into a sitting position, shifting the pillows at his back, remembering how the door had slammed and how the car took a long time to turn over. She'd flood the engine, he thought. But then the car had come to life and he had listened to it back up out of the driveway. Gone. She was always going somewhere these days. He put his hand out to the bedside table and picked up the bowl of food she'd brought up early this morning, placing it on the table like it was a great favor, a gourmet dish—but when he'd eaten it, or tried to eat it, it had been lumpy and tasteless in his mouth. Some kind of pap, like tapioca, oatmeal. He hadn't complained because his own appetite had surprised him, but halfway through the food he felt sick. It occurred to him that maybe she'd put something in it—but what? A poison? Now he was hungry again and he spooned the miserable stuff into his mouth quickly, then he put the bowl back down on the table and lay against the pillow and belched. Poison or starvation—what was worse? He rubbed his eyes, turning his head to the window, feeling a sense of light coming into the room. Outside, the street was silent. He felt disoriented, not knowing the time of day. Nine-thirty. Ten. He wasn't sure. He hadn't been listening to the usual noises of early morning. Now, though, he listened to the house. The silence was overwhelming. Once, he remembered, when they'd first come to this house, there had always been noise—the kid's radio playing, the TV running, but the silences were deep and profound now, like the kind you found in funeral parlors.

He pushed himself upwards and tried to swing his legs over the edge of the mattress, but it was so damned hard to get the wasted muscles to perform. He made it a little way, but then he felt exhausted and slumped back again. He lay, breathing heavily, and imagined for a moment that she had invented a terrible new game—that she'd driven her car around the corner, parked it, then walked back to the house and let herself in quietly, making no noise at all, closing the door soundlessly, coming up the stairs so that he couldn't hear her, and then—

And then what?

Then she'd burst open the door of his room and scare him. Shitless.

You're stronger than that, he thought. You can't let her scare you. You can't let her run your life like this.

So what do you do?

You're helpless. Goddam helpless.

He moved his legs again, turning over on his side, reaching for the radio on the bedside table. He flipped the On switch, but nothing happened. The radio was dead. He felt the movement of a brief panic, then recalled that when she'd come into the room before she'd moved around the side of his bed, close to the window, she'd done something—made some small scrambling noise. *She must have pulled the plug,* he thought.

She killed the radio.

He let his hand drop wearily from the bedside table, he let it hang over the side of the bed. She's mad, he thought. She doesn't have any control anymore. She's lost it. Out of her mind. That was it. Madness. Pure and terrible. Malicious insanity. He felt sick again, a burning in the center of his stomach. What the hell had she put in that food? What was it? He prodded the back of his throat with a finger, pushing the finger deep inside, touching the soft flesh at the back of the mouth. He retched, but nothing came up. He tried again, and there was a spasm in the upper part of his belly, but nothing came out. Insane, he thought. Gone out of her tree.

The radio. The food. The silences she created.

Now his head ached and he was sweating badly.

You can't just lie here and be murdered, he thought. You can't die like some fucking sick dog. Goddam, he wouldn't let that happen. The telephone. But who could you telephone anyhow? Even if she hadn't taken the extension out of his room, who *could* he have called? He sighed, rubbing his lips with the back of his hand. There was a telephone downstairs. But would his legs carry him even as far as the bedroom door, for God's sake?

Dangerous games, he thought. She's playing a dangerous mad game. Without rules. Without regulations. *She's making it up as she goes along.* And the object is my torture. That's what it is. My torture. My death.

He was angry now. Even weak, he could feel a slow sense of rage. "I'll get her before she gets me," he said aloud. Then he was conscious of his own voice, and wondered how long he'd been talking to himself. Talking to yourself, he thought. That was a symptom of something.

He was silent. It was hard to breathe. Some kind of warmth was burning, like a tiny dying sun, in the center of his chest. He thought: I'll get her first.

Somehow.

3.

Beyond Pastorville there was some magic countryside—deep woods that stretched on either side of a narrow highway, woods that in the fullness of fall would turn the colors of old pennies, brass, dark reds reminiscent of dried blood. Even now the first dead leaves littered the grass mounds at the edge of the highway. Adrienne drove with abandon, sometimes taking both hands off the wheel to fumble for a cigarette or change the radio station. And Emily, divided between the dying landscape and the woman's restless talk, sat back in her seat and tried not to listen to the sound of Adrienne's voice, just as she tried not to think of the car spinning off the road and plunging over an embankment.

A one-sided conversation, an endless litany of what Adrienne had achieved after a rough start in life, poverty, an early doomed marriage, then a dull if somewhat steady second marriage, kids, her own business, her success. It was a hymn to the work ethic. After a time Emily managed to tune most of it out, nodding automatically now and then, smiling politely when she felt she had to. An amazing social glaze, this learned behavior of nodding and smiling and somehow getting them in the right places. If Adrienne noticed she wasn't really listening, it didn't deter her from going on. And on. And on.

Emily gazed at the hamlets that flicked past, the small towns—or town*ships,* as they declared themselves to be—with a single grocery store, a post office, American flags suspended from poles on tidy lawns, white frame houses. You had an uneasy sense, somehow, of being watched from deep shadows on front porches. Then Adrienne turned off the highway and over a narrow unpaved road, passing beneath a sign that said *The Cream Pantry, Prop. M. Leopold.* She parked the car, in a crowded parking lot, outside a frame house that had been converted into a restaurant. They got out and Adrienne said, "Are you counting calories?"

"Only when I get some kind of Puritan urge—"

"Like me, just like me," Adrienne said. "Aren't we weak sometimes? But in a place like this, dear, temptation simply *leaps* at you. And you can't afford to be calorie-conscious. Believe me."

They went up the steps to the porch, and then inside—a large room with what seemed to Emily upwards of a hundred women seated at small tables, drinking coffee and digging, almost obscenely, into elaborate pastries with silver forks. They found a table tucked away in the corner and Emily had the curious feeling that she'd discovered some secret place, something hitherto concealed from her—a cabal of pastry eaters, female fugitives from all the surrounding towns and suburbs who'd gathered here for an orgy of cream and coffee and gossip. So this is what they do with their spare time, she thought. This is how they contrive to banish emptiness. They eat pastries. They make furtive trips to the Cream Pantry and they gorge themselves. She became suddenly conscious of the way she was dressed, her own incongruity in this place. The women were all smartly dressed: alone, she looked like a beachcomber, a realization that embarrassed her in a small way. It was almost as if she'd stepped inside a private club, every one of whose members knew that she was alone in failing to pay her dues. She listened to the clack of forks, the babble of talk, she smelled the perfume of pastries, the dripping of coffee —and she thought: It's an anachronism. It's like taking a long step back into some dim past. A Neanderthal time of the *kaffeeklatsch,* when women didn't go out to work, when membership in the country club was of universal importance, when lives were regulated by some obscure principle of Keeping Up With the Joneses. It's weird, she thought. It doesn't belong in the *now.*

Adrienne slid a menu across the table and said, "Try the Parisian Custard Surprise."

"It sounds like a cholesterol nightmare," Emily said.

"Of course it is. But we didn't drive all this way *not* to indulge, did we?"

"It sounds corny—but do you come here often?"

Adrienne said nothing for a moment, studying the menu. "On those days when I play hooky—which are rare—I come out here. It seems part of the whole absenteeism bit, like it's naughty to take a day off and gorge yourself."

Naughty, Emily thought. She hadn't heard that word in years. She always associated it with the wrongdoings of a two year old. She stared across the room, watching busy waitresses rush from table to table. Who are all these women? she wondered. Where do they come from? What the hell do they *do?* And what she imagined was a world of golf and tennis lessons, PTA meetings, afternoons of backgammon, orderly breakfasts and Crockpot suppers prepared in the mornings and simmering slowly through the afternoons. Maybe, in election years, they licked envelopes for Republican politicians.

A waitress came to the table and Adrienne ordered two Parisian Custard Surprises and a pot of coffee. When she had gone, Adrienne said, "You don't look too happy, Emily. Does this place bother you?"

"It surprises me, I guess."

"Relax. Enjoy it." Adrienne put her hand across the table and touched the back of Emily's hand lightly, a gesture that reminded Emily of the touch of some old aunt—dry, consoling, reassuring. You could let this woman dominate you, Emily thought. You could let her through the cracks of your life and she would just assume control. Already, even if only in a distant way, she was irritated with herself for having agreed to come out here, having acquiesced so mildly. Don't think of Ted. Enjoy the disgusting pastry, the coffee, and go home.

"How long have you lived in West Boredomville?" Adrienne asked.

"About ten years—"

"It's the pits, isn't it?"

"No, not exactly."

"Emily, don't you *ever* drive along the streets and feel that the whole purpose of the place is to put you to sleep? I get that feeling all the time."

"It's not exactly the most *exciting* place—"

"Wonderful understatement, dear. If it weren't for the fact I go to the city I'd be insane by this time. Believe me. It's such a sterile environment, frankly. Let me ask you. How many friends have you made in West P, Emily? Honestly now."

"Friends," Emily said. "Well. I don't really know."

"Let me answer for you. One? Two?"

Emily didn't answer for a time. Then she said, "People seem to come and go so much, I guess that's it. They improve their homes, then sell them to the next young married couple that comes along. They don't settle."

"Exactly," Adrienne said. "They don't settle. There isn't really *time* to form friendships."

Emily watched the waitress come back with the lavish pastries. Custard-stuffed and sprinkled with some kind of glaze. They were set down on the table where they seemed, in an odd fashion, to stare monstrously up at you—as if they were alien creatures, misshapen things zapped in from some outlandish galaxy. How can I eat this? she wondered. Adrienne poured coffee. Two cups. She picked up her fork and tackled the pastry. Yellow custard oozed from the slit in the confection.

"I did have a really close friend," Emily said, feeling some need to defend the suburb, though not knowing why. "She lived in the next house. About five years, I think. She got a divorce last year, took her kids, left. She went Upstate somewhere and I haven't been in touch with her since."

"Typical," Adrienne said.

"Apart from her," Emily said, shrugged, gazed at her pastry. She sipped some coffee.

Adrienne patted the back of her hand again. "I think we'll be good friends—provided you don't up and leave."

"I don't think we'll be upping and leaving in the near future," Emily said. If ever. If ever. She was thinking of Beryl now, Beryl who had been her only true friend in West Pastorville, Beryl who had despised the place for its lack of life, vitality. She wondered what had become of her. Upstate someplace, but that was all she knew. Beryl's departure had created an absence in her life.

"The trouble with West Pastorville," Adrienne was saying, wiping a slick of custard from her lipsticked mouth, "is the feeling of emptiness I get. People should live their lives to the full, don't you think? Nobody does that in WP. Nobody. They drift through life half-asleep. They slumber through the days, dear. I don't call that living."

"They're not all like that," Emily said.

"No?" Adrienne opened out her napkin. "They've banished passion from their lives. They don't get excited anymore. About *any-thing*."

Emily picked at the edge of her pastry. She raised a piece to her mouth. It was rich and heavy and cloying. She washed it down with the strong coffee.

"What excites you, Emily? What do you feel passionate about?"

What a question, Emily thought. Was she supposed to ransack her life and come up with an answer, just like that? Was she supposed to say that she was intensely intrigued with a new shopping plaza? The recently constructed Little League baseball park? What did you do—search the dark corners of yourself for an easy answer to what it was that excited and impassioned you? She found, to her horror, that she couldn't think of a goddam thing.

Adrienne was smiling secretively. "Can I ask you a personal question?"

"Could I stop you?"

"Not really." Adrienne stared across the table. She had given up the pastry halfway through and was fishing in her purse for a cigarette. "Does your *marriage* excite you?"

"I don't know if I can answer that—"

"You don't have to," Adrienne said. "I think I can tell."

"What can you tell?" Emily asked. The other woman's manner, one that suggested some deep perception, some striking insight, annoyed the hell out of her. Christ, what had she let herself in for—an interrogation of the heart? How much more personal could the questions become? Do you get any satisfaction, dear, from your sex life? How long is Ted's cock? Do you ever experiment, Em? Does he eat you out? Do you give a good blow job? Does bondage grab you?

"I can tell," Adrienne said slowly. "I can tell that your marriage is in the same condition as mine, dear."

"I wouldn't say—"

"Dull City, right?"

"Adrienne—"

"You don't have to lie to me, you don't have to pretend."

You're bullying me, Emily thought. I refuse to be bullied.

Adrienne leaned confidentially across the table and said, in a whisper, "There's an easy solution."

"I didn't say I had a problem, for God's sake."

"Whatever, dear. But if you *should* have a problem, and I'm *not* saying you do, *understand,* but if you should have you ought to consider the possibility of an affair."

"An affair?"

"You're too easily shocked, Emily. An affair. An affair, right. Preferably with a young man. No involvement. No love. No attachment. You go to bed whenever it's convenient and you have a little fun and you put your clothes on and you go home. And is hubbie any the wiser? Of course not. He's in a state of torpor in front of a TV, watching a ball game. What does he know?"

Emily said nothing. She sipped her coffee, lit a cigarette she didn't feel like smoking, and gazed out over the crowded room. Was this the kind of conversation being pursued at the other tables? Did these women contrive to fill their lives with other men? Having their ashes hauled in the afternoons? It might have been amusing—the idea of some deliveryman doing a whole street of bored matrons, of legendary window washers climbing in through open spaces with more than chamois leather on their minds. But she didn't find it altogether funny. In fact, Adrienne's "solution" had distressed her, almost as if the suggestion had touched some moral core in her—and she found herself fantasizing briefly about the other night with James Hamilton, of what might have happened if she'd accepted the glass of wine, then an invite to his apartment or wherever, and all the rest that flowed from a simple yes to his invitation. It wasn't something she wanted to think about. What was it anyhow? What was this Puritan streak she kept encountering in herself? You're just an old-fashioned lady, Emily. That must be it. You believe in marriage, even as you entertain short fantasies, even as you create phantom lovers for Ted in his motel rooms . . . an old-fashioned woman. Dear God. It sounded like an early death.

Adrienne said, "What do you think *I* do to fight away tedium? What do you imagine, Emily? I go to the city, I move in a world that is not without some glamour, dear. I meet younger people trying to get ahead. And sometimes, frail and human as I am, I yield to temptation."

"I just don't see the point," Emily said, hearing herself sound feeble. She thought suddenly of her kids, two photographs that popped unexpectedly into her head. The kids. It was always the kids somehow, as if the last thing you'd do was jeopardize their lives by entering into some fruitless relationship with a man.

"The point is fun," Adrienne said. "That's all. Do you mean to tell me you've never looked at another man and wondered what it would be like to lay him?"

"I don't—"

"It's perfectly natural, dear. You see somebody attractive and you wonder what he'd be like in bed. You must have thought about it. Surely."

Emily shook her head. "I can't say I have."

"Then you're a rarity."

"I must be, I guess."

"Or a freak."

"Maybe even that," Emily said. Was she telling the truth? she wondered. Hamilton was an attractive man, in some strange gaunt way, but she hadn't really thought about him in bed, had she? No, whatever she'd thought, whatever she'd projected, it hadn't gone that far. It had amounted to a teen-age kind of fantasy, played out briefly, then squandered in nothing. It hadn't even been a *fantasy,* for God's sake: what was she *thinking* about?

"I don't think you are a freak," Adrienne said. "I get the feeling you're just scared a little."

"Scared of what?"

"Of yourself, dear. Of yourself."

"That's bull," Emily said.

Adrienne laughed and finished her coffee. Then she said, "It probably is bull, Emily. You're probably right."

There was a silence between them now. Emily watched the other woman for a time. It wasn't anything to get worked up over, was it? If Adrienne wanted to lead her life in one way, what the hell. It struck Emily as an empty kind of pursuit, that was all. Barren, pretty useless. But if it was what she wanted to do, let it be. She knew she couldn't do it herself—yet caught herself wondering if, now and then, she'd seen an attractive man in a crowd, in a restaurant, a bar, at a party, someone about whom she'd speculated. She couldn't remember. She honestly couldn't remember.

"Let's drop it," Adrienne said. "We have different attitudes, dear, and never the twain shall meet. Promiscuity just seems to me one of the few rewards of being alive."

A reward, Emily thought. A merit badge. What happened when you were old, though? When you couldn't even entice young men into your bed? Emptiness, that's what. Long hours of sad reflection.

Adrienne looked inside her empty cup for a moment, then she said, "I guess you're ready to go back?"

"Whenever you're through," Emily said.

"I'm through." Adrienne picked up her purse and rose. Emily went behind her and out on to the porch. The sunlight was striking, burning in the changing trees, diffusing itself in myriad lights that reflected like tiny mirrors. Adrienne turned to her and said, "Have you been invited to baby-sit yet?"

"Not yet," Emily answered.

"Me neither."

Adrienne shrugged, as if she were disappointed, and went towards her car. After a time, Emily followed.

4.

Adrienne said very little on the way back. It was strange, Emily thought, like sitting beside somebody who'd changed entirely, irrationally. Maybe I offended her, maybe that was it. Maybe she'd pictured me trekking down to the city some day and joining her in some sexual frolic or something. Whatever. The quiet was pleasant now, the silence enjoyable. Only when they'd hit the freeway around West Pastorville did Adrienne speak, and then it was some inconsequential observation about pockmarks on the highway. On Larue Drive, she parked outside Emily's house, leaving the engine running.

"I hope you enjoyed coming out," Adrienne said.

"You know what they say about a change," Emily answered, staring at the facade of her home. She smiled. "Thanks for inviting me."

"You can spring for it next time, dear," Adrienne said.

"You can bet on it." Emily opened the door and stepped out.

She watched Adrienne wave, the hand moving slowly in a regal gesture, and then the blue Oldsmobile was gone quickly down the street. She stood for a time on the lawn. The street was empty and quiet. If you narrowed your eyes and distorted the view you could easily imagine a lunar landscape of some kind—a lost relic of a dilapidated civilization. Then a delivery van, brown paint glistening, went lumbering past, disturbing the peace the way a fly might buzz in a room on a summer night. When it was gone she could feel the emptiness of the street as an almost tangible thing, a presence, something that lay like a nesting creature in the silent trees. Then she turned towards the house, taking the keys from her jeans.

She didn't know why she glanced in the direction of the wagon parked in the driveway. But she did—and it caught her eye at once, lying as it did with a parking ticket jammed between wiper and windshield. She thought: When did I get a ticket? Last night? But she'd have noticed it last night, driving back from Pastorville. She'd have seen it. Anyway, she was parked legally in the college parking lot. She hadn't parked anyplace else. She went towards the wagon and picked the piece of paper out from under the wiper, seeing at once that it wasn't a ticket, that it was a scrap of blue-lined paper of the kind you might find in an exercise book, or a diary, that it had been ripped carelessly from its binding, that it was ragged and folded over a couple of times. She straightened it out on the hood of the car, seeing the scrawled handwriting that had been done in crayon or eyebrow pencil, smudged and difficult to read, like it had been written in some hasty anger—

She read it, she read it again, then a third time. Who could have written such a thing, such a meaningless thing? And for a moment she imagined it had been Carole after she'd left last night, but she dismissed that immediately. It didn't make sense. Then Adrienne, before she'd come to the door this morning, but that made no sense either. They had no reason to leave a message like this, something so cryptic as to defy understanding. A kid, then. A friend of Charlotte's, maybe. But the hand, albeit scrawled, didn't look like anything that might have been done by a ten-year-old. It looked more adult, more sophisticated.

She read it another time.

You think you've got it all, don't you, but nothing lasts

She folded it over and tore it into scraps, letting the pieces fall from her fingers. You think you've got it all, she thought. What the hell was that supposed to mean? *Nothing lasts.* True, she thought. Nothing *does* last. That wasn't news. She looked at the litter underfoot, nudging it with her sneakers. Then she thought she knew where it came from, a creation of one of the religious nuts that were forever prowling the neighborhood, remembering now the emaciated woman who'd come to the door about a month ago and offered her grace through a strict diet of fruit and nothing else. She'd been quite insane, Emily thought, a wild look, a gaunt face whose skin had seemed almost transparent. She'd called herself a Fructarian, or something like that. She'd espoused the merits of mangoes and bananas, explaining how God was to be found in the texture of fruit. A loony. But there were always religious loonies selling their dreams of salvation up and down the suburb, dreams which, if you didn't buy them, turned out on their reverse sides to be filled with the horrors of hell, hellfire, eternal damnation. She stared down at the scraps and thought: Okay. It's a message from some doomsayer, a member of some sect too impoverished to afford a printer. That's all it is. Stuck under my windshield wiper and left there to remind me not to be smug, not to be complacent, and not to think in terms of my own immortality.

Everything is fragile, everything transient. One day you have to die. Nothing lasts.

All is flux, et cetera.

She found herself wishing they could bring more cheerful news to her door, that they might leave some indication of optimism under her windshield wiper. But they were invariably an unhappy bunch, operating on the dark side of disenchantment. Damn, she thought. She didn't like the idea of somebody prowling around in her absence and leaving a message—a message of any kind. No matter how you cut it, it was a tiny violation, a faint intrusion on your privacy.

She kicked at the scraps again, shrugged, and went to the front door where she stuck her key in the lock. The door, abruptly, was hauled open from the inside. And Ted was standing there, smiling.

"You almost gave me heart failure," she said. She put her arms around his waist and kissed him lightly on the mouth. He shut the door with his foot.

"I called from the station—"

"And I wasn't here."

"You weren't here. Right."

"And you wonder where I was—"

Ted ruffled her hair, a gesture that reminded her of a parent gently chastising a kid. "It crossed my mind," he said.

"I was with a bunch of women stuffing themselves with pastries."

"Pastries?"

"You should have been there. A positive orgy."

He was already moving away from her, going into the kitchen. She followed him through. He was filling his pipe. We're safe again, she thought. The master is back. The castle is secure.

He sucked on his pipe, got it going. He did it so slowly, with such deliberation, that she thought: He comes home and lights his pipe and it's like he's never been away, no great embrace for the homecoming, no realization that the kids are in school and the house is empty and the bedroom is empty and nothing might disturb them if they went upstairs. Nothing like that. *He smokes his pipe.* And then she thought: No, I'm letting Adrienne get to me, that's all. I'm letting Adrienne's words sink through my head. *I can tell that your marriage is in the same condition as mine, dear. Dull City, right?*

"How was the trip?" she asked.

"The usual," he said. He screwed the lid on his tobacco can. "I took a cab from the station. Who did the big Olds belong to?"

"One of the coven," she said.

"A new pal?"

Pal? What kind of a word was *pal?* "An acquaintance," she said. She went over to the table and stood behind him and placed her hands flat on his shoulders. He didn't move. He didn't make any move to respond.

"Did you write some poems?" he said.

"I haven't tried yet," she said.

"How was the class?"

"It's OK. I think it'll get better when everybody feels more at ease, you know?" This is small talk, she thought. Chitchat. Morsels of language. The dregs.

"You're going back?"

"Oh, sure."

He turned around and his fingers brushed lightly against the back of her hand. "How was the other thing?"

"It was OK. . . ."

"You don't sound too sure."

"It hasn't got going yet," she said.

Ted got up from the table and walked to the back door and stared out across the yard. Of course, she thought: checking his trellis. What else? Checking his trellis, as if in his scheme of things a series of wood slats was more important than a wife. She had a terrible feeling suddenly of something diminishing so rapidly that it was nothing more than a speck now—a speck you tried to keep in view, because when you didn't it was lost forever.

"Was the sitter OK?" he said.

"She was fine, Ted, just fine," she answered. "I expected her to turn up in a Halloween mask, I guess. But she didn't. She had all the outer appearance of normality. Who knows what lurks beneath the surface though—"

Ted turned and looked at her. "Is something wrong?"

She shrugged. "No. Nothing. Why?"

"I just wondered."

She moved to the door and stood beside him. "So what was exotic Maine like?"

"Damn cold."

Ted, she thought. Not like this. Not this way. This vacuous small talk. We used to Say Things. We used to Touch. Let it be the way it used to be. He opened the door and went out into the yard. She followed him. He strolled to the trellis. She watched him trace the slats of the trellis with the tips of his fingers. It was almost obscene, the loving way he did this.

"It's still standing," she said.

"Sure it is. I built it to last."

"Like a monument," she said. He didn't hear the quick razor's edge in her voice, the sharp parting of air. He didn't even hear that. A monument to what? She clenched her hands, wondering all at once why he'd bothered to come back, finding herself wishing he'd leave again, as if his presence were suddenly a stain, an intrusion on her life. No, she thought. Fight that. Keep that one away. This isn't the downhill slope. This isn't the shit you hit at the bottom. But why wasn't he holding her in his arms? Why wasn't he *touching* her? He was ice, ice she couldn't cut; maybe the rest of their married life was to be eked out in some emotional permafrost, some hard tundra where nothing ever flourished. Love me, she thought. Say you love me. I need to hear you say it.

He isn't a stranger. He's Ted. He's somebody you know. He's the man you love. She reached upwards and put her arms around his neck and kissed him straight on the mouth.

When she drew her face away, she said, "I missed you. I missed you badly."

"I missed you too," he said.

"Let's go inside. Let's go upstairs. I want you to fuck me, Ted."

He looked startled and she realized, with a slight chill, the paucity of language that had grown in the spaces of their marriage: how little they communicated on that level where a word like "fuck" had a tender side to it. And she remembered a time when Ted had always insisted she open her eyes and look at him while they were making love, how he always kept saying *I love to fuck you I love to fuck you* —but now it was darkness, silence, a ritual thing. There was a strange emptiness in his eyes, a bleached quality, like he didn't understand anything she was saying. And she thought: The kids, without the kids I'd have nothing, not a goddam thing. Only solitude. Make it better, Ted. Make it real again. Don't let it slip away. Turn back all the clocks.

She watched him a moment, then she turned and went back in the kitchen. She closed the door behind her, entered the front room, stopped at the bottom of the stairs. He doesn't want to, she thought. He doesn't find me attractive, he doesn't want *me*. She went upstairs and lay on the bed, staring up at the ceiling. She wondered: This sense of loss, this insecurity—did it happen to everybody? Did it simply strike, like some preordained calamity, when you reached a certain age or when you passed a certain point in a marriage? She closed her eyes. Waited. She expected to hear the buzz of his electric saw, the rattle of his hammer. Instead, she heard him come inside the house and then the sound of his footsteps on the stairs. She raised her hands in the air and looked at the tight whiteness of her knuckles. The blood had drained from her fingers. She stared at the door, watching Ted come in, seeing him stand there and just look at her. He moved slowly across the floor next, stopping beside the bed, gazing down at her. She turned her face to the window, watching the still branches of the oak. When she felt his weight settle on the edge of the mattress, she looked at him. He touched her waist. He touched her the way he touched the trellis. She shut her eyes tight. *It doesn't mean anything to him,* she thought. *I want to weep. It doesn't mean a goddam thing.* He pressed his lips against her forehead and the kiss was a cold thing. She turned her face away.

"What's wrong?" he said.

How can he ask? How can he even *ask?*

She looked at him and he repeated his question and she thought how dumb he seemed, his face suddenly flat and vacant and devoid of feature.

"I don't know what's wrong," she said. "Something. I don't know. Something missing. . . ."

"Missing?" He seemed puzzled. He shrugged and stared at his hands for a time. "Like how? What's missing?"

"Jesus Christ," she said. "I don't know. You come home. You hardly look at me. You barely touch me. You go outside and you give your trellis more attention than you give me—"

"Hey," Ted said.

"Hey nothing. It's true. It's a fact. I missed you. I was looking forward to seeing you. I was *really* looking forward to that."

He shook his head slowly from side to side, sighing as he did so. He got up from the bed and walked to the window where, with his hands in his pockets, he stared out. Without looking at her, he said, "Maybe we need a vacation. I don't know."

The nub of it, she thought. The crux of the matter. Ten days in another town and everything's solved. A trip up the St. Lawrence to watch nature perform its autumnal miracles on the Thousand Islands and everything is set right. Like hell.

"I don't think scenic wonders will cut it, Ted. I don't think that's going to do the trick."

He turned to look at her. He was frowning. "You know what I think? I think you're overreacting to something, that's all. You're stuck in this house all the time. You brood too much. You've always had too much imagination, Emily—"

"Oh, fuck, Ted," she said. "What has my imagination got to do with the fact that you don't seem interested in me? Huh? What has my goddam imagination got to do with the plain old fact that you don't exactly go out of your way to make me feel I'm a highly desirable commodity?" She had risen from the bed, conscious of Making A Scene, like she was auditioning for a role in some awful melodrama. "Maybe it's just stale, Ted. Maybe that's what it is. It happens to married people, doesn't it? They get tired of the same old slab of meat. . . ."

Crude, she thought. Crude, pointless. Be reasonable. Take the rational approach to life; the adult sophisticated way to deal with conjugal erosion. Try a little of that honey called understanding.

"This is a crock of shit," Ted said.

She walked up and down the room. She paused at the door and turned around to face him. She was close to the edge of something here; it was as if she could hear in the far distance the first crack of earth in a quake, the first splitting of the crust. "It's not that, Ted. It's not that simple. See it through my eyes. Try that for a moment. Can you make it? Reason number one. You don't love me."

"Emily—"

"Let me finish." She paused, conscious of how she was trembling, like someone standing in front of a closed door behind which some dreadful secret lies locked: and all you have to do is turn the key. Turn the key in your cold hand. "Reason number two. You've got somebody else. There's another woman. Somewhere there's another woman."

She sat on the bed again, fingers clasped, hands jammed between her knees. Suddenly she heard him laugh. The incongruity of the sound annoyed her. She turned to look at him, watching him sit beside her on the bed, his hand going to her wrist, his fingers folding around it. He was still laughing.

"Emily, Emily, Emily," he said. "You're way off beam, baby. You're way off target. First, I love you. I've never stopped loving you. Okay?"

I'm listening, she thought. I'm listening. Let me hear what I need to hear.

"Second," Ted said. "There's nobody else. There's nobody else but you. I even feel goddam stupid having to say it. What did you imagine? I'd risk my wife and family for somebody else? Did you imagine that? Come on, Emily. I mean it." He cleared his throat. "Maybe . . . maybe I neglect things around here. Maybe I spend too much time away. I'm not denying that. But when you say I don't love you, or when you say there might be some other woman, I feel sick. . . . I mean, I wouldn't jeopardize anything, Emily. I wouldn't do that."

She opened her eyes and looked at him. He was saying, "I'll clear my desk and take some time off. We'll go away for a few days. That would help. Just you and me. Don't you think that would help?"

"You shouldn't have to ask that question," she said.

He was silent now. He leaned over, carefully kissing her hair, running one hand over her shoulder, down her side, down to the hip. She closed her eyes, wanting to drift away, just her and Ted floating on some frail cloud. She felt him tug at the buckle of her belt and slide her jeans from her hips—everything done slowly, easily, his voice saying over and over *I love you I love you there's nobody else nobody else.* And she heard herself say *I know, I know, Ted,* feeling his hand between her legs, feeling her own hand go to him, her back arching as he entered her gently, and then it was slow, easy, warm, a cocoon where her own anxieties dwindled to nothing, where her own passion astonished her. *I believe you, Ted. I believe you.* Harder, harder now, faster than before, and then she felt herself coming as if from some terrifying depth inside herself, coming and coming again, wave after wave after wave, each wave draining her. She clung to him, her legs twisted behind his back, crossed against the base of his spine. An exultation, a sequence of flashes, echoes, something blazing inside her like it might never stop. Ted, she heard herself saying. *Ted, Ted, Ted.*

I love you.

She heard him say: I love you too.

I never loved anybody else.

Never.

Sweating, her sweat adhering to his, she opened her eyes. Never. Never loved anybody else. She looked at him as he lay on top of her and then she closed her eyes again, retreating, withdrawing, pulling herself into a kind of blindness.

That look on his face.

That *look.*

But she didn't want to think about it, not even when he drew away from her and went into the bathroom, not even when she heard the sound of running water, the toilet flushing, the sound of him clearing his throat. That look in his eyes. I imagined it, she thought. I imagined what wasn't there.

But it was there and you didn't imagine it.

You imagined *nothing,* Emily.

The look had been one of boredom. Plain and simple boredom.

All he'd done was go through the goddam motions of movement and language and what it signified in the end was his means of appeasing you—

No, she thought.

No. It hadn't been like that.

And then she couldn't remember if he'd come, if he'd performed just for her sake, if it had all been an act, a singularly convincing and utterly depressing act.

She watched the bathroom door open. He was standing there smiling at her, looking pleased with himself. She shut her eyes. She felt cold and vulnerable and empty; and behind her closed eyelids there lingered the impression of his smile—a mirthless thing, a vacancy.

She turned on her side and she thought: No. I'm wrong.

I have to be wrong.

But she knew she wasn't.

5.

She watched them board the bus. A yellow bus streaked with old mud, caked and grimy. She could feel the sunlight as it came through the glass, as it burned against her forehead and brought sweat out of her flesh. She was sweating everywhere. Hands, underarms, the insides of her legs. Everywhere. She thought: I should roll the window down, let air inside the car, but she didn't. She didn't move. Paralyzed, she sat watching the kids as they streamed out of the school building—soundless, because she had her windows shut tight. So many silent kids. She watched as they ran, broke into little groups, climbed the mesh fence around the school yard, clambered aboard the bus. So many of them, but she was only looking for one, just one.

Where is she? Why hasn't she come out of the building?

She put her moist hands on the steering wheel. It seemed to her that she was safe inside the car with the doors locked and the windows shut like they were. Nothing could penetrate, harm her. Nothing could touch her in this cocoon. She tapped the rim of the wheel, feeling her own sticky sweat against plastic.

Where is she?

She stared at the steps, noticing now how the flow of kids had dwindled. A few stragglers, a few loners. And then suddenly *she* was there, walking slowly in the company of a fat girl, swinging a small satchel from a strap—a casual movement, but even so there was infinite grace in the way she did it. Such grace. The striking sunlight had turned her hair to a color that was close to white. It lit her, illuminated her, creating around her a soft nimbus.

She let her hands drop from the wheel and into her lap. The sound of her heart—how could it keep hammering that quickly? It would break. It would break and explode, a bloodied muscle. She tried to catch her breath, but that was impossible. Charlie was walking towards the bus. Charlie was stopping now, inclining her head towards the face of the fat girl. Charlie, aflame in the sunlight, stood motionless. For all the world to see. She wanted to close her eyes. But she hardly blinked. She was watching a series of pictures unroll and she couldn't afford to miss a single frame. She unlocked the door and the hot air made her gasp, an unexpected heat in the late afternoon, as if the sun were pulsating, becoming frenzied. Drenched in sweat, her clothes gummed to her body, she stood outside the car and watched the girl move towards the door of the bus. She had to restrain herself —but how could she? The child was a gift from the place of the dead: how could you restrain yourself faced with that kind of wonder?

A gift from the place of the dead. A resurrection.

She felt her dry lips part, her mouth open.

Charlotte said, "I'll see you tomorrow, Bea."

Bea Cunningham pushed the tip of an index finger into her flabby cheek and a misshapen lump of pink chewing gum appeared on the tip of her tongue. She let it drop to the ground. She shielded her eyes from the sunlight and said, "You could come over to my place, Charlotte. You could call your mother from there."

Charlotte shrugged and looked at the open door of the bus. A couple of latecomers were still climbing on. "Except my father's supposed to be home today," she said. "So I ought to catch my bus."

"Nuts," Bea Cunningham said. "We might've had some fun."

"Maybe tomorrow."

"Nah. Friday's no good," the fat girl said. "They always drag me over to my grandmother's place on Friday nights."

Charlotte moved towards the bus. The sunlight made her feel a bit strange in a way she couldn't explain to herself. It was like dizziness somehow, but not really that strong. Lightheaded, maybe that was it.

She didn't want to go over to Bea's anyhow. The trouble with Bea was how, if you were her friend, she wanted to own you. She made demands on you. And sometimes you had to make your excuses. At least she had a valid excuse today. Through the open door she saw Johnson, the driver, look at her impatiently.

"Look, I'll miss my bus if I don't haul ass," she said to Bea. She liked that expression: *haul ass.*

Bea, who lived within a block of the school, shook her head and said, "Yeah, I guess."

The fat girl looked forlorn. Charlotte understood that she had been elected Bea's best friend, a process that had evolved out of a series of demands Bea had made, demands Charlotte had complied with because she felt sorry for her—she didn't have any *other* friends. Possessive, that was the way to describe Bea best. A jealous edge. It upset her to see Charlotte talking with other girls.

Charlotte tapped her foot on the ground. Johnson was talking to her from the bus, saying, "This ain't no personal limousine service, duchess. I got a schedule to keep. Maybe that don't mean a whole lot to you—"

"I'm coming," Charlotte said. She turned to see Bea drifting away, moving in the direction of the teachers' parking lot, which was crammed with cars; and there were parents in other cars on the street beyond, picking up their kids if they didn't want them to ride the bus.

Johnson moaned. "I coulda been a chauffeur, lady. I coulda been a private *chauffeur.*"

"I'm coming, I'm coming," Charlotte said again. She stepped towards the bus, turning once to wave to Bea, who had disappeared amongst the cars. It was funny how in the sunlight the roofs of all the cars seemed to shine in such a way that they appeared to melt into one another, making one large gleaming metallic canopy. She put her foot up on the first step.

And then she heard it.

Somebody called out *Charlie!*

She turned, surprised, and looked in the direction of the cry. But she couldn't see anybody. Only the shining cars. Not even a sign of Bea anymore.

"I wouldn't mind, but not a single one of you kids ever tips," Johnson said, revving up the engine. Charlotte got in and the automatic doors hissed shut behind her in a savage way.

"One day I'll squeeze the life outta one of you kids with them doors," Johnson said, laughing. "Wouldn't that be something?"

Charlotte found a vacant seat. She sat, crossing her legs, looking out of the window as the bus moved off. If somebody called out Charlie, she could only assume that it hadn't been meant for her. It was close to her own name, but nobody ever called her that. Not even Frankie, who sometimes came up with Charles—but poor Frankie's efforts at making fun were silly and easy to deal with. Maybe Bea Cunningham, miffed a little, had shouted it out just to annoy her. Except it hadn't sounded like Bea's voice at all. It was more grown-up. A woman's voice.

That was it. A woman calling to her son. That was all it was.

She followed the yellow bus for about a mile, until it stopped on the corner of Larue and Diamond, then she swung the car in an arc and drove away in the opposite direction.

Chapter Six

1.

For a couple of days following the Bedroom Farce—which was how Emily had come to view the episode—it seemed to her that Ted was unusually morose, even furtive, hiding behind newspapers he clearly wasn't reading, making trips to the public library to exchange books she knew he hadn't opened, sitting in the back yard and silently smoking his pipe and scanning the lawn as if he were gathering his energies for some new extravaganza. But he hadn't bothered to finish the trellis, which in Emily's mind had taken on the permanence of a Stonehenge. He hadn't even looked at the most recent copy of *Popular Mechanics* which had come in the mail. A closed book, she thought. A sealed envelope. It infuriated her to think of him shutting himself off the way he was doing; but no more than it did when she recalled her own tragicomic behavior in the course of the Farce. Some things were perhaps best left unsaid. But she'd dragged it out into the open, behaving like some maudlin teenager: *Is there another woman, Ted?* How odd that something so simple as a question should render a person vulnerable, but that was how she felt—ragged and insecure, almost as if she expected at any moment to find Ted packing a suitcase in the bedroom. Even the kids were acting strange, sensing tension, walking as if on eggshells, whispering in their bedrooms. It was unhealthy, she thought. If it went on she knew she'd explode in some kind of outrage. What was needed, she concluded, was a new approach. Something fresh that would administer a salve to the marriage. But what? She couldn't come up with anything. Besides, she wondered why it should be left to her to make discoveries, to correct things, when it was clear that Ted wasn't even trying. Maybe nothing was worth saving in his mind; maybe he thought the whole thing inconsequential. Since he didn't communicate, how could she know?

On Monday morning he went to his office in Albany, where VacationEase had its headquarters, to attend to some paperwork. She took the kids and drove him to the station where his departure was hurried, the way he kissed her on the side of the face little more than a hasty gesture. They watched him board the train. He waved once from the window, then the train was gone and the tracks empty in the grayish morning light. She felt like driving, like not going back to West Pastorville. It was a gloomy morning; even the countryside, entering its first rage of fall, seemed muted and dark. And she was beset by a sense of failure, a feeling that embraced not only the marriage but her projects as well. Number One, she thought: I haven't even tried to write a goddam poem. Number Two, there hasn't been any activity on the baby-sitting front. Sometimes the wreckage, like a contagious thing, spread through everything. And there didn't seem any way of stopping it.

She drove down through the old town of Pastorville, the kids silent beside her in the car. What we need about now, she thought, is some forced gaiety—party favors and conical hats and tiny fireworks. Something. *Anything.*

Then beyond Pastorville, in a westerly direction, the woods were dark and sullen and she knew cheerfulness wasn't going to cut it. It needed something else, some other quality, a kind of determination, a fortitude, a quality that would prevent things from slipping even further. She hadn't even sent the kids off to school today, as if she needed to have them with her—like reinforcements, comforts of some kind. They hadn't argued about it; they hadn't argued much about anything the last few days.

She drove until she came to the cutoff for Whitney, a postcard village beyond which there was a stream that sliced through the woods —picturesque even on a day so overcast as this one. She parked near the picnic area at the edge of the trees, remembering how all four of them had come here several times in the past. Better days, she thought. There was no one at the trestle tables. The barbecue pits were covered with old ashes. Hers was the only car; what else could you expect on a morning like this one?

"We haven't been here in a long time," Charlotte said.

"I wanted to go to school," Frankie said, getting out of the car.

"You don't like a day out now and again?" Emily said.

Frankie shook his head. "I'll miss Miss Rosenblum's pictures of Egypt. She went there, you know, and she took all these pictures of camels and pyramids—"

"I've seen them, Frankie," Charlotte said. "She shows them to every class she has. She showed them to me when I was in second grade—"

"Maybe," Frankie said. "But—"

"They're pretty dull. You've seen one camel, you've seen them all."

Frankie bent down and picked up some sticks. He shrugged, letting the matter go. Emily watched him a moment, then went to one of the trestle tables, its surface covered with hardened bits of bird excrement, and lit a cigarette. She cleaned off a part of the bench and sat down and listened to the woods. A few birds scattered through the trees. A rook screeched in the distance. The stream, which she couldn't see from where she sat, made one constant glassy noise as it slid over pebbles.

She watched the kids go into the woods. Then the gray trees folded around them and she couldn't see them any longer, she could only hear the sounds of their voices. For a moment she imagined some redneck rapist prowling through the trees, some moonshine artist with a fetish for blonde hair and young girls. But this was to invest the woods with a menace they didn't possess, a sense of threats unseen, an invisible force that jeopardized the unwary, the innocent.

Then she heard Charlotte shout: *Wherever you are I'm coming to GET you, Frankie.* And the voice, high and clear, created a small echo. Frankie answered with a brief scream that died in a flurry of birds rising from the branches. After that there was silence except for the breaking of twigs and stalks. Emily closed her eyes, seeking an elusive tranquillity. In olden days, she thought, we'd come to this place and bring a picnic basket and have fun, Ted pretending to Frankie that the shallow stream contained monstrous fish and all he had to do to catch one was be patient and silent and let his line dangle in the water. And Frankie believed it, sitting for hours on a rock and watching the surface of the stream.

Divorce. Was that where it all ended? Was everything pointing in that direction? She stared at the woods. Overhead there was no sunlight, only massed gray clouds. And the air was chilly. Divorce. What she couldn't imagine was life without Ted. She couldn't envisage that emptiness, a life of division, of sending the kids to see him on weekends, of losing out somewhere along the way. What am I thinking? she wondered. What the hell am I doing, sitting here and thinking these things? If a marital relationship turned into some form of gladiatorial combat then you worked your ass off to see the emperor giving his thumb's up sign, didn't you? You didn't just lie down and roll over, like some servile dog. You fought—isn't that what you did?

Sure, she thought. Sure you did. She got up from the bench and strolled to the edge of the woods. The problem was the choice of weapons, really. With what did you fight? And how could you begin to think of combat until you'd identified the enemy? She moved through the trees now, looking for the stream, pushing aside overhanging branches as she went. When she reached the edge of the stream she watched it awhile—tiny whirlpools creating froth as they spun in the funnel of land, leaves and broken pieces of wood skidding along in the rush of water. Hypnotized, she found she couldn't take her eyes from the stream, from the way it created fragmented images of trees and sky.

She sat down on a flat rock, throwing tiny stones into the water. She listened for the sounds of the kids but she couldn't hear them now. She knew they couldn't be far away, playing some game of hide-and-seek—but why couldn't she hear them? She tilted her head, listening, waiting. Nothing. She stared through the thick trees, seeing only interlocked branches, piles of fallen leaves, dark soil. She got up from the rock and went across the stream, skipping over stepping stones.

Then she was walking deeper into the woods. Moving quicker. In a narrow clearing she paused, thinking how easy it would be to get lost in here, to forget your way back.

She began to call their names, but all she heard was the dull echo of her own voice come back in a teasing way, an acoustic mockery. That and the sound of the stream, fainter now, distant. A conspiracy of sounds and silences. Kids, she thought. Why do they disappear? Why do they so thoughtlessly just run off in a place like this? She looked around the clearing, then went back into the trees again. She called their names once more. There was no answer.

OK, she thought. OK. They're around here someplace and they're playing a game with me, a game of silence, a stupid kind of game— but what they don't realize is that there's a point when the game crosses some borderline into torment. They just don't *think*. They don't *consider*.

Still calling, she went forward. But they couldn't have come this far.

Sure they could. What did they know about distance and time? Nothing, they knew nothing. She stood still now, silent, irritated with herself for having let them wander off. Wrapped up in your own miserable problems, she thought. No time to turn round and see where they went. Self-centered and out of control. She shouted their names again.

Nothing at all.

She turned and went back towards the stream, because from there it was easy to find the car, and she was sure that's where the kids would head for when they had tired of this game. If they weren't lost. If. She forded the stream again, losing her footing on a moss-covered rock, getting her sneakers waterlogged. The stream was like ice, chill against her skin. She went up the bank, her sneakers squelching. Then, through the trees as they thinned out, she saw the station wagon.

But no kids. No kids.

No sign of her children.

She walked towards the car and leaned against the hood and watched the trees until her eyes began to hurt. Nothing. Then it became hard to control her imagination, as if it were some frightening thing gone berserk inside her skull—creating pictures over which she had no control. The woods filled with state troopers, helicopters, skimming the tops of trees, dogs howling as they tracked scents. And then headlines No Sign of Missing Kids. . . . But she wouldn't yield to that kind of thing. She moved away from the car and back to the edge of the trees again, and this time she heard something crashing through the woods, like somebody running hard over brittle wood and stubs of shrubbery. She shouted their names again. Through the shadows, through the density of the growth, she saw something move.

Then she heard them calling out as they ran. She wanted to be angry with them but she couldn't, she found it hard to replace her relief with anger. It was Charlotte who emerged first, her hair untidy; panting, out of breath. Then Frankie appeared just behind her.

"Didn't you hear me calling you?" Emily said. "I mean, I was shouting and shouting, didn't you hear me, for God's sake?"

"We didn't hear anything," Charlotte said.

"You must have," Emily said. She tried to keep her voice even, her tone subdued. "I was shouting at the top of my lungs, Charlotte."

Frankie, catching his breath, sat down on a bench and said: "We saw somebody out there, didn't we, Charlotte?"

"Saw who?" Emily said.

"I don't know. Just somebody."

"You're imagining things, Frankie," Charlotte said. "There wasn't anybody out there—"

"There was too! I saw somebody!"

"You did not," Charlotte said.

"I did," Frankie said, his face all determination, earnestness. "Somebody was hiding behind some trees—"

"It's not true," Charlotte said to Emily. "He just got scared in the woods and imagined it."

"It doesn't matter for God's sake," Emily said. "I don't know why you're squabbling like this. What difference does it make if somebody was out there? Other people are perfectly entitled to use the damn woods, you know." She paused, hearing the sharp edge in her voice.

Frankie said, "I saw somebody."

"Bigfoot, right?" Charlotte said.

"Knock it off, Charlotte," Emily said. "Let's forget the whole thing, right?"

Charlotte, who seemed not to have heard, said: "I bet it was Bigfoot, Frankie. I bet he was coming for you. I bet he said to himself—hey, there's a tasty-looking kid."

"I said to knock it off."

Charlotte stared at her mother. "I'm only teasing him."

"Drop it. OK? Just drop it. I don't want to hear any more."

Charlotte kicked at some dirt, looking down at her foot. "I don't know why you have to take your temper out on me," she said.

"Is that what I'm doing?"

"What else?"

"What makes you think that?"

"It's obvious, isn't it?"

"Look, you run off in those goddam woods and I have to come looking for you and I don't know what I'm thinking—" Emily stopped. She stared at her daughter, seeing some hurt on the vulnerable face, an expression of subdued pain. A wound, she thought. I've wounded her. And then she wondered if all she was doing was working off her tensions, letting off the steam that had gathered between herself and Ted, using her own daughter as an escape valve. She sighed, tried to unwind, get some perspective. Decay, she thought—

does it go this far down already? She touched the child on the shoulder. A gesture, that was all, but Charlotte still looked glum.

"I was worried," Emily said. "When you've got kids of your own, you'll understand."

"I don't think I'll have kids," the girl said.

"Why not?"

"Maybe they're more trouble than they're worth."

A knife, Emily thought. A cut. "I don't want you to say that, Charlotte, I don't want you ever to think that or say that—"

The girl looked at her mother, as if she were faintly puzzled, as if some slow understanding were dawning. "I mean it," she said. "They're a hassle. *We're* a hassle."

"No," Emily said. "You're not that. Anything but that. I love both of you—"

"Then love is a hassle," Charlotte said.

Dear Christ, Emily thought. It was everywhere, the strain working like some slow poison, like some virus that passed down from the parents to the kids, changing and wrecking everything in its movement. "Love isn't a hassle," she said. "You don't want to think that either. Sometimes there are problems, and differences, but they can always be put right, Charlotte. Always."

She could see the child was unconvinced. Betrayed by my own tone of voice, Emily thought. *They can always be put right.* Show me how. Light my way. Give me a sign.

Frankie, who had been silent, said, "There was somebody out there."

"Don't start that again," Emily said.

"Nobody believes me," the boy said. "I don't understand why nobody believes me."

Emily walked over to the car, opening the door. She sat for a moment behind the wheel, watching the kids approach slowly. They got into the car—and the silence was suddenly awful, like some shell of lead. A weight. A terrible weight.

"Hey," she said. Inject them with enthusiasm. Rah-rah-rah. "I've got a marvelous idea. You guys ever hear of the Sundae Shoppe?"

"Can we go there?" Frankie said. It was one of his all-time favorite places.

"Sure we can."

"Great."

Emily glanced at Charlotte, who was sitting glumly, coiling a strand of hair around an index finger. Emily said nothing for a time. Then: "Do you think we can get your sister to smile again, Frankie?"

"I could tickle her," Frankie said.

"You dare," Charlotte said

"Hey, she talks," Emily said. "She must have a good ventrilo-quist."

There was no response from Charlotte, only the same grim silence, the same appearance of withdrawal. Hell, Emily thought. Something is just slipping away here. Something is just slipping haphazardly away.

2.

When she had parked her car she sat inside for a time and looked up at the old Victorian house that had been carved into a collection of offices. It reminded her of that place where Nick had lived—

She looked towards the front door where there was a brass plate listing the occupants and their professions in alphabetical order. Clitheroe, Architects. Esterhazy World Tours. Pastorville Family Counseling Service. And then Spassky's name, last on the list. She put her hand on the handle, about to open the car door, when she thought: *No, I don't need to come here, I stopped coming here, why didn't I remember that?*

There had been a decision. No more visits to Spassky.

Somewhere she'd made that decision.

She shut her eyes. The boy, she thought.

The boy didn't belong in the framework. Why did there have to be a boy? It was suddenly not right, it was incorrect, like a fuzzy pic-ture, a fading photograph. She would have to think about this boy very carefully, very carefully. A family had no place for outsiders.

Maybe he'd seen her. Maybe not. She hadn't really been conscious of him, only of Charlie, of how Charlie moved through the woods. And then . . .

But what happened then?

She opened her eyes and looked down at the mud on her shoes. She hated the mud.

What happened next?

Then they'd been running, running through the trees, that was it. No. He hadn't seen her.

The boy. The boy didn't belong.

She turned the ignition key. And she thought: Nick. Nick. But that confused her for a moment because Nick was dead, and just for a split second there she'd thought he was alive. Dark specks drifted in front of her eyes. Nick's dead, she thought. But Charlie isn't.

Charlie isn't dead.

Maybe there's a place, she thought. Yeah, maybe there's a place where we can all be together again.

She found a tissue and reached down awkwardly to wipe at the mud on her shoes. Dry now, it came off in small flakes. She picked the flakes from the rug of the car and, gathering them in the palm of her hand, opened the door and let them drop outside in the street.

When she finally drove away, she thought: Why did there have to be a boy?

3.

It was only by an intense effort of will—an effort that left him gasping for air, struggling like a goddam beached whale—that he got out of bed. He thought of his legs as if they were frail stilts, sticks that could hardly support any weight at all. He leaned against the wall, pushing his hand out until the palm had made contact. There was a singular buzzing inside his head, the electrical sound of rushing blood, cells dilating and contracting like so many pulses. For a time he thought he was going to faint. But he concentrated, breathing as deeply as he could, he concentrated by saying over and over to himself: You can make it, you can make it. He slipped, his hand losing contact with the surface of the wall, and he felt the knuckles knock against the bedside table, upsetting the radio, spilling his water, making it fall to the floor with a sound of breaking glass. He moved his bare feet cautiously but he couldn't avoid a shard of glass that sliced his sole. He moaned with the sudden pain of it all, then he sat down on the edge of the bed and fumbled for the broken skin, the sliver of glass, catching it between thumb and forefinger and easing it out—but he could feel the wetness of blood on his hands. He lay back against the pillow, exhausted now, exhausted but pleased with himself that he had gone a couple of steps, small steps admittedly, but it was something, goddammit, it was something to be proud of.

He heard the door slam shut below and the sound of his daughter crossing the living room. Quickly, nervously, he pulled the bedsheet over his body, pretending to be asleep. The broken glass, the mess. What would she say about that? I'll tell her an accident, that was it, an accident. She couldn't know he'd got out of bed and moved across the floor. She couldn't know that.

He heard her open the door of his room. He heard her cross the floor to the bed. She said nothing for a time. She sees the mess, he thought. She sees the mess.

"What have you been trying to do?" she said.

He wished he was asleep, really asleep, not just pretending.

She said, "I don't intend to clean this up. I don't have the slightest intention."

He turned, playacting coming awake. "Is that you?" he said.

"Who did you think it was?" she said.

"I was dreaming. . . ."

"Yeah. Sure you were. How did you knock the radio off the table? Huh? How did you break the glass?"

"I didn't mean to," he said. "I was reaching out for—"

"Look at the mess," she said. "It's a godawful mess."

He waited for her outrage, the burst of anger, waiting and trying to gauge her mood from her tone of voice.

And then suddenly it was different. It was changed.

She laid the palm of her cold hand flat on his forehead and with her other hand began to smooth his thinning hair away from the brow. He became tense, his muscles stiffening, sweat forming in his armpits, a clawing kind of emptiness in his stomach.

"Poor father," she said.

Poor father. What was she saying? Why was she touching him? He wanted to shove her chilly hands away but he didn't move. He held his breath, waiting uneasily.

"Poor dear father," she said, her voice funny, dreamy, like she was talking to herself. "I wish you could see. I wish you could have your eyesight back somehow. Like a miracle."

A miracle? What was she talking about? Her fingers, frostlike, moved across his face, feeling the surface of his dry skin. He licked his lips.

"I brought you in some food," she said. "You'd like that, wouldn't you? I brought in some sirloin. It's cut up for a stew. You like stew, don't you? I know you do. Mother always said stew was your favorite meal. She always said stew was a hearty meal."

She was silent now. She took her hands away from him. He heard her rise, he heard her whistle to herself briefly, then she stopped and there was a long silence. He was filled with dread. He couldn't put the feeling away; it swept over him in waves, wave after wave, like some swelling tide. A hearty meal, he thought. Maria had never cooked stew. Never. He hated stew. He hated dishes where things floated in liquid. Maria had never said stew was his favorite food. Why was his daughter saying this now?

"I'll go down and get it started," she said.

He listened to her go from the room. All the way down the stairs she whistled. The sound, thin and grating, seemed to him filled with menace, with threat. Why was his daughter doing this? A hearty meal. What was it about that phrase anyhow?

He pushed himself up to a sitting position. He wouldn't eat any of her goddam stew, not even if she tried to force him, she couldn't make him open his mouth, she couldn't make him do that if he didn't want to.

A hearty meal.

He remembered it now.

The condemned man, the hearty meal.

Was that why she'd used the phrase? The condemned man. He strained to listen, his mind all at once blank with panic, and what he heard in the distance was the noise of his daughter working in the kitchen—the clatter of a dish, the sound of a blade knocking on a wood surface as it sliced through something. I won't eat it, he told himself. Nothing in this world would make me eat anything you prepare. No matter what you bring, no matter how hungry I am, I won't eat anything you prepare anymore.

4.

From the kitchen doorway Emily looked across the dark back yard. The suburban night was filled with sounds, each one of which she recognized. The slurring of the night breeze across the surface of Mrs. DeSantis's pool which, if she looked through the slats of the common fence, she could see was green and unused. The raspy sound of a distant lawnmower, someone conscientiously clipping his grass after dark. Across the alley, from another house, the sound of a stereo playing, at full volume, some hard rock music that vibrated in the air. The sudden cry of a small baby, piercing the night, then lapsing into silence. Or was that a cat howling somewhere. And then Ted, seated at the kitchen table, flicking through the "important" papers he'd brought from the office. There was, it seemed, a crisis at VacationEase. It might have been the end of Western Civilization the way Ted was behaving—but it was only an outbreak of suspected food poisoning at some resort complex in the Poconos. Already, several guests had taken to their beds with nausea, vomiting, and diarrhea. And a couple of public health officials out of Stroudsburg were poking around the kitchens. A calamity, she thought. Wholesale goddam disaster. And Ted—the workhorse Ted was going to have to get down there and put a good PR face on the whole sordid affair. One of the many vice-presidents of VacationEase had been on the telephone to him, exhorting him to make good speed to the Poconos. She was intrigued and a little disappointed by the way Ted yessirred this lord of VacationEase, as if his life were controlled, as if no matter what he was told to do he was ready to comply—and this was a curious subservient side to him she'd never seen before.

She turned to him. He was looking at his watch. She thought, he's only just come home and now he's leaving again. Still, what she felt was a small hint of relief, like his departure would create space for her, a time in which to think, to get some kind of perspective on the state of the marriage.

She said, "Is the Salmon Walewska the principal suspect?"

He looked up from his tidy papers. "The public health people seem to think so."

"So what are you expected to do, Ted? Absolve the Salmon Walewska? Apologize for a fish? Make a public statement to the effect that it will be stricken from the menu?" She couldn't keep the edge from her voice. She tried, but she couldn't do it.

"I'll have to play the situation by ear," he said, his voice serious.

"I guess you will."

He was gathering up his papers, looking at his watch again. She thought, he belongs to VacationEase. He's enslaved by his work. Chained, manacled and handcuffed to a corporate concept. That's the secret name of his mistress—it wasn't any mysterious woman of the freeways, the seductive ghost she'd imagined at times in his motel rooms. It was VacationEase itself, nothing more. And somehow this seemed more overpowering to her, more overwhelming, than any woman could have been. It was an insight that depressed her. She thought, for no good reason, of the scrap of paper she'd found on the windshield of the station wagon. *You think you've got it all. . . .* No, she thought. Whoever you are, you've got it wrong. I don't think I have it all, not even remotely.

"What time's your train?" she said.

"Eight-fifty."

She looked once more across the back yard. She said, "How long will you be gone this time?"

He rose from the table and crossed the floor, standing behind her and placing his hands on her shoulders. "When I come back, I'll take some of that vacation time I've accumulated. I promise you that."

"That didn't answer my question, Ted."

"I don't know how to answer it," he said. "I'll go down there for as long as it takes to straighten the thing out. Three days, four. Maybe less. I don't know."

She turned around, looked at him. From the upstairs part of the house she could hear the kids. She said, "We'll talk when you get back."

He sighed. She said, "Ted, it's something we *need* to do."

She watched him a moment. The expression on his face was that of a forlorn child and she felt suddenly sorry for him—not really understanding why, but guessing it had something to do with the way he'd given himself, body and soul, to a corporation: he'd done that, for his family at first, but somewhere over the years he'd lost sight of that purpose. He'd gone on blindly, working blindly, forgetting why he was working in the first place. And in this kind of blindness he'd lost his way. She reached out and touched the back of his wrist.

"Ted, we can clear everything up."

He smiled at her. "I don't want to go," he said. "You know that, don't you?"

"I know," she said. And for the first time in days she felt a form of optimism, a sense of opportunity, as if the marriage could be welded back together, strengthened. "And I'm sorry. Sorry to see you go. Sorry about the way I behaved the other day. Plain old sorry."

"You're not as sorry as I am," he said. Then he was fidgeting with his papers, gathering them up and sticking them inside his briefcase. She thought: Why the hell had some prick of a chef in the god-forsaken Poconos taken it into his head to cook some goddamned polluted salmon? It was a ridiculous chain of events. Somebody miles away cooks a fish; and, in a set of causal improbabilities, it affects your home. It takes your husband away. The stench of some distant salmon poisons the air in your own home. Maybe she could laugh at this. Maybe she could find a way of turning it into complete absurdity.

She closed her eyes a moment, listening to the noises of the kids.

"You want to drive me to the station? Or should I get a cab?"

"I'll drive you. What else?"

He went out of the room. She could hear him going upstairs to the bedroom now. Then he was talking with the kids, his voice low, and she knew he was telling them that he'd have to be gone for a couple of days, explaining to them in that patient way of his about the food poisoning. She walked to the foot of the stairs and watched him come down, an overnight bag in one hand, his other loosely slung around Frankie's shoulder.

In the car Frankie asked, "Will the people die?"

Ted said, "I don't think so."

"Why do you have to go, if they're not going to die?"

Ted laughed quietly. "I have to make sure it doesn't happen again. I have to help find out what caused it."

"How do you do that?" Frankie asked.

"I work with the public health people, you see—"

"Are they like scientists?"

"Something like that," Ted said.

Emily parked outside the station. She didn't want to see Ted off, she didn't want to watch him board the train, but the kids were already getting out of the car and following him through the entrance-way to the platform. She went after them, turning up the collar of her coat against the wind that had begun to blow, with a sharp trace of cold, through the darkness. The train was running late. She stood beside Ted on the platform, not knowing what to say to him, listening to the kids as they asked him desultory questions about food poisoning, hearing him explain salmonella and what it did inside your intestines. Then, in the distance, she heard the faint rumble of the train along the track. She saw its lights as it came slowly around a bend.

Ted picked up his overnight bag from the platform. He moved towards her, his hand suddenly tight against her arm. The kids were silent now, gazing in the direction of the train.

"I'll get back as soon as it's humanly possible," Ted said.

"I know—"

"I didn't want to leave again this soon," and he muttered something inaudible about the emergency.

He was silent a moment. Like a black ghost, the locomotive was grinding towards the platform. The sound of the wheels on the tracks pierced her head. "Listen," he said. "I left something for you in the bedroom."

"What?"

"It's something I want you to read," he said. "I put it in an envelope."

"Tell me what it is—"

"I'd like you to read it because if I mentioned it—hell, it would only cause an argument."

A letter? she wondered. Had Ted left her some kind of explanatory note? A point-by-point analysis of their marital situation, written neatly on VacationEase notepaper?

"I'll read it," she said. "Whatever it is."

"All I ask is you think about it. OK?"

"Sure."

And then he was getting on the train, kissing her full on the mouth, embracing the kids quickly, climbing up into the carriage and pressing his face against the glass. She raised her hand in a stiff way. The loudspeaker system stuttered. She caught the words *for Grand Central Station,* but the rest was lost to her. The locomotive hissed and the wheels began to turn slowly. Then the train was gone, the platform empty. They walked back to the car.

In the car Charlotte said, "Why can't he get a job that doesn't make him do this traveling? Why can't he get an ordinary kinda job? I don't understand it."

"He likes what he does," Emily said. "And VacationEase needs him."

"They must need him real bad," the girl said. "Maybe he doesn't think *we* need him."

Emily felt a twinge of pain, something deep inside her chest. "Charlotte, he knows we need him. Do you think he *doesn't* know it?"

The girl was quiet for a while. Then she said, "Sometimes it doesn't seem that way."

"I know how it seems, Charlotte. I know that."

"Then you should talk to him, you should try and make him understand—" The girl broke off.

"I do try, Charlotte. I really do."

"Yeah. Well. Maybe you don't try hard enough."

All at once the sharp tone in the kid's voice made Emily feel angry. She had the urge to stop the car dead, to swing around and strike out at her own daughter—but what would she be hitting out at? Not the kid, because you couldn't blame her for seeing the truth of a situation. You couldn't hit her for that. She fought the anger away.

She heard herself say, "He'll only be gone for a few days, Charlotte. He told you that. Then he's going to take some time out from work. He made me that promise."

Charlotte didn't say anything.

"Sometimes, kid, you have to make a real effort to look on the bright side of things," Emily said. How feeble. What a wretched pep talk. Maybe she could convince the kids, and herself, that all was well. She glanced round from her seat. "What's wrong with us all anyhow? I mean, what the hell is *wrong* with us? We didn't used to go moping around like this, did we? I seem to remember we were pretty happy, we used to make jokes, we used to laugh a lot—so where did this particular train go off the tracks? Huh? Where did it begin to go astray?"

The kids said nothing. They were erecting their fragile little barriers of silence. She resented them for their failure to *enthuse;* they were all going downhill fast. She turned the car into the parking lot of a shopping plaza. She stared at the merciless neon of nocturnal commercialism, the bright lights that, brighter than the moon, lit up the sky.

"Why are we stopping here?" Frankie said.

"I have to pick up some groceries, that's why," Emily said. "You guys want to wait in the car or do you want to come in with me?"

"Can I get something?" Frankie said.

"Like what?"

"I dunno. A toy maybe. A comic book."

"We'll have to wait and see," Emily answered.

They trooped out of the car and into the supermarket. Lagging behind, Charlotte was deliberately dragging the heels of her shoes, making a scuffling noise.

"I've never been in this market before," Frankie said.

"It's new," Emily said. Which was true; until recently this plaza had been nothing more than a large vacant lot. Now, almost overnight, it had been transformed into a series of stores—a large shining supermarket, a drugstore, a shoe store, a loan office called Eastern Beneficial, and a place that, festooned with heavy drapes and looking altogether secretive, was called Margarita's Beauty Salon. Inside the market, the kids went off to look at the toys from Taiwan, the cheap books and comics, while Emily pushed the gleaming shopping cart towards the dairy produce section. Milk, eggs, bread, peanut butter, and then home, she thought. The empty house. The locks. She placed a carton of milk inside the cart, then a box of eggs, a loaf of bread, a large jar of peanut butter. She wheeled all this back to the checkout counter where an oversized girl was nonchalantly tapping the buttons of her cash register. All around the desk were those newspapers and magazines designed to catch your eye with their sensational headlines, each promising some lurid revelation. She stared at them idly. Why We Had to Eat the Flesh of Our Daddy, she read. And Manson Vows to Return to a Normal Life. She picked one up and flipped through the pages. What I See This Fall for the Stars. What Did Cher Say to Warren Beatty? She closed the thing and stuffed it back on the rack, watching the plump girl haul the groceries from her cart and sling them along the small conveyor belt on the desk. Cocaine Can Kill, Says Beverly Hills Medic. Three cheers, Emily thought. What these papers promised was a passport into a flashy world, a place of such extravagant extremes that you were made to feel privy to some real hotshot secrets. I don't give a shit what Cher said to Warren Beatty, she thought. It could only have been something boring anyhow.

The girl was bagging the groceries, then holding her inkstained palm out for money. Emily paid and picked up the bag and looked round for the kids. She saw them coming towards her, Frankie clutching a comic book, something called *Tales of the Vampire*. She gave him some coins to pay for it and then she waited as he stood in line at the checkout desk.

Charlotte pushed her way through and said, "Guess who I saw."

"Who did you see?" Emily asked.

"That woman."

"What woman, Charlotte?"

"The one with the funny hair."

"I'm not sure who you mean." Emily looked through the plate glass. It was beginning to rain outside. Great drops slid across the window. Charlotte tugged at her sleeve.

"You *know* the one I mean," the girl said.

"I don't think I do—"

"The one who came to your baby-sitting meeting. *You* know."

"Who? Adrienne?"

"With the reddish hair kind of piled up? I don't remember her name."

"Adrienne," Emily said again.

"I just saw her."

"Where?"

Frankie was paying for the comic, dropping the coins slowly into the checkout girl's hand. "You saw Adrienne here?"

"In that aisle over there." Charlotte pointed. Aisle Number Three, where there hung a sign saying: Tea Coffee Spices.

"Well, maybe she shops here," Emily said.

"I don't think so. Take a look."

"Why?"

"C'mon. Over here." And Charlotte was pulling her by the sleeve towards the chromium turnstile.

"I don't feel in any mood to talk to her, Charlotte. Really I don't."

But she followed the girl anyhow towards Aisle Three. For a moment Emily didn't understand, for a moment she felt a sensation of loss, of misunderstanding, as if some vital part of her brain were failing to function properly.

"There she is," Charlotte said. "That's the one, isn't it?"

"No," Emily said. "It only looks like her."

"With that hair?"

"It isn't *her,* Charlotte."

"It is. I know it is. Go talk with her."

"No—"

Emily turned her face away, unable to look any longer. She had a feeling as of some facade crumbling, of an epoxy coming undone, a falling apart. It wasn't Adrienne. It was someone who looked like her. That was all. Somebody dressed in the dark brown uniform of the supermarket employee. Somebody routinely stamping cans with a price-stamp and shoving them on to a shelf. But it wasn't Adrienne.

Adrienne worked in the city. Adrienne had her own business.

That's what Adrienne had said.

The woman glanced briefly in Emily's direction, the face all at once white and smooth under the fluorescence, without expression, without feature, like a mask unfinished. *Adrienne.*

Adrienne.

How could it be? She had a sense of worlds colliding, of two realities coming together like battleships on a disaster course. *How could it be Adrienne?*

She worked in the city. She moved in a world of glamour. She'd said so. Emily moved away, feeling herself suddenly lightheaded. *It isn't Adrienne,* she thought. *How could it be her?* She looked back again. But the aisle now was empty. The opened box of cans lay on the floor. The woman had gone. She saw me, Emily thought. She saw me and she's hiding now. She's hiding because she can't sustain her lies, her fabrications, her whole existence of prevarication—no, how could that have been Adrienne? How?

Figure it out. It isn't hard. A pathological liar. Or just some pathetic lonely person, constructing a dream world for herself. Embittered. Sad. Making up an attractive world for herself to move in, light years away from stamping prices on cans in a goddam supermarket.

Emily walked to the front door and out into the parking lot. She felt weak suddenly, afflicted by an odd emptiness, a vague embarrassment. She lied to me and I caught her out in the lie, she thought. She lied to me, fooled me. She wasn't telling the truth, not to me, not to herself, not to any members of the co-op. It didn't make sense anyhow, not if you really thought about it, not if you retraced your steps and went over the things Adrienne had said—there was that one glaring hole, something Emily recognized only now, something she might have considered before. What would somebody like Adrienne have needed with a baby-sitting co-op anyhow? What would some-one, with the kind of money she was supposedly making with her model agency, have wanted with a bunch of middle-class house-wives? You should have seen that. You should have been worried about that. But you glided around it, didn't think about it, didn't re-ally think about *any* of the women because—on the bottom line, in that hard place where your determination lay—you needed to show yourself, and Ted, that you could build things in your life. Jesus Christ. *The woman lied. She lied.*

Emily walked slowly to the car. The groceries were heavy in her arms. I shouldn't have stopped here, I shouldn't have come to this market, I could have gone on believing the woman—why did I have to come to this goddam place? Why did Charlotte have to see her?

And now Charlotte was saying, "That was the one, wasn't it? That was the one I heard talking about her model agency, right? Big shot."

Eavesdropping. "I don't know what you mean, Charlotte."

"Sure you do. I heard her say she went to New York every day. All that shit about models and stuff."

"Don't say shit, Charlotte—"

"You know what I mean, don't you?"

Emily slung the groceries in the back of the wagon and then got inside the front, sitting motionless behind the wheel. The consid-eration of a lie, a series of lies—it could lead you anywhere, it could take you down avenues you didn't want to travel, into cul-de-sacs of mistrust, where nothing was quite what it seemed to be, where every-thing, as in some bad dream, became ambiguous and incom-prehensible. She put her hands on the wheel. Her palms were damp, her fingers shaking. Adrienne. What were you supposed to do when you saw through the lie? Exactly what? She started the car and drove quickly out of the parking lot.

All those women who came to your house.

What did you know about any of them?

What?

Sweet nothings. Their lives, their homes, their relationships, even their kids, even those kids whose lives had brought the co-op into existence—you knew nothing: Everything was a closed door. She felt like someone had struck her, slapped her straight in the face. Cheated. *She cheated me.*

And she saw me. She knows I know. Where does that knowledge lead? She wouldn't come back, that was all. She wouldn't take any part in the cooperative. She'd disappear quietly. One less name in the Book of Points.

She drove back to her house in a daze. The bewilderment gave way to a muted anger, and the anger in turn yielded to an uneasiness. What she felt like doing was going inside and taking the holy Book of Points and setting it alight, forgetting the whole thing, putting it out of her mind. You could do something else anyhow. Play bridge. Take tennis lessons. Learn how to embroider.

Four women. How many of them were liars like Adrienne?

What would the law of averages say?

Followed by the kids, she went inside the house. She dumped the grocery bag in the kitchen, then she sat down at the table and lit a cigarette. *I can't let Ted win this one. I can't.* Four women, only four —did you scrap the whole thing because one was a terrible liar? And not even a liar, maybe, but somebody who firmly believed in her own fantasies. Ted would have said that that was worse than just being a liar. Ted would have called the woman a crazy. A nut. And then he really *would* have forbidden the whole cooperative thing.

She went into the TV room where the kids were sitting, watching a show concerned with a private detective who, between endless car chases, surrounded himself with attractive young women in skimpy bikinis. She stared at the picture in a glazed way. The electronic Valium. I should call the woman, she thought. I should wait until I'm calm and call her. Put it to her point-blank. Put what exactly? *I saw you in the supermarket, Adrienne. Ergo, I deduce you're a teller of tall tales.* The broadside approach, all guns firing. The air filled with cannon shots. Why, though? Why wasn't it better to let it fade away? You didn't have to face the woman again, did you? And there was a slightly funny thing: Why, having caught the woman out, did it make *you* feel a little guilty?

She went back into the kitchen. If the job was a sham, then maybe everything else in Adrienne's life was equally fabricated. The husband who didn't know anything about her supposed indiscretions. The kids. The house on Arbor Road. Maybe all that was a part of her own creation too. It wouldn't surprise you, would it? No, damned right it wouldn't.

She lit another cigarette.

Nothing would surprise you now.

She smoked quickly, stubbing the cigarette in a violent way. She went to the back door and drew the bolt, then pulled the curtain across the glass. She returned to the TV room and convinced the kids that bed was a viable alternative to the adventures of a private eye. They grumbled. They always grumbled. But they must have seen something in her expression, some grim determination, because they complied with her request almost at once. She waited until they had brushed their teeth, then she went to their rooms and kissed them good night and turned their lights out. After that, she locked the front door.

She sat for a time in the living room and tried to read a novel, but she kept coming back to the sight of Adrienne in the supermarket.

How could she do it? she wondered.

How could she do it?

5.

Frankie had difficulty in falling asleep, in part because he was still puzzled by the figure he'd seen in the woods; but the thing that puzzled him even more was how nobody believed him, not Charlotte, not his mother. He wished his father hadn't gone away. His father always believed him. But then he hadn't mentioned the figure in the woods to his dad. It was funny how sometimes you couldn't convince another person about what you saw. No matter how hard you tried, they always looked at you in disbelief. . . . Charlotte couldn't have seen the person, because whoever was moving behind the trees had been doing so when Charlotte was facing the other way. Maybe, Frankie thought, it wasn't anyone. Maybe it wasn't anything except some shadows working away in the leaves and he'd *thought* it was somebody. That might be the whole ball game right there.

Creepy, though. The idea of somebody just staring at you. It was the thing that maybe scared him more than anything else, more than horror movies, more than the vampire comics, just the idea of being somewhere, in a room, say, and then raising your head and seeing this face at the window, this face just *staring* at you. . . . He didn't really want to dwell on it, because sometimes he got himself worked up, and then he'd toss and turn in his bed and not sleep, which made it hard to get up in the mornings. Still, he thought, I really did see somebody, no matter what Charlotte said. I really saw *somebody*.

He played a game with himself, the one where he was being asked hard questions by cops. It was something he did at times, if he wanted to get a thing really straight in his head. They'd fire these questions at him and he'd try his best to answer.

Man or woman, Frankie? they'd ask.

I don't know, he'd answer.

How tall? Big? Small? Come on, Frankie.

I didn't look long enough.

What color clothes?

I don't know. I think maybe a dark coat.

Dark, Frankie? Like what? Navy blue. Brown. Black.

I can't remember.

You putting us on, Frankie? You sure you really saw somebody?

I did. I swear it.

How can you be sure?

He opened his eyes, turning over on his side. He looked at the crack of light beneath his bedroom door. It was the landing light, the one his mother left burning all night. A shadow passed in front of it, then he heard his mother going into her bedroom, followed by the soft click of the metal in the lock. She wasn't herself these days, he thought. A bit too snappy, a bit too cranky. It had something to do with his dad going away. He wasn't sure what. He wasn't even sure he wanted to know what it was.

He shut his eyes now. I saw somebody in the woods, he thought. I really honestly truly did. No mistake. Somebody ducking behind the trees. Cross my heart. I did.

6.

Emily wasn't sure what woke her, whether a dream, some deep sense of panic, some noise from outside the house, but she opened her eyes in the black bedroom, confused, her whole body covered with slicks of sweat. She must have been sleeping restlessly because the blanket had been kicked aside and the sheet was twisted around her leg. She reached out for the bedside lamp which flickered on and then, with a faint snapping noise, died. The bulb just died. She got out of bed and opened the bathroom door, reaching in and switching the light on, and then looking round the bedroom by what little light emerged from beyond the open door. What woke me? What was it? A dream?

But then it seemed to her that she'd heard something, a crash, something coming down with a crashing noise—and it was only then she realized her window was open, that a high wind was rushing through the tree outside, that the curtains were flapping upwards in the room. She pulled the window down, still sleepy, still confused. Outside, the branches of the oak were swaying back and forth, driven by the wind and the rain; and the glass pane in the window was shaking as the rain beat against it. She lay on the bed again. She heard somebody moan. She sat upright, then she rushed to the bedroom door, opened it, stepped out on to the landing. The house was incredibly noisy, creaking, rattling, as if in its fervor the storm had provoked it into reaction. There was the sound, once more, of somebody moaning. She went into Charlotte's room. The child was turning this way and that on the bed, and Emily turned on the light.

"Charlotte," she said.

The girl opened her eyes. "Mom—"

"Hey, you were dreaming, you must have been having a bad dream." Emily sat down on the edge of the mattress. She put her hand on the child's forehead. "What was it, Charlotte?"

The girl said nothing for a time. She looked pale, wasted in some way. "I don't know. I think . . . something was falling on me. I couldn't get out of the way. I felt this weight just kinda coming down on me."

"A nightmare," Emily said. "It's OK. It's all right. Just remember. Dreams can't harm you."

Charlotte closed her eyes.

"You going to be OK?" Emily said.

The child, drifting back into sleep, mumbled something. After a moment Emily got up and tiptoed quietly to the door, closing it behind her. A bad dream. A nightmare. Maybe that's what woke me, she thought. But she couldn't remember anything now. Nothing, no trace, no remembrance. She looked inside Frankie's room. He was perfectly still, his breathing steady and shallow. She returned to her own bedroom and sat on the edge of the bed, her head inclined

slightly forward. Sleepy. You won't remember this in the morning, or
if you do it'll be like a dream. She closed her eyes. A crashing sound.
There had been some kind of crashing sound. And Charlotte, in her
dream, had felt something was falling on her. She rose and went to
the window and looked out. Across the street a car was backing up,
its white reverse lights glimmering a moment, and then the car
turned in a circle and moved off down the street. She let the curtain
fall from her fingers. The wind came again, shaking the glass. A car,
she thought. Whose car? But it was nothing. How could she attribute
menace to a car going along a street, for God's sake?

She returned to the bed. She felt she wanted to smoke a cigarette
but she'd left the pack in the kitchen and she didn't want to go downstairs for it. Do yourself some good, she thought, by self-denial. But
why won't I go downstairs? Am I afraid of something?

She stared at the darkened floor. There was a square of white
paper lying under the bedside table and she thought: Ted's envelope,
Ted's mysterious envelope. She'd forgotten all about it in the wake of
seeing Adrienne in that market—and the wind must have blown it on
to the floor. She picked it up and, opening it, carried it into the bathroom doorway, into the light. It contained a scrap of paper in Ted's
neat handwriting, and a newspaper cutting held to the paper by a
plastic clip. She looked at Ted's words.

Emily, I want you to read this and then think very carefully
about what you're involved in. I know it's important to you, but
I'm sure the kids are much more so. I would have talked
this over with you, but the mood wasn't right. Love, Ted

She removed the paper clip and spread the newspaper cutting out.
Ted's note fell from her fingers and fluttered to the floor. A clipping,
she thought. What did he want her to read a cutting from a newspaper for? And why the curt, almost clinically polite, note? She
stared at the cutting. Words swim, she thought. Sometimes they just
swim before your eyes. They undulate, as if you were seeing them
under water. A newspaper item, neatly scissored out of *The New
York Times*. (And she could see Ted doing just this, cutting away
neatly, as if it were a pattern that had to be just right, exact in every
way.) She read it through and she thought: He doesn't want me to go
on with the cooperative, he'll stoop to this, this cheap trick, to make

his goddam point. Ted, Ted, Ted. It was a low blow, a terrorist's tactic. An empty piece of rhetoric. Okay, so he didn't like strangers looking after the kids—but this? This, Ted, *really?*

It was datelined Denver, Colorado, and had the line *Special to The New York Times* under the reporter's name and it was a lurid horror story of a baby-sitter who'd freaked out in the Denver suburb of Aurora, smothering to death the three kids that had been left in her care. The stricken parents were quoted as saying *"We'd never used her before as a baby-sitter. We didn't really know her. We thought she'd be all right."* There were photographs of the parents, a blurry picture of a suburban home. Jesus Christ, Ted—you'd go to this length, you'd really go this far to spook me out of something I want to do. She folded the cutting, tore it into strips, flushed it away.

All right, I'm sorry for the parents, I feel for their suffering, she thought. I can understand what they're going through. But what do you want from me, Ted? That I should close the whole venture down? But the cutting had quite the opposite effect on her. It increased her determination to make the thing work, make it successful. I'll be damned if I bow to this kind of cheap shot, she thought. I'll be damned.

She leaned against the doorjamb and, with her eyes shut, listened to the roar of the wind through the oak tree.

Chapter Seven

1.

The man who called himself Quayle was standing with his back to the unlit fireplace. He seemed to dominate the room—or somehow his presence changed the room's dimensions, making things diminish. The other, Steadman he called himself, was lounging on the sofa, his legs stretched. She tried to listen to what Quayle was saying to her, understanding that a question had been asked and had gone unanswered, that the question lay in the air now like some shrinking balloon. She couldn't concentrate; nor did she entirely understand why these men had come back, what they wanted with her, why they were asking questions.

"When did you last see him? When did you last see your husband?"

Steadman took a handkerchief from his raincoat pocket and blew his nose. She glanced at him and then, biting her lower lip, stared at the floor. Quayle's shadow moved. There was some kind of muffled pain inside her head, knocking and knocking, like a gloved hand rapping on a raw nerve. Early this morning, she remembered, she'd gone inside her father's bedroom, expecting to find him—expecting what? He'd been asleep, his mouth slack and open, his breathing constricted. And the stew lay untouched on the bedside table. The stew, she thought now. He hadn't eaten it. . . . There was a lapse here of some kind, a link she couldn't locate. I made the food, she thought. I took it up to him. Then . . . *Then what did I do?*

It was important to remember. But the presence of these two men caused her to forget whatever it was. She thought: It isn't right they should come here. They drag something into the house, something I don't need. What did I do after taking the food upstairs last night? Something . . .

"When did you last see him?"

She raised her face and looked at Quayle. He was patient, polite. But his very size scared her. "I can't remember. I don't think about him much."

"Yeah, I'm sure you don't," Steadman said.

His tone. The way he said that. Biting on the word *sure,* like it was a tiny piece of bone fallen from some tender meat in his mouth. What did he mean?

Quayle said, "It's important. We need to know the date. His landlady said you went there once."

"Did I?"

Quayle was silent now. He picked up something from a shelf and she realized after a moment that he was holding Charlie's photograph, his large hands dwarfing the tiny frame. Charlie's in school, she thought. That's where Charlie is. School.

"Your husband had a license for a gun," Steadman said. "Only we can't locate the gun. You know anything about that?"

She shook her head. "I don't remember any gun," she said.

Quayle leaned forward, bringing his face close to hers. She could smell his breath. A stale peppermint. "We're trying to find your husband," he said. "It's important."

"It isn't important to me," she said.

"I understand that," Quayle said. Silently, he looked at the picture of Charlie. "Pretty girl. Very pretty."

She nodded her head. She looked across the room at Steadman, who was holding something in his hand, something he might have picked up from the side of the sofa. What was it? There was a sound of air hissing, escaping.

"Whistle's broken," Steadman said.

"What whistle?" she asked.

"What good's a rubber ducky when it don't whistle?" He squeezed the thing. Yellow body, orange beak, eyes that had once been bright blue were bleached out now. "No fun in the bathtub, huh?"

She didn't say anything. These men confused her. The rubber duck. The picture of Charlie. The questions. Why were they here? Why had they come back?

Quayle said, "Pretty."

He paused. She felt the silence beat against her like something dark and moist.

"I'm sorry about your daughter," Quayle said.

Sorry? Blinking, she looked at him.

"A terrible accident," he said. "I don't think you get over these things easily. I'm truly sorry."

The accident, she thought. She wondered how they knew about that, but then it was easy for them, it was simple to find anything out, they had files, dossiers, computers. There wasn't anything they couldn't find out. They pressed buttons, watched consoles, rummaged old files; then everything was laid bare. The accident. *Charlie's in school.*

"It's a waste, a real waste," Quayle said.

She smiled at him slightly. She wanted to say to him: *You don't understand, Mr. Quayle. Everything's fine now. I'm planning a reunion, you see. We'll be together again. All of us.* But she was silent.

"Can you give us an approximate date?" Steadman said.

"For what—"

"For when you last saw your husband—"

"I don't remember. Late August, I don't remember. Early in September, maybe. I can't remember everything."

"Why did you see him?" Quayle said.

"I can't recall."

"You must have had some reason."

"I must have."

Quayle stood upright again, setting the picture back on the shelf. She said, "It was about money. That was it. He was sending me money. He promised he'd send money. He promised me that. Then he forgot about it one time. I went to see him about that."

"It must be tough," Quayle said. "Financially, I mean. You don't have a job?"

She rose from her chair and went to the shelf where she adjusted the photograph, setting it just right, the way it had been before Quayle had touched it. A job, money, an accident, she thought. They're talking about somebody else. They're not talking about me at all. They're making a bad mistake. They have it wrong, terribly wrong.

Steadman stood up, a joint in his leg cracking. "You think maybe a UFO came down and lifted him, huh? You think maybe he's up there right now, doing the galaxy without a return ticket?"

She stared at Steadman. He shrugged and turned away, and Quayle sighed—a deep sigh, weary. Then, in a slow patient way, Quayle said, "We're trying to find him, that's all. People vanish. We need to know where they are. We need to rule out the chance of foul play."

"Foul play," she said.

"Right. That's what we need to rule out before we close the book."

"I understand," she said. "I understand that."

"And what really worries me here is the missing weapon."

She stared at the window. At the gray morning light that, like some dense liquid, filled the glass between the drapes. After I took him the food, she thought, where did I go? There had been a storm, the night suddenly alive with the roar of trees, rain hammering through the darkness . . . A storm. She'd gone out in the storm.

"I don't know about any weapon, I'm sorry."

"OK," Quayle said. "OK."

Steadman, making a funnel of his fist, coughed loudly into it. He was looking out of the window now. A window, she thought. A window had something to do with it. Looking through a window, watching. Standing in the rain, in the miserable dark, and watching. And then . . . then going up close to a door, a door that led into a kitchen, and staring through the glass at the woman as she sat at a table and lit a cigarette, then turned her head towards the door like she saw something there. And the girl had come into the kitchen, opened the refrigerator door, took a glass of milk. She'd stared at her mother for a time. Saying nothing. Looking sad. *You don't have to be sad,* she thought. *You won't be sad for much longer. Not when we're together again.*

She looked at Quayle now. He was going across the room, out into the hallway. Steadman followed. I hit something in the dark. I knocked against something. Bruised my shoulder.

"Thanks for your time," Quayle said. "I'm sure we don't need to trouble you again."

She watched them go down the driveway, watched them get inside their dark car. Then she shut the door.

2.

There were dreams and dreams, images of chaos and cataclysm, and when Emily forced herself awake, her head ringing with echoes, her mind fuzzy, she realized the house was silent, that the kids must have gone to school earlier—but she'd no idea of time, wakening to see the gloomy morning light slice through the curtains. She sat upon the edge of the bed, listless, uncertain. Terrible dreams, terrible ones, like the dreams of a stranger, but now she couldn't remember the substance of them, she couldn't recall what had been so awful about them. Her throat was dry. She went into the bathroom and inclined her face beneath the cold water faucet, then let some tepid water fill her mouth. It was curious how, in some sense, she felt violated by her own dreams, raped by her unconscious, as if what she carried inside her head, and had no control over, were some sinister cinema whose images pressed upon her to the point where she couldn't stand them. Merciful amnesia, she thought. Merciful.

She went downstairs and into the kitchen, tying the cord of her housecoat. She plugged the coffee maker into the wall and lit a cigarette. Even her hands trembled. She dropped the match in the ashtray, scalding the tip of a finger as she did so. The filter of the cigarette adhered to her dry lips. What was it, she wondered, that had come in the night and left her feeling so goddam shattered. She poured coffee. Shattered, that was the only word she could think of. She felt drained, bloodless. Something switched off inside her. You deal with dreams, she thought. And you deal with indefinables. She carried her coffee cup to the sink and threw her cigarette into the garbage disposal, where it sizzled momentarily. A storm. She remembered a storm, she remembered Charlotte waking from her own bad dream. Maybe there were such things as contagious nightmares, like the sympathy pains a father was said to suffer when his wife was undergoing labor contractions. The coffee was bitter, strong. But already the feeling of the dreams was beginning to disappear.

And then she recalled Ted's clipping, his little moral scissored from *The New York Times*. Maybe it was that, maybe that had gone to work in her dream world, that message of anguish and torment. *Three kids smothered by unknown baby-sitter*. She wondered how you could go on living if that happened, how you could begin to reassemble your life, what you could do to deal with that stalking emptiness, that bottomless guilt. You couldn't. Everything would be different, changed, your life would be meaningless. Bad dreams. The worst kind of dreams, suffused with guilt, shot through with the menace of memory. You'd lose your grip on things. Realities would come and go, and you wouldn't be able to tell the difference between one and the other.

Ted's clipping.

She heard a car draw up outside. The door slammed. Then after a moment there was the sound of the Westminster chimes. Who? she wondered. She went to the front door and put her eye to the peephole, the glass lens of which created the effect of a fishbowl. For a moment she wasn't going to open the door, she was going to pretend she wasn't home, the house was empty. But she opened the door anyway, looking at the sheepish expression on the woman's face outside, the downcast eyes, the faint smile that lingered on unlipsticked lips. Ask her to come in, Emily thought. No, why should you? But she was already halfway in anyhow, crossing the threshold, her head lowered slightly.

"I don't know why—" Emily started to say.

"Why I'm here?" Adrienne said.

"That's right."

Adrienne sat, a little hunched, on the edge of the sofa.

Silences. Emily thought of an aquarium for some reason, of the restless silences of fish slipping through water. So much motion and no noise. She looked at the woman. *I won't feel sorry for her. I refuse that courtesy.*

"I'm here because, my dear, you saw me last night—"

My dear, Emily thought. It sounded fake, ridiculous. She stamps cans in supermarkets. She imprints the tops of . . . cans of beans.

"I saw you," Emily said.

"And you're pretty pissed with me?"

"To phrase it mildly."

"I don't blame you." Adrienne took a cigarette from her purse, lit it, exhaled blue smoke.

"You lied to me."

"Obviously."

No remorse, Emily thought. No goddam remorse. She'd come here to brazen it out. What was it going to be? The model agency had gone bankrupt and she was obliged to find a new position? Something like that?

"You tell me, Emily," Adrienne said. "You see any harm in what I did?"

"Sure it's harmful," Emily said. "How could it not be? Jesus."

Adrienne smiled somewhat sorrowfully. "Explain, dear."

"What's to explain? You tell me a whole story of lies—what am I supposed to say? *Let's forget it, Adrienne?*"

"I didn't come here to ask forgiveness, Emily, even if you were in a position to give it." The woman gazed at her coldly now.

"Amen," Emily said. "You tell one lie, it leads to another. After a while, who knows what the truth is? *I* don't know. Do you? Do you know? I could've asked you to mind my children one night. And the terrible thing about that is, I'm leaving my kids in the care of somebody whose life I know nothing about. Whose whole life is just a set of goddam lies—"

"Lies? You'd call them lies?"

"You know a more charitable name for them?"

Adrienne shrugged. She flipped her ash on the rug. "Harmless fantasies, dear."

"Harmless fantasies, for Christ's sake!" Emily couldn't look at the other woman now. She didn't have the appetite for this kind of reproach, this kind of anger.

"That's all," Adrienne said.

"I don't call them that—"

"Did they hurt you? Did they hurt you *personally,* Emily?"

"Not exactly—"

"Of course they didn't. Why would it interfere with your life if I concocted stories about my *own* life?"

There are kids involved, Emily thought. Little kids. I'm supposed to leave them with somebody like you?

"Why did you bother, Adrienne?" she asked. "Why go to all the trouble when you must've known that somebody would see you in the supermarket sooner or later? I don't understand it."

"You're not trying, dear. You're not using your head, are you?"

Adrienne looked down at the rug for a time, humming some tune to herself, her fingers fidgeting nervously with the hem of her dark coat. She said, "I haven't had that job very long, you understand. I haven't been there more than a couple of weeks. The last job I had was in a diner outside Pastorville. A life of hash browns and eggs over easy. I quit. The supermarket hired me. I've had plenty of jobs, Emily. More than I can remember."

"All that garbage about models—"

Adrienne raised her face and smiled. "Harmless, really—"

"And the rest of it? What about all the rest, Adrienne? What about the house on Arbor Road—"

"I live in a duplex on Williamson."

"It figures. And the husband?"

"I haven't seen him in a while—"

"And the kids? What about the kids?"

She shook her head. Emily saw that her eyes were watering. A handkerchief was fished out of the purse and applied to the eyelids— and yet it was hard for Emily to avoid the feeling that some kind of playacting was going on, a dramatic performance, a piece of pure soap.

"No kids," Adrienne said.

"No kids?"

"We didn't have any—"

"Tell me why, Adrienne. Tell me why you even came to our meeting?"

"Is that so damn hard to grasp?" She folded the handkerchief away. "I live alone. I don't go anywhere. I don't belong to anything. I saw your little card. It was like a light, you see. It attracted me, Emily. A group of women. The chance to meet other people. Besides, I've always liked kids. I've always felt bad I never had any of my own, dear. But you wouldn't know that feeling, now, would you?"

Emily shook her head. Then she remembered how Adrienne had excluded herself from sitting Thursday nights because *she stayed over in the city*—when what she really meant was that Thursday night was when she worked late in the supermarket. That was it. No husband, no children, nothing but a series of experiential hollows. She wanted to feel sorry for the other woman, but she couldn't bring herself to do it. Where was charity? The moment of compassion? Emily sat down, sticking her hands into the pockets of her housecoat.

"I don't know what to say, Adrienne. I mean, how can I know you're telling the truth even now? How can I be sure of that?"

"I didn't come here to compound my fantasies, dear. Why would I do that?"

"I don't know. I find it so goddam hard to believe you, Adrienne. You'd blame me for that?"

"I wouldn't blame you, Emily," Adrienne said. "I expected, maybe, a glimmer of some understanding. You think it's easy for me to come here like this? You think this is a waltz, dear? Something I skate through? I couldn't sleep last night. I had to come here."

Emily closed her eyes. Disbelief was a hard thing to put down once it had taken root, once it had begun to work inside you.

"Naturally, I won't take any further part in the cooperative, Emily," Adrienne said. "I wouldn't put you in an embarrassing situation, dear. It's your idea, and I don't want to hurt its chances for success. I think it's a damn good idea too."

"Sure it is," Emily said.

She opened her eyes and saw Adrienne rising. *It's a horrible idea,* she thought. You put your telephone number in some supermarket and before you know it—before you know it you're immersed in a world of uncertainty, insecurity, surrounded by people you don't even know, people who are strangers. Strangers, she thought. She was operating along Ted's lines now. She might have been pondering his own sentiments, as if he'd rehearsed her. Slow brainwashing.

"I wish you hadn't lied," she said.

"I didn't *lie,* Emily. I don't call it *lying.* Lying hurts at times. I didn't hurt anybody or anything. I'd never do that." Adrienne stood at the door, shifting her weight around uneasily. The spangled purse hung from her hand like some dead creature whose existence had never been classified. "I believe in it sometimes, you see. I have to believe in it. Perhaps you don't understand that, after all. I wouldn't expect you to."

Adrienne opened the door and went outside. For a second, Emily struggled with the urge to call her back, thinking: *Who am I to punish her? What gives me that sanctimonious right?* But she didn't move, she stared at the closed door, then she heard the car door slam and the motor come raggedly to life. Adrienne, she thought. What form of pity are you looking for? But then she wasn't thinking about Adrienne next, she was thinking about something else, something it seemed important to do. She went into the kitchen and opened a drawer, finding the Book of Points. Remove Adrienne's name, leaving three others. Three other names. On a separate sheet of paper, ripped out of the back of the book, she wrote the three names down. Beneath them, she wrote down all the things she could remember about these women, as if she were compiling a list, drawing up an inventory, looking through the scant facts of other lives for a sign of more fabrication, more inconsistency, more lies—

She stopped. I don't need to do this. Why am I doing this?

Because it's important, she told herself. Because you need to know. Because because because: Ted came somewhere at the top of her list of reasons. Show Ted something can be worked out successfully. Show him that much at least. Just flash it in front of his face and make him admit that it was all right after all, that it would work.

She wrote quickly.

Then she put the pencil down, rubbing her wrist, searching her memory. All you do is check up on these women, that's all, a simple little task you can perform in next to no time. She strolled to the back door and drew the curtain back from the glass.

It was gone.

Ted's wonderful trellis was gone.

Surprised, she opened the door and stepped outside. But it hadn't gone. It was still there, lying flat against the grass, presumably knocked over by last night's storm. You build a thing to last, don't you Ted? You really know how to build something lasting. She crossed the moist grass barefoot and stared at the fallen slats of wood. No roses will grow here, she thought. The poor old thing. She walked around it, feeling the damp soil adhere to her feet. The grass had been trampled, flattened by the fall of the trellis. It was, she thought, a perfect symbol of something. Of collapse all round.

She went back indoors. Later, she'd call Ted and she'd tell him what had happened to his trellis.

3.

They were in the car, going across the freeway towards Pastorville. Steadman was driving in his usual careless manner, handling the car as if the streets belonged to him and nobody else. One day, Quayle thought, we'll crash and that will be the end of it. Steadman braked for a red light, took a crushed pack of Marlboros from his raincoat, and stuck one between his lips without lighting it.

"What do you think?" he said, staring forward through the windshield. "You ask me, I think she's a flake. I don't think she's playing with a full deck, Quayle. Somewhere along the way she's lost a coupla cards."

"How do you figure that?" Quayle said.

"You only got to look at her, Quayle. She's a space cadet."

Quayle stared at the cloudy sky. A dog day, he thought. "She's troubled, I'll say that. So what? Half the human race is troubled. If I took it into my head to worry about every troubled human being, I'd fall out of my tree."

"Yeah. Well, you weren't on the receiving end of the look she threw me. Poison. Pure poison." Steadman put his foot on the gas, propelling the car under the green light. The suddenness of the movement caused Quayle's head to swing back. Quayle clutched the door handle.

They were going down through Pastorville.

"I guess anybody'd be troubled after a kid drowns," Quayle said. "Then the husband kisses the whole thing off. That would trouble anybody."

"Sure," Steadman said. "So what do you think? Missing Persons?"

Quayle shrugged. He was staring at Pastorville's main thoroughfare, lamenting the way some of the old buildings had been torn down and replaced with little Plexiglas boxes. Some of the old storefronts remained, housing businesses they hadn't been constructed for. He looked at the group of people lifting crates outside the food cooperative. He remembered that the store had once been the premises of a shoemaker, an old craftsman, an artisan of the Neanderthal school. You didn't get that kind of work anymore, not in the Age of the Slipshod. At the end of the block there was a garish storefront called *High There,* which sold drug-related paraphernalia. God, he thought, there was even a category in the Yellow Pages: Head Shops, it said. A changing world. *High There* had once been a family grocery store owned by Italian immigrants. But no more. He stared at a long-haired girl coming out of the head shop. A pretty young thing. But all the pretty young things had bloodshot eyes these days.

"What d'you think?" Steadman asked again.

Quayle looked at his partner. The set of Steadman's jaw was one of constant belligerence, a certain attitude of aggression.

"Funny," Quayle said. "When we first went there I remember picking up the kid's photograph. I remember complimenting her on such a good-looking girl. Why didn't she say something then about the accident? She acted like the kid was out back playing with her dolls or whatever."

"Like I said. A space cadet. Fried brains. We call it losing touch with reality, Quayle. You ever hear that phrase?"

Quayle said nothing. Sometimes he was sick to the gut with Steadman, with the way the guy spoke, the way he had of sticking a thin needle into him. Then he was thinking of the gun again. That's what bothered him now, more than anything else. A missing gun. It seemed somehow more important than a missing person.

"File it," Steadman said. "Stick it in a drawer, I don't care. While you're farting around with this Nick character, people are peddling drugs at the college, Quayle. You got your priorities somewhat muddled."

"I'll file it," Quayle said. "Sooner or later."

They went beyond Pastorville Community College, beyond a small neighborhood bar called the Happy Hour—a converted frame house— and parked outside the Victorian gray brick monstrosity that passed as Pastorville City Hall.

"Sooner instead of later," Steadman said. "You know what your problem is, Quayle? You brood too much. You're gonna brood your gray matter right outta your head one day. You'll see."

"Yeah. You'll be the first to know when that happens," Quayle said.

"If it hasn't already," Steadman said, getting out, slamming the door.

4.

Emily spread the sheet of paper on the table and looked at her own crabbed handwriting. What else? she wondered. What else could she remember about these women? She read what she'd written, trying to fill the spaces in her own recall. What gaps did she leave? The information she remembered seemed somehow so skimpy, so thin.

Carole Kirkham—one kid, a daughter, divorced,
about 30, says she works full time at Sears, in
the credit office, says her husband lives in
Pastorville
Susan Gallo—thirty, roughly, full-time housewife,
says her husband teaches (somewhere nearby, over in
Hunter? Was that it?), says she has two kids
Marylou Fretz—on welfare, separated, can't remember if
she said divorce or not, says she has two kids, belongs
to the food co-op

She stared at the list for a while, struck by the fact that—if you included Adrienne—three out of the four women who'd come to the meeting were either separated or divorced. A weird statistic. Maybe they *were* like Adrienne, coming to the meeting out of some sense of wanting to belong to something, anything, filling up absences in their lives. But they couldn't all be liars. How could that be? They couldn't all be lying about their lives, could they?

She copied their addresses onto her sheet, taking them from the Book of Points. They all lived, she noticed, in the suburb, even Marylou Fretz, whom Emily had suspected would live somewhere in the old town—which might have been more in keeping with her image. Still, it was easier if they all lived in West Pastorville, they were easier to visit that way. She folded the sheet of paper and stuck it into the hip pocket of her jeans.

Beginning now, she thought. Why put it off?

She took the car keys from a drawer and was about to go to the front door when the telephone rang. It was James Hamilton. He sounded slightly inebriated, his words a little slurred.

"How's the poem coming along?" he asked.

"Actually, it isn't," she said.

"For shame, Emily Allbright. You haven't done a goddam thing, right?"

"That about sums it up—"

"What's the block? Lack of the old liniment of inspiration? Your muse got wings of lead? Tell me about it."

"I don't know," she said.

"You sit down. You look at virgin paper. The idea of putting a word down is like blasphemy. Why defoliate a virgin, after all?"

She said, "I haven't even sat down. I haven't even stared at blank paper."

"Emily, Emily," he said. "I only called to ask. The poet as detective. Investigating the life of a student under suspicion."

"Suspicion of what?" she said.

"Malingering. Loitering in the doorway of a poem with malicious intent."

"Have you been drinking?"

"I've had a light intake of cheap Chianti," he said. "We reached a mutual understanding, the grape and I. I drink it down, see? And in turn it numbs my senses when I sit down to read the ravings of students. Teeny-bopper outpourings, Emily. The discontented heart. Everything is covered in the latex of chewed-out gum. They ask such serious questions, that's what it is. *Why am I alive? What does it all mean?* Stuff like that."

"Are you looking for my sympathy?"

"Not really. I'm looking for your presence in class tomorrow night. As for sympathy, it's a debased currency, Emily. Poem or no poem, will you be there tomorrow night?"

She hesitated. "I don't know. I can't answer that."

"Why? It doesn't strike me as an especially taxing question, involving as it does either an affirmative or negative response."

"That's a terrific choice. I just gave you a maybe."

"Maybes are tightropes, Emily. Be there."

"I'll try," she said.

"Do better than endeavor. Be valorous. Show up. God alone knows, I don't have much to look forward to in that class when you pause to consider. Realtors high on Willie Wordsworth. Religious epics written by nice old ladies. You should come to my daytime class sometime and catch the teen-age angle. You can't hear yourself think surrounded by the popping of Wrigley bubbles."

"I'll try. Really."

"Don't be a poetry pooper, Emily."

"Go back to your bottle," she said.

"I intend to. See you tomorrow."

And he hung up. She put the receiver down and wondered why he'd called: just to ask about her supposed poem? It seemed a flimsy pretext to her. Ah, but a pretext for what? Dream on, Emily. How does a poet make a pass?

She went outside, locking the front door behind her. She sat inside the station wagon for a time, considering: Why am I doing this anyhow? Why am I about to drop in at the homes of these other women? What do I expect to find?

Only this, she thought. A clean bill of health. An unencumbered title to the baby-sitting cooperative; a sense that all was well. Then her husband couldn't bitch about the thing anymore. Then he wouldn't be tempted to leave pointless newspaper clippings in sealed envelopes. Above all else, though, she would feel easier herself.

A whole lot easier.

She turned the key in the ignition. She set off on her house calls, like a physician probing some unidentifiable malady, a virus without name.

Chapter Eight

1.

Somewhere in the course of the night the food had gone rancid and now he could smell the sweet odor of decay. A fly buzzed over the plate, then presumably it landed—but he didn't hear it again after that. Dead, he thought. Whatever she put in the stew would kill flies as well as humans. Stone cold dead. It isn't going to be me, he thought. He moved his legs a little, feeling how the muscles hurt from the exertion of the day before. During the hours of darkness he'd thought: I could just give in without a fight, I could just close my eyes and drift out into whatever that darkness is that waits for me out there—because where was there a good reason for living anyhow?

And he'd thought, ransacking his mind, dreaming up good arguments. In the end there was only one, there was only one thing to hold on to, to clutch: *I won't give her the goddam satisfaction of burying me. She won't get that from me. I'll see her in hell first.*

It was this that sustained him now, burning in his head like a small flame. He swung his legs over the side of the bed. The arch of his right foot hurt from where the sliver of glass had gone in and he reached down to rub the spot, feeling a hard speck of clotted, dried blood. Holding his arms forward, he stepped onto the rug. Careful. The glass. Cautiously, he circled the rug, then his feet found the cold linoleum. But now he could hardly breathe and his lungs, like dried sponges, seemed to shrivel in his chest. Then his outstretched hands touched something. The wall.

The wall.

But all at once he was lost. He didn't know where the bed lay, where the window was, the door—he was as lost as he might have been in unmapped terrain, stranded in a forsaken place without a compass. Panicked, he moved along the wall, touching the surface with his fingertips, feeling that any moment he would lose his remaining strength and fall, and then she'd hear him and come running up. No. I don't want that, he thought. Find the bed. Find the bed again. Then there was an obstacle in his way. A wooden thing. A chest of drawers. He had reached the corner of the room by this time. Go back. Back the way you came. But which way had he come anyhow?

The muscles in his calves felt like some viscous liquid. He pressed his face flat to the wall, breathing hard. Find the way back. Find the bed. Before she comes upstairs, before she sees me. This is the only weapon you have, he thought. Your secret, your only means of attack, of defense. Your mobility. And she doesn't know about that, does she?

He groped. He cursed this stupid impenetrable darkness that was the condition of his life. His hands shook, the muscles in his thighs weakened. He crouched now, his forehead still pressed to the chill wall. Bedridden, am I? Is that what you think? Can't rise, can't get up?

Let me show you.

He put his foot out through the darkness. Glass. Bits of glass. Then he was back on the rug again, but this time his legs wouldn't support him, this time there was a collapse, and he went down slowly on his knees, reaching forward across the small rug to touch the edge of his bed. The pain, sweet Christ. The fucking pain. The glass went through the cotton of his pyjamas and slid into his knee bones. He grabbed a corner of a bedsheet and stuffed it in his mouth so he wouldn't cry out. Then, with an immense effort, he hauled himself against the side of the bed. He swung himself upwards onto the bed, rubbing his knees, feeling the dampness of his own blood. How could he get those tiny fragments of goddam glass out of his skin? *I can't even see them. I can't see where they went in.* He drew the bedsheet over his body. He turned, feeling his useless eyes water from the pain, in the direction of the window. Normally he sensed the light, but she must have drawn the curtains. Sometime in the night, she must have drawn them so he wouldn't know if it was night or day any longer.

To confuse. Perplex. Maybe she hadn't done that, though. Maybe he'd lost his sense of time, and several hours had just slipped away somewhere. Goddam her, he said to himself. She'd created a prison for him—an almost perfect prison, but not quite. Not quite that.

He lay, breathing heavily, listening for her sound. But there was nothing in the house save for some hollowed-out silence.

2.

I was in the neighborhood, just thought I'd drop in, say hi. . . .

One kind of approach. Was there any other?

Hi, there, I'm here to check up on you, doing some minor gum-shoe work to see who's on the level and who's not. . . .

It wasn't even that, was it? It wasn't minor detective work at all. You've got another name for it? she asked herself. The search for a sense of security, perhaps.

Call it that, she told herself.

She drove past a diner on the edge of the freeway. Somewhere around here was the house where Marylou lived. Sycamore had been one of the first cheap constructions in the suburb and consequently looked more shabby than the surrounding streets. Some of the houses were duplexes, presumably rented out to college students by absentee landlords domiciled in Miami Beach. As she drove along slowly, Emily checked her sheet of paper. She was looking for 95, the ad-dress Marylou had given. It was a corner house on a relatively large lot, fronted by an untidy hedge, an overgrown lawn, shaded by un-ruly trees. She parked and got out and went through a space in the hedge, seeing a VW bug stationed in the driveway. Beneath the car there was a slick puddle of oil, as if something were leaking.

She rang the doorbell. Waited. Nothing. She isn't home, she thought. Why did she feel a sense of relief? But then there was a sound from inside, a movement in the hallway, and the door was opened. Marylou stood there, her hands in the back pockets of her blue jeans, a black T-shirt worn loose and hanging outside the pants. Her glasses gleamed, her black hair glinted as if it had just been washed.

She doesn't remember me, Emily thought with some dismay. I smile, and there's no returning gesture. *So hard to remember, so easy to forget.*

"Marylou," she said.

"Emily?"

"That's right. I was just passing and—"

"Come in," the woman said. "Welcome."

Emily followed Marylou into a darkened hallway that led to a liv-ing room. It was tidy, well-furnished, comfortable. This perception surprised Emily. She wondered if what she'd expected were Jimmy Hendrix posters, the face of Chairman Mao, perhaps even Che—all the clichés of a decade. You're prejudiced, she thought. You didn't expect Sears, Montgomery Ward, did you?

"Grab a seat," Marylou said. She took off her glasses and rubbed her eyes and Emily noticed the eyes were faintly bloodshot.

"I thought you didn't remember me," Emily said.

"Oh, that. I've been experimenting with contact lenses this morning, and I think maybe they've affected my eyesight," Marylou said. "I didn't see you properly, I guess."

Silence. *Why am I here?* Emily wondered. She looked round the room. There were a number of books, framed pictures on shelves, an embroidered motto hanging on a wall. She took this in quickly, not wanting to be rude, staring, the way some people were when they first stepped inside your home. It doesn't fit somehow, these surroundings didn't fit the image she had of Marylou; nor, for that matter, did the woman herself seem comfortable, looking as if she were trying to adapt to an unusual environment and feeling, like some chameleon going through the changes, quite miserable.

"You were just kinda passing?" Marylou said.

"That's right. Then I remembered you lived around here. . . ."

"You want coffee? I have some white wine chilled, if you'd like."

Emily shook her head, smiled. The descent of awkwardness. The palms of her hands felt moist.

"How's the cooperative working out?" Marylou tilted her head at an angle that suggested insatiable curiosity.

"It's hardly got off the ground yet—"

"Yeah. I haven't had any calls so far. The thing is, these things tend to take a while to get going. People are, like, hesitant at first. That's only natural. But it'll grow. There's something really sound about the cooperative principle. We'll get new members, then it'll take off like a rocket."

New members, Emily thought. I'm not even sure about the old ones. Marylou, enthusiastic, was going on about how it would run itself eventually, how a maximum number of thirty members would be enough for real success. Emily found herself listening in a glazed way. Marylou paused, then said: "You got two kids?"

"Right."

"I think I saw one of them peeking the other night at your house."

"You probably did."

"Pretty little girl with real blonde hair."

"Charlotte," Emily said.

"Real pretty."

"She hears that all the time. I hope it doesn't go to her head."

Marylou smiled. A silence now. The whole house seemed silent. Emily remembered the time she'd called Marylou about baby-sitting, just before her first college class, and a man had answered in a gruff voice. She wondered about it—a lover? a friend?

"I called about a week ago," she said.

"Yeah?"

"I'm taking a night class Wednesdays in poetry writing." Emily laughed, as if what she wanted was to apologize for a pretension. "So I thought I'd ask you to sit for me. But you weren't home. A man answered."

"A man?" Marylou said. "When was this?"

"Let me think. Last Tuesday night, I guess. Right after our meeting. That was it."

"A *man* answered?"

"That's right—"

Marylou frowned. She ran the fingers of her hand through her hair and blinked at Emily. She said, "I think you got it wrong."

"How?"

"There wasn't anybody here. There wasn't any man."

"Oh?"

"The house was empty. I left the kids over at the food co-op, went to our meeting, picked the kids up, then came home. There wasn't anybody here, Emily."

Emily laughed again. It was a brittle sound. "I dialed the number you left. A man said you weren't home."

"He said *I* wasn't home?"

"By name."

"Weirder and weirder. You sure?"

"He wasn't exactly polite—"

"It must have been a wrong number."

"How?" Emily said. "The man said, 'Marylou isn't at home. Goodbye.' Then he hung up."

Marylou got up from the sofa and walked to the window, where she stood for a moment and looked out. "That fucker," she said. "That rotten fucker."

Emily said nothing. What had she touched off here? What nerve?

Marylou took her glasses off and came back to the sofa, looking agitated. "I knew it," she said. "That miserable bastard watches the goddam house, and when he sees me go out he lets himself in with his fucking key. I *knew* he was doing that. *I just knew it!*"

"Who? Who's doing what?"

"My old man," Marylou said.

"Your husband?"

"Yeah, if he deserves a title."

"But why? I mean, why would he come here?"

Marylou was quiet for a time. "It's part of his game, OK? He's playing some stupid game. He skips, I can't find him, he doesn't send money, he doesn't write, he couldn't care less about the kids—but I knew he was still in the vicinity. I knew he was. That cheap shit."

"I still don't—"

"You'd have to know him. You really would. Like, he's kinda strange. And part of it is the fact he comes here, because he thinks he can bug me that way. OK, it's his house, and all this junk furniture is his, but that doesn't give him the right to come here when I'm out. Shit. Once or twice I had the feeling someone had been in the house. You know? I would come back and find something different. Not different so you would really notice it, Emily. I don't mean a table knocked over or something like that—"

"What kind of things *do* you mean?"

"OK. Once I found a date circled on the calendar in the kitchen. I knew I hadn't done it. The date didn't have any significance. I thought maybe one of the kids. It wasn't anything important. I guess I forgot about it. Another time I came back from the food co-op, a meeting of the steering committee, and the cellar door was open. You don't think about small things like that, really. OK, maybe I left it open. But I knew I hadn't. I thought, well, it blew open." She smiled, shaking her head. "It's him. All that goddam time, it's him. Coming here to bug me, trying to remind me he's still in my life somewhere."

"I think that's bad. Awful," Emily said.

"I just never got round to changing the lock," Marylou said. "Because I never really suspected. Just feelings, that was all. I could *sense* him. Does that make sense? It must have been him that answered the telephone when you called."

A stranger in the house, Emily thought.

Somebody coming in your absence. Turning his key in the lock. Moving around the house like a shadow. It was a distressing thought.

What kind of mind would dream such things up? Things so small, disturbances so tiny, you'd never noticed them until later? Marylou sighed, rubbed her glasses on the black T-shirt, replaced them.

"He's got some balls," Marylou said. "I mean, *answering* the phone."

Emily gazed at the bookshelf. The silence of the house pressed in on her again. She ran the palm of her hand across the Herculon fabric of her chair and said, "You should change the lock today."

"When you're on my kind of budget, it was either contact lenses or a lock."

"I guess," Emily said. She watched the other woman for a moment then asked: "Are your kids in school?"

"They're not school age yet. I found this group connected with the community college that runs a free pre-school day-care thing. A couple of times a week I leave them there. They like it. And it gives me some breathing space—"

"I know about breathing space," Emily said.

"I try and get some housework done. I hate it. But I try."

Emily smiled in sympathy. She looked quickly around the room again. It wasn't exactly tidy, like she'd interrupted Marylou in the middle of her cleaning. A mop stood inside a bucket in the corner. There was a can of Pledge on the table, a roll of kitchen towels, a container of Ajax. A bag of groceries could be seen on the kitchen table—half-unloaded. Sticks of celery. A red cabbage. A pack of bean sprouts. Yoghurt. A large package of oatmeal.

"The group seemed nice the other night," Marylou said. "Except for that woman . . . Adrienne?"

"Adrienne, right."

"There's a certain kind of person I don't get along with. Maybe she's OK, I don't know. But she seemed fake to me. You know what I mean? A bullshit artist?"

"I think I know," Emily said.

"That's why I kinda dashed away. I was beginning to feel she wanted to smother me. I didn't want to come off as rude, but there was something *gross* about her."

Emily nodded. She looked at her wristwatch. It was close to noon. "A question, Marylou. Can you sit for me tomorrow night?"

"Sure," Marylou said. Then she frowned, shutting her eyes in the manner of somebody concentrating. "Wait. I can't. I'm sorry. I have

this steering committee thing and I promised I'd go. I'm really sorry.
Any other night."

"It isn't important," Emily said. She wasn't sure why she'd thrown
the question out like that anyhow—except she found herself liking
Marylou, an unexpected feeling of sympathy, a certain trust. She rose
from her chair and said, "Come visit with me sometime."

"I will." Marylou walked with her to the door.

Outside, Emily turned and said, "And get your lock changed."

"Hey, top priority," Marylou said. "Number one on my list."

Emily smiled and went to her car, feeling reassured, feeling her
own unease begin, even in a small way, to sink—as if there were an
invisible set of weights and balances in her mind, and Marylou more
than canceled out the presence of Adrienne. One down, she thought.
Two to go.

This is easy. Real easy.

3.

Susan lived on the other side of the suburb, away from the freeway,
away from the center of things—if you could say that West Pastorville had a center, a heart. It didn't, really, Emily thought. Everything is scattered, there isn't a core, a hub. She drove along Lincoln
Boulevard—an unlikely name for a narrow street, suggesting as it did
a line of trees, small cafes on the sidewalk. But the boulevard was
just another suburban street filled with orderly homes, tidy lawns.
She slowed the car when she left Lincoln, and checked the address
on her sheet of paper: 651 Maryland. It lay somewhere to the south
of the boulevard, beyond the Sears Plaza. Unlike Sycamore, this area
was the most recent addition to the suburb. Brand shining new almost: the houses hadn't yet lost their patina of freshness. Maryland
was a quiet drive, as she'd known it would be—a wide street, parked
cars, a couple of Stars and Stripes fluttering here and there in some
limp semblance of patriotism (why? she wondered; why this urge to
fly Old Glory?), a few sprinkler systems sending arcs of water over
lawns turning brown. Number 651 was near the end of the street. She
parked the station wagon and stepped out, looking up at the house.
A blue Ford was in the driveway, an LTD of recent vintage.

She approached the front door. As she did so, Susan opened it.

"I saw you drive up," Susan said.

"I was in the neighborhood—"

Susan smiled. "Come in. Please. I'm glad to see you."

Emily followed the woman through a dim-lit living room and out into a kitchen. A bright gleaming kitchen, fitted with stainless steel surfaces that snared your reflection and threw it back sharply. (She thought of her own messy kitchen, making a terrible contrast.)

"We don't get many visitors," Susan said. "This is a bit out of the way."

"Oh, nothing's out of the way in West Pastorville," Emily said.

Susan smiled again and opened a cabinet, taking out two cups.

"I just made some fresh coffee," she said. "Milk? Sugar?"

"Straight and black," Emily said. She sat down at the kitchen table. No Formica here: real wood, highly varnished, and a sight of your own reflection again. She watched Susan pour the coffee. She had delicate white hands. You couldn't imagine these hands doing housework somehow. You could imagine them assisting a magician in his act; or, gloved, sifting through lace handkerchiefs in some expensive department store.

Susan sat down across the table. "I'm pleased you're here," she said. "I thought sometimes of coming to see you."

"You should have," Emily said. "I'm almost always at home. Alas."

"Me, too. It gets pretty monotonous."

"Monotony and I are fellow travelers," Emily said and sipped her coffee.

When she smiled, Susan looked quite beautiful—as she did now; and under the drawn quality of her face you could see how she must have appeared once, fresh and vital, with the kind of innocence that finds its sexual outlet in the handling of a baton. The high-school homecoming queen, maybe. What does she do all day long? Emily wondered. The kitchen, with its robotic appearance, surely ran by itself. So, after you'd cleaned up a few spots, a couple of greasemarks, what was there left to do? Emily gazed at the window, at the pale green venetian blinds through whose slats there came streaks of gray light.

Susan said, "I've been trying to make cheesecake."

Ah, Emily thought. "From scratch?"

"From scratch—"

"Brave soul," Emily said. You couldn't tell, though. If she'd been trying to build a cheesecake from the basic ingredients, she'd covered her tracks pretty damn well.

"I gave it a shot once," Emily said. "I was up to my neck in graham crackers and cream cheese. Shall I tell you what a disaster it was?"

Susan tilted her face back and laughed. Revealing, this gesture: you could see tightly drawn skin beneath the chin. Emily set her coffee down and took out a cigarette, lighting it, thinking: You could be seduced by the coziness of all this, two married women doing a domestic thing, chitchat and coffee and a cigarette in an empty house. It was dreamlike, somehow it didn't belong to any known world. And yet she'd seen it before, remembering the TV commercials that advocated a reality in which women, their kids presumably in school, discussed such profundities as margarine, hand lotion, or tollhouse cookies. It was an ordinariness elevated to the sublime.

"It's easy when you have the knack," Susan was saying.

"I guess I just don't have it."

"They say practice makes perfect."

She means it too, Emily thought. There was the light of some conviction in her lovely eyes.

"I like your kitchen," Emily said.

"My husband's idea," Susan said, looking round.

"Yours too? My husband can't stop picking up tools. Sometimes I think I'll go to sleep at night and wake the next morning and find he's totally remodeled the house during the night." Looking, Emily thought, for a common bond, a social adhesive.

There was a pause. Emily could hear a clock tick somewhere. On the wall by the back door there were a couple of kids' drawings, elongated figures with stalklike edges, tiny heads, all done in lavishly colorful crayon. Emily stared at them for a time.

Then she said, "I started to go to night school."

"Really?"

"Poetry writing. Don't ask me why."

Susan raised her coffee cup and drank in a genteel way, her small finger crooked slightly in the air. "It sounds interesting," she said, setting the cup down. "I should do something like that."

"Why don't you?"

"Oh," Susan said. "It's the old story, I suppose. At the end of the day I don't have any energy left. I feel beat. All I want to do is sleep."

Emily had the feeling that Susan's life was as interesting as a display of somnambulism, that she was bounded in and hemmed by this house. By husband and kids. By catering for them. She wanted to reach across the table and say: *You have to do something. You have to, for God's sake.* Susan was smiling again, this time at nothing Emily could guess: it was as if she used her smile as a kind of buffer, creating an empty zone between herself and reality. Monarch of her home, Emily thought. Which was OK, if you didn't want anything else, if you felt comfortable with what you had, and if you were able to create a controlled environment into which nothing intruded. Contented, she thought. Perhaps, at a pinch, happy.

"Why did you join the co-op?" Emily asked.

"Why?" Susan touched her hair, tossing it back. "Actually, my husband and I thought we should go out more. We hardly ever go out. He likes movies. Restaurants. So I joined because I wanted to please him, I guess." Susan paused, staring into her coffee cup. "That's right. I wanted to please him. Does that sound awful? Does that sound servile?"

Servile, Emily thought. An echo. She shook her head. "It doesn't sound servile at all," she said. "I think it's perfectly natural."

"It's a good marriage. Why shouldn't I please him?"

Susan got up from the table and fetched the coffeepot, unplugging it from the wall. Emily laid her hand over the top of her cup and said, "One cup's enough for me. It makes my nerves jangle."

Susan poured for herself, then sat down. "So many people seem to fail at marriage, don't they? I sometimes think of the friends I went to high school with and how many of them have already been married and divorced. It makes me sad."

Emily said nothing. One of the drawings on the wall had the word Dad scrawled under it. Another said Mom. A severe case here, she thought, of Happy Families—catching herself in the act of thinking, wondering if what lay beneath the thought, on some other stratum of awareness, was a kind of bitterness. Not yet, Emily, she told herself. It's a long way to bitterness. Just because you don't live in some Barbie Doll world doesn't mean you have to be miserable, does it?

"You need to work at your marriage," Susan said.

"Of course you do," Emily said.

"And sometimes it feels like a full-time job." Susan laughed in a light melodic way. She laughed, Emily thought, a little too long. There was something pent-up in the sound. Nervous, maybe. Kitchen crazy. Cheesecake mad. Seeing your own harried image one time too many in gleaming surfaces.

Emily finished her coffee. She put the cup down in the saucer. From somewhere an ashtray had been produced. She stubbed her cigarette against its clean glass surface, feeling as if she were defiling something; like leaving the stains of your hands on white towels in somebody's bathroom.

"Both your kids in school?" she said.

Susan stared at her across the table. The tick of the clock, a clock Emily couldn't see, was maddening. It not only counted out the seconds of your life, it seemed to emphasize them, like it was making endless, repetitive accusations. "Yes," Susan said. "The younger one just started this year in first grade."

"It's a wrench when they first go all day long," Emily said.

Tick tick tick tick. Why didn't the woman smother the clock? The tiny noise echoed like a small hammer on thin metal.

"It sure is," Susan said.

Then Emily realized she had run out of things to say to Susan. She wasn't sure what to add, what to ask. A polite social call, nothing more. She sat for a moment, gazing at the twisted stub of her cigarette. Susan reached forward and took the ashtray and emptied it into a trash can, then placed the ashtray in the stainless steel sink. A Clean Freak, Emily thought. What was that compulsion to create a spotless environment anyhow? What kind of drive did you need for that? Control, she thought. If you keep it clean, squeaky clean, you have control over the whole domain. The silence now was more awkward than it had been in Marylou's house, more pointed somehow, like it attacked you.

Emily stood up. "I better get going," she said. She looked at her watch. Susan walked behind her through the living room, out into the hallway, the front door. There was a strange antique by the front door, an old mahogany coat tree of a kind Emily hadn't seen in years. She paused, looking at the burnished wood.

"I *like* that," she said.

"It's unusual," Susan said. "People always notice it."

"Where did you find it?"

"There's a dealer over in Pastorville," Susan said. "My husband found him. He often has really quite unusual things."

"Does he have anything else like this?"

Susan reached out to touch the coat tree, curling her hand around one of the hooks. "I wouldn't know," she said. "I haven't been over there in a while."

"I like it a lot," Emily said. What was she doing—standing here and blathering about a piece of wood? "I'd like to find one like this." No, she thought. You really wouldn't. What would you do with it anyhow?

"I've got his name written down somewhere," Susan said, suddenly eager to please. Emily pushed open the front door. There was a hint of rain in the air.

"I'll get it for you," Susan said.

"Hey—don't go to any trouble." Emily smiled, stared at the coat tree.

"It's no trouble," Susan said. She went back through the living room. There was a noise, like a drawer being opened. I opened my big mouth, Emily thought. What did I go and do that for? A coat tree, Christ. The drawer was slammed shut, somewhere at the back of the house, and Susan rushed through with the dealer's name on a sheet of paper. Emily took it, then swung her head round to look at the street, drawn by a sudden sound, a huge grating noise. She saw an enormous street-cleaning truck come down the edge of the sidewalk, its engine straining, the vast brushes revolving as the thing moved. It was elephantine, hideous. Even the trees seemed to vibrate.

"How often does that come along?" Emily shouted over the roar of the thing.

"They've only just started doing it," Susan said.

"They haven't made it to my street yet," Emily said.

"They will, I expect."

Emily watched it pass, lumbering, clumsy. Then she turned to look at Susan again. "Thanks for the coffee," she said.

"Come any time, Emily. I'm usually at home. You don't need to call."

"And I won't forget to make the Book of Points rotate in your direction next," Emily said.

For a moment Susan seemed puzzled. Then she smiled. "Right. I'd almost forgotten I asked you about that."

Emily shrugged. "It's not the most absorbing pastime in the world, I guess."

"I'd still like to have it," Susan said.

"You got it," Emily said, and went to her car, turning once to wave, then driving away.

4.

She picked up the useless rubber duck where the man called Steadman had dropped it. She held it in her hand for a time. It seemed to her like she could feel the warmth of the child's hand around it, but that was only an illusion. A trick. A rubber duck. How long had it lain down the side of the sofa? How long since Charlie had left it there? Stuffed it beneath the cushion? She stuck the toy in a drawer, shut the drawer. She realized she was hungry all at once, but she didn't feel like eating. She went to the bottom of the stairs, looking up. She could see the closed door of his room. Once or twice he'd called out to her, but now he was silent. He hadn't made a sound in hours. Alive or dead? But she didn't care. When she'd taken the stew up to him last night she'd sprinkled it with the powder taken from broken capsules of Placidyl, then stirred it through the meat and vegetables. But he hadn't eaten it. He *knew. He knew,* she thought.

She went into the kitchen and sat down at the table.

She laid her hands in front of her, clasping them.

She had been thinking of the boy again. She had been thinking about what to do with him.

What to do.

Two kids instead of one. Two kids, not just one.

What to do with the boy.

She shut her eyes and listened to the house. It was deadly silent, closing in all around her in one dizzying rush, bringing darkness, a sense of being enveloped in all this quiet.

The boy.

5.

Carole had written down an address on Fillmore, which was located in the eastern part of the suburb in the network of small streets and cul-de-sacs that lay behind Arbor Road. As she drove along Arbor, Emily looked at the spacious houses. They'd been built in accordance with some demented architectural dream of colonial dwellings; indeed, the builder's brochure describing West Pastorville had called them "the neo-Colonial homes"—five-bedroom houses with great expanses of lawn and colonnades that suggested minor plantations. In front of some of the houses there were even transplanted willows which, bending languidly to the ground, echoed a past grace. Arbor Road. Where Adrienne "lived." She turned along Jackson, where the houses were smaller and less pretentious. Fillmore lay at a right angle to Jackson, a quiet cul-de-sac.

She didn't expect Carole to be home, not if she was working at Sears. But when she passed in front of 33, the address Carole had written down, there was a car parked out front, a powder blue Pontiac she thought she remembered from the night Carole had baby-sat. She braked, reversed to the front of the house, then got out. The yard was a ruin, tangled grass, a barren tree, a plenitude of weeds. Outside the front door she paused, her hand lingering over the doorbell. Wait, she thought. Hold on. Why would Carole be home if she had a full-time job? Why would she be home? Emily momentarily wanted to turn around and walk away, as if what she feared most was the discovery of more lies. Just because Marylou and Susan were all right, it didn't follow that Carole was on the level, did it? OK. She's home. There's a reason why she's not at work. There's got to be.

She pressed the bell. When the door was opened Carole stood there, an expression of surprise on her face—almost as if she'd been found out, discovered in the act of a trifling crime.

"Emily," she said. "Is something wrong?"

"No, I just dropped by—" Emily faltered. *Is something wrong?* Why had the woman opened with that question? Why not *Oh, this is a surprise.* Or *How nice to see you.* Suddenly, Emily had the feeling that there was a surface here, a facade, like a sheet of dark ice stretched over murky water.

"Am I interrupting you?" she said, smiling.

Carole held the door wide now. "Of course not. Come in. Come in."

Emily stepped into the hallway. It was dark, shadowy.

"Through here," Carole said. She went ahead and Emily followed. They passed through a living room and into a kitchen—a kitchen that was wondrously untidy, the surface of the table littered with broken eggshells, with vegetable cuttings piled on a wooden board, unopened bills spread, like an unplayable hand of cards, on the Formica work surface.

Carole shrugged. "Messy, huh?"

"It's just like home," Emily said.

Carole said, "I've been in your home, remember? Compared with your place, this dump looks like the kitchen of the Titanic just after it struck the iceberg." She moved away a couple of tea towels from a chair, and Emily sat down.

"I'm kinda surprised to see you," Carole said.

"I was in the neighborhood. I thought, well, why not?"

"I was just making a sandwich," Carole said. "You want one?"

Emily shook her head. She watched Carole remove two slices of thick bread from a bread wrapper, spread mayonnaise on both sides, then from a plastic bag take some cold cuts—bologna, roast beef, some Swiss cheese slices—and slap them between the slabs of bread.

"Lunch," Carole said. "I try to come home for lunch. I don't always make it. But I like to get out of the office sometimes. It's a drag."

She took an enormous bite of the sandwich and sat down, chewing heavily, at the other side of the table. Emily gazed at the heap of vegetable cuttings, the tops of carrots, the ends of green beans, the outer skin of an onion.

"I still feel bad about the other night," Carole said. "I don't know what to say. I guess maybe I shouldn't drink beer. It makes me sleepy. Besides, it doesn't exactly help burn off the calories." The woman laughed to herself.

"I've forgotten it," Emily said. "It's over."

"I appreciate it . . . the way you understand, I mean." Carole put her sandwich down. "I'd offer you something, but I looked in the refrigerator and I don't even have milk. A shambles, huh? I'm not well-organized, Emily."

"It's okay." Emily smiled. The woman seemed flustered, disoriented. And, as if to cover it, she wouldn't stop talking. She wouldn't stop apologizing—for the mess, the lack of something to drink, and Emily had the unsettling sensation that if she continued to ramble on she'd begin to apologize for the fact of her birth.

"Listen, I don't want anything to drink," Emily said. "I was just being social, coming here. I didn't even expect to find you home."

Carole looked at her watch. "To tell you the truth, without seeming rude, I have exactly five minutes to be sociable with you. After that, Sears owns me."

"I chose a bad time, I guess."

"I hate this damn rush," Carole said. "I'd like to sit here and just bullshit for the rest of the afternoon with you. I wouldn't mind that at all. But I'm going through the Bs this afternoon."

"The Bs?"

"Yeah. All the bad debts under the initial B. I write them up for reminders to be sent. Or, in real backward cases, I arrange for a collector to make a house call. You want some advice? Don't let yourself get into debt with Sears. It's not worth it. Some of the collectors are gorillas."

"I'll remember that," Emily said.

Carole had finished the sandwich now, and was wiping her lips with a paper towel. "After the Bs, the Cs. What else? I sometimes see my life going in alphabetical order, you know?"

Emily smiled. She lit a cigarette. It was night and day, sun and moon, coming into this house after Susan's spotless palace. Even so, she felt more at ease here, knowing that if she smoked and stubbed her cigarette Carole wouldn't rush to empty the ashtray. There wouldn't be this hygienic compulsion.

"You ever drink, Emily?"

"I don't have much of a taste for it—"

"We ought to go out some night. You and me. There's a neat bar over in Hudson. Do you like bluegrass? They have a terrific bluegrass band. Hey, we could use the baby-sitting thing, couldn't we? I keep forgetting about that."

"Let's do that some night," Emily said.

"Great idea," Carole said. "If I have my daughter here, I'll call Adrienne, or Marylou. And you can use Susan. We could go out on the town. It'd be fun."

Emily watched the woman a moment. She'd taken a piece of chewing gum from her purse, unwrapped it, slipped it into her mouth; her cheeks wobbled as she chewed. "Is your daughter still with your husband?"

"Unfortunately. But I get her back tomorrow. I'm looking forward to that."

"You must be—"

"When she's here she takes the emptiness away, you know?"

Emily was silent. What she couldn't get out of her mind was the picture of Carole fast asleep on her bed. It was as if there were some kind of baby-sitting license and, on hers, Carole had received a black mark. It was ridiculous. Why couldn't she just forget that? She was an ordinary person, someone without frills, without pretension—sad and ordinary. A weight problem, a broken marriage, solitude at times.

"I hate to do this," Carole said. "But I've got to be off and running."

Emily got up. "Do you ever have a day off?"

Carole said, "Not during the week I don't. Saturdays and Sundays, that's all."

"Maybe I'll come over some Sunday," Emily said.

"Yeah. Bring your kids. I really like your kids."

"I'll do that."

Carole followed her out of the kitchen and into the hallway. At the front door, Emily turned, looking in the direction of the stairs. They rose up into thin shadows.

"I'm glad you came, though," Carole said.

"Short and sweet," Emily said.

"We'll get together on a Sunday—"

There was a noise, a faint sound from the upper part of the house, like that of somebody moving slightly, something knocking faintly against a wall.

Carole turned towards the stairs. Then she looked back at Emily, who was gazing still at the upper shadows. Somebody is up there, she thought. Somebody is upstairs in one of the rooms.

Carole said, "She's a lazy bitch."

"Who?"

"My housemate. Didn't I tell you I had someone who shared the house with me?"

Emily said nothing. She looked at Carole.

Carole said, "Well, it's too big, and it's too expensive, for little old me and my daughter. I just wish she did some work around the place, that's all. She sleeps all day. Then when I get home at night the same mess is still there that I left in the morning. I wish I had the guts to get rid of her. But I don't."

Emily pulled the front door open. Then she glanced once more at the stairs. A housemate. It made some kind of sense. Maybe it made good sense.

"One day I'll come home and I'll sling her out," Carole said.

Emily stepped outside. She said, "Give me a call, Carole. We'll make it some Sunday afternoon."

"Great. And listen—don't forget if you need a baby-sitter."

"I won't," Emily said. She went towards the station wagon, taking the keys from her jeans and rattling them as she walked.

6.

But then she wasn't thinking about the boy anymore. She wasn't even thinking about him, because he wasn't a problem. Two kids weren't any problem. Nick would understand that. And what she remembered was the time when she'd lost the baby, the baby she hadn't been able to carry the full term, the way Nick had been mopping up the mess, crying as he did so, crying for this sad lost life, this lump of nothing—

It could have been a boy.

It might have been.

It didn't matter. Two kids didn't matter.

She was thinking now of Emily Allbright, of how she'd had to sit and talk with the woman and pretend, and how great the effort was to keep it up, growing confused, mixed-up, wondering whether she'd told the fucking woman two kids or one, but even that didn't matter.

And it had been a struggle, a terrible struggle. It had been a dreadful hard struggle to keep from blurting out *You've got my daughter, you took my daughter.* . . .

She wondered about this now. Maybe she was all wrong. Maybe the woman didn't have the girl.

But that couldn't be right. How could that be right?

You saw her. You saw her in the cinema. You saw her get on the school bus. You saw her through the window in the kitchen door when you were in the back yard. You saw her in the woods, when she was with the boy. *You saw her everywhere.*

Everywhere you looked.

You couldn't avoid it now.

She went to the window and looked out at the swimming pool. The water was gray-green, opaque, its surface shimmering in some slight breeze, scum floating on the top—scraps of disintegrating paper and sodden leaves and broken twigs and dirt that had been dumped there by wind, by storm. Like a swamp. Like a terrible swamp. She dropped the blind back in place and turned away from the sight.

She thought, when he sees the kid again, Nick will be pleased.

Oh, he'll be pleased.

7.

Emily got home shortly before the kids were due back from school. She cleaned up the kitchen, a halfhearted gesture in the direction of housewifery—or homemakership, as it might be called—and then she sat down in the living room, feeling tired. She wondered what she'd found out. You visit the homes of three women, what do you learn? Maybe only that there were differing degrees of normality, three women trying to cope with the weight of suburban life as best they could, but coming in on that target from varying directions. Normal, sure. Normal but different. And then she thought: *I didn't see any kids.* I saw kids' drawings, I saw photographs briefly. But no kids.

What did you expect? Houses overflowing with children? Floor to ceiling with broken toys? Suppose somebody came here, suppose they chose this particular moment to visit you—would *they* see any kids? Of course not. The kids aren't back from school yet. Traces, sure, like a small sneaker lying under the kitchen table, a grubby palm print on a wall, a skateboard lying in exactly the right position to jeopardize your health if you accidentally stepped on it—only traces of children. But no children. Yawning, she got up and went inside the kitchen, listening to the rinse cycle of the dishwasher. Entertaining, she thought. The broken melody of the rinse cycle. Maybe she had the start of a domestic poem in there somewhere. But she dismissed that from her mind, and with it James Hamilton. It was almost as if, were she to sit down and write a poem, she would be admitting the specter of temptation into her life—what a ridiculous thing to think. I won't even go tomorrow night. There wouldn't be any point, would there?

He'd invite me to have a glass of wine again. And I'd have to refuse. *And a refusal often offends.* She stared through the kitchen window at the street, waiting for a sight of the school bus. Any time now. She glanced at her watch. Then the telephone was ringing. She picked it up and, across some great crackling distance, as if he were calling from a galaxy other than this one, she heard Ted's voice.

"I thought I'd give you a call," he was saying, the voice fading in, fading out. She was reminded of those relayed messages from the first moonwalk.

"I'm glad you did," she said.

"I miss you," he said. "I miss you badly. I wish this goddam situation hadn't happened. It looks like it's going to drag on for a few days. Like I really need it. Shit."

"You haven't caught your fish yet?" she asked.

"Not yet," he said. "Everybody thinks it's the salmon except for one guy, a health inspector from Philadelphia. He's looking into some clam chowder that was on the menu a few days ago. It's a real pain in the ass."

She said nothing for a time. The connection was dismal. Salmon, clam chowder, she thought. You couldn't dream up anything more absurd than that: How could fish get in the way of your marriage?

"I just wish you were back," she said. "I don't think I've missed you this much before. . . ." And then she remembered his expression in the bedroom, the empty smile. She fought it away, relegated it to that place where all the flaws of memory were stored. This marriage isn't going to die, she thought. I'm not going to let this marriage fall apart around me, no way. "How much longer will you be gone?" she asked, and she could hear the subdued urgency in her own voice. I want to clear the air, she thought. I want everything put right. Come home. Just come back.

"I can't say just yet. Figure on two days. Three at the most. But probably two."

"Make it two," she said.

"I'll try. . . ." Then his voice was swept away. She could hardly hear what he said next. She had to shout into the line, asking him to repeat himself.

"I'm trying to give you this number," he said. "It's a shitty connection."

"Let me have it quick. Before we get cut off for good." She picked up a Bic pen from the table, tore a strip off last month's electric bill, and began to write. The place was called Silver River Lodge. The telephone number had a 215 area code.

"How are the kids?" he asked.

"They're fine. Everything's fine."

"Listen, will you kiss the kids for me. OK?"

"I'll do that," she said.

She waited. She heard the crackling, as if it were distant thunder.

"I love you," he said. "You know that, don't you?"

"I think I do—"

"You don't sound so sure."

She was quiet for a time. "I want to be sure, Ted. I want everything to work for us."

"It will," he said. "You've got my word on that."

Then he said something else, something she didn't hear, and after that the line was dead. She put the receiver down and stared at the scrap of paper covered with her own handwriting, the various versions of skulls and crossbones she'd woven around the words Silver River Lodge. Skulls and crossbones, she thought. It would take an analyst to tell her what they meant. She went to the window, looked out at the empty street, expecting at any moment to see the school bus. *You've got my word on that.* I need more than your word, she told herself. I need more than that.

Then she remembered. The trellis! She'd forgotten to tell him about the fallen trellis. She could picture his face when he returned to find it knocked over and she wondered if she should call him back, forewarn him—the way you might if a close relative had died. Prepare him for the worst, she thought. Uncle Trellis just collapsed, things look bad. Hell, it wasn't important. He could stick it back up again; he'd probably relish doing it anyhow.

The school bus came into view, the brakes squealing as it slowed at the corner. She watched the kids jump down. A whole stream of kids. Frankie was the last to get off, Charlotte among the first. She watched Charlotte skip across the street, not looking for traffic, moving with such careless grace. Behind her, turning his face this way and that, as if he were indoctrinated with old pedestrian regulations, Frankie stepped off the sidewalk.

She went to the front door to greet them.

"Did dad call?" Charlotte asked.

"You just missed him."

"Oh." The girl threw her satchel down on the sofa and sat, crossing her legs. "Is he OK?"

"Sure, he's fine." She looked at her daughter for a time. She thought: The kid wants to hear that everything is fine between her father and me. She wants to know. She's been brooding over it, worrying it. She sat down beside Charlotte and touched the back of her wrist.

"He's fine, really. He'll be back in a couple of days."

"Sure?"

"Sure I'm sure."

Now Frankie was coming in, slamming the door behind him. "Did you say dad called?" he said.

"About a minute ago," Emily said.

"Did you see the terliss was down?" the boy said. "Did you see that?"

"*Trellis,* not *terliss,*" Charlotte said.

"I guess the wind blew it over," Emily said.

"Did you tell dad?" Frankie said, looking serious, gloomy, as if the collapse of the wretched trellis were tantamount to some natural catastrophe.

"I forgot," Emily said. "Can you forgive me?"

"I think you should tell him," the boy said.

"Why?"

Frankie shrugged. "He put a lotta hard work into it."

"Maybe you should tell him, Frankie. Maybe he'd take it better if it came from you."

"Well, I helped him at times," he said. "Maybe I *should* be the one to tell him."

Emily got up from the sofa. Charlotte said, "I don't see the need for any fuss. I mean, he's just going to come home and put it back up. So why worry?"

Emily went out into the kitchen, picked up the telephone. The kids came behind her, Frankie watching as she picked up the strip of paper, read the number, dialed it. Charlotte was rummaging in the refrigerator, finding an apple, biting into it with a sharp crisp noise. OK, Emily thought. They want to talk with their father, the trellis is neither here nor there. They just want to say hello to their father. She heard the number ring. She heard the lilting voice of an operator say the words *Silver River Lodge.* She asked for Ted. She listened to the silence. She listened to how, like stray punctuation marks, the silence was riddled with static noises. The operator came back. *Mr. Allbright?* she said. Charlotte crunched the apple. Frankie had his hand in the air, ready to take the receiver. *You must have the wrong number.* No, she heard herself say, that doesn't make any sense. He was there, he was there just a moment ago, he talked to me a moment ago, he has to be there. Mr. Allbright, right, works for VacationEase, the food poisoning thing, he's down there dealing with the food poisoning thing, but then the operator was laughing slightly, saying *what food poisoning, you really must have a wrong number, and there's no Mr. Allbright in residence, nobody even with a name like that.* She heard herself mutter something nonsensical about Salmon Walewska, about a public health official from Stroudsburg, about sick guests, and it was as if she were speaking down an empty line, an unused line, hearing the slight echoes of her own voice come back. That is the Silver River Lodge isn't it? I mean, there couldn't be another one, could there? *I'm sorry, no. I'm sorry.*

Shaking, she put the receiver down.

Well? Frankie said. Charlotte was staring at her across the kitchen. Well? Well? The questions danced, frantic, in the air. Well well well?

She heard herself answer, "He isn't there. He must have gone out. I'll try again later."

And then she rushed out of the kitchen.

8.

A death in the family. Someone in the terminal ward.

She tried not to think.

You live on a certain level, a plane, and all of a sudden it tilts. Everything goes slipping away.

Empty air, nothing to clutch.

An explanation, then. Oh, sure.

The telephone operator got it wrong.

No.

Then Ted himself, confused for some reason, gave her the wrong number. The wrong name of the resort.

It doesn't cut it.

She turned over on the bed. She looked at the slit of light in the bathroom door.

How long, Ted? How long? The Other Woman. The Faceless Siren.

How long was it now, Ted? How many of the other telephone numbers you gave me were fake?

It must have been elaborately prearranged, the myth of the food poisoning, the supposed phone call from VacationEase. She must have said, *Let's use the old Salmon Walewska alibi, she'll never know, she'll never find out.*

She. Whoever.

Goddam you, Ted. Everything.

She tried not to think. What she could hear in the distance was the sound of a wind screaming through a house of cards.

And the kids.

The kids.

They'd seen her face when she'd put the telephone down, they'd seen how she looked, the sight of her hurt, her bewilderment, the way she rushed from the room. The kids. What were they thinking now? Dad's a liar. Dad's a liar.

The TV was booming from downstairs. Played loudly, she supposed, because it drowned out everything else. *Me and Jethro'll get on down to the bank, Grannie.* She pressed her hands over her ears.

I won't cry, she thought.

I'll just make myself good and numb.

No anger, no pain, no sense of hating.

Zero hour.

She clenched and unclenched her hands. She thought: The trouble with deception is how it *demeans* you. How it humiliates its victim. How it makes you feel so utterly stupid, so completely used.

Like you're a nothing. A nobody.

She lit a cigarette, her fingers trembling, and she tried not to create a picture of Ted and his woman—a figure who, already forming in her mind, shimmered like heat haze rising from concrete, like something lovely taking shape out of ectoplasm. And Ted screwing her, Ted screwing this woman.

Intimacies. Things shared. Things she'd never know about.

I knew it all along, she thought. Goddammit, I knew it all along.

Only I tried not to. His only lover was his job. Bullshit.

She got up from the bed and stood at the window and looked out across the front yard, her hands touching the curtains, her face close to the glass. Out in the darkening street a car passed. A stab of light struck the oak leaves.

She stared for a long time, conscious of nothing.

9.

The telephone. The telephone on the coffee table. It was funny how, when it didn't ring, it seemed to have no purpose. A strange shape. A weird black thing. She put out her hand and touched it, feeling the smooth plastic surface. She played with the dial. If you didn't lift the receiver you couldn't hear the little melodic notes. And that was strange too because they'd have to be making some kind of sound somewhere. Only nobody heard it.

She drew her hand to her side.

She realized she was waiting for the telephone to ring.

That's what she was waiting for.

The call.

But nothing happened. The house was without sound.

Silence downstairs, silence up. A house without sound wasn't really a house at all. It wasn't really a home.

Call me, she thought.

Tell me to come. Don't you know I'm waiting?

She stared at the telephone. Call me soon.

Chapter Nine

1.

Charlotte wakened in the dawn and watched pale light, the color of pearl, impress itself upon the curtains. Then she couldn't get back to sleep for some reason. She knew why, though she didn't really want to admit it to herself. Because of her father. Because of his lie. And maybe where there was one lie there could be any number of them, like those dolls that contained other dolls, each growing smaller all the time. She felt sad. But not because of the lie, more on account of what her mother must be feeling. Adults did that to each other all the time, didn't they? They destroyed each other. They cheated and they lied and they damaged themselves on their own actions.

She went downstairs to the kitchen. Her mother was up already, sitting at the kitchen table and smoking a cigarette. Silently, Charlotte sat down facing her, waving her hand in the air so she wouldn't have to breathe tobacco smoke. She noticed the ashtray was filled with stubs. She looked at her mother's face and wished there was something she could say, something really positive, like *Every cloud has a you-know-what*—but words didn't have any place. They didn't have the kind of depth she needed.

"You're awake early," Emily said.

"You too."

"Yeah." Emily stubbed the cigarette.

Charlotte tapped her fingers on the table a moment. "It could be a simple mistake," she said hesitantly.

"What could?"

"You *know*."

Emily watched her daughter for a second, then turned her face away. "You're right. You're right on the button, kid. A simple mistake."

Charlotte said, "These things happen."

"All the time," Emily said. She got to her feet and tugged at the cord of her housecoat. "You feel like breakfast?"

Charlotte didn't, but she said she did anyhow, because she understood that her mother needed something to do—something banal and simple like cooking breakfast. She watched Emily go to the stove and stick a frying pan on a burner. Cracked eggs were whisked in a bowl, then poured into the skillet.

Charlotte whistled tunelessly for a time, then realized the sound might be a nuisance, so she stopped. You gotta think of something bright to say, she told herself. You gotta be *positive*. She could smell the scrambled eggs now and realized she had no stomach for them. She said, "Hey, tonight's your class, isn't it?"

Emily nodded. "I don't think I'll go—"

"You should. You really ought to—"

"I thought about it—"

"What are you going to do? Sit around and mope?"

Emily smiled. "I was never much good at moping—"

"See," Charlotte said, as if she'd proved something. "You ought to go to the class."

Emily poured the scrambled eggs onto a plate and brought it to the table and placed it in front of Charlotte.

"I know you don't want it," she said.

"Sure I do."

"After ten years, Charlotte, you get to know somebody else pretty well."

Not always, Charlotte thought.

"And sometimes I can read you like a book," Emily said. She sat down and lit another cigarette. "Don't feel obliged to eat the goddam things."

Charlotte made a couple of passes with a fork, chewed for a time, then put the fork down. She reached across the table and touched the back of her mother's hand, laying her fingers over the knuckles, wanting her to know that this simple act of touching was an act of loving, of concern, of something too profound for words. But then she saw her mother's eyes were blurry, watery, and she took her hand away.

"Listen," Charlotte said. "We'll be OK. I know that. I can feel it."

"Can you?"

"Sure I can. You think the worst. But the worst doesn't always happen."

Emily was silent for a while, then she said, "You grow up real fast." She put a hand to her eyes, smiled, and added: "This is a godawful time of day to feel maudlin."

Charlotte stared at her plate, uncertain of what "maudlin" meant.

Then she raised her face and said, "Don't worry. Please. Everything is going to be just fine."

Silence. Emily put her cigarette out.

The kid, she was thinking. The kid's fine tuning. The distant edge of solace. The pep talk from a ten-year-old. She watched the crushed cigarette smoulder. It had been a hard restless night filled with decisions that invariably met with counter-decisions, like she was weighing things on scales. And every time she thought of something, something positive, she would hear Ted's lie again as you might cringe at the screech of a fingernail on glass. It wasn't a wild surf you could ride out and hope for calmer waters. It wasn't a situation you could just sit and watch, like some inactive spectator. You had to do *something*.

Charlotte was saying, "Go to your class tonight. Get out."

"You really think so?"

"Sure, I do," Charlotte said. She thought: I don't want you to go, not really, but for your own sake you should. "Anyhow, you've got this baby-sitting thing going. Call one of your members. It's real easy."

Charlotte got up and took her plate towards the sink, scraping the eggs into the disposal unit. Emily watched her daughter, watched how the early morning light fell through the window against the soft hair. Love seemed to her just then a transparent kind of adhesive, a thing you couldn't see and you couldn't explain, but something that locked you into another person—and there wasn't imprisonment, or confinement, but a sense of being able to rely, to trust with total confidence. She went towards Charlotte and hugged her and the child, yielding, put her arms around her neck. You could lose yourself in this, she thought. This alone would make anything tolerable. And suddenly she was furious with Ted, a dark rage against the fact that he'd jeopardize this family, these kids. And for what? Because he'd found somebody he liked to fuck? Somebody who was new and different?

It wasn't fair.

She looked into Charlotte's clear eyes and she said, "You really think I should go to class?"

The child nodded. "Yeah, I do."

"OK," Emily said. "I will. I'll do just that. Even if it means using up another of my blessed credits."

Charlotte laughed. "That's what credits are for."

There was a thumping noise from upstairs, a door slamming, the sound of footsteps on the stairs.

"Hark," Charlotte said. "Our little elephant is awake."

Emily went to the foot of the stairs and watched Frankie, rubbing his eyes, come down.

"Good morning," she said, with a brightness she didn't feel.

"Hi," Frankie said. "Do I smell food?"

"Sure you do." She put her arms around him and kissed him on the side of his face and he made an embarrassed gesture with his hand, like he was swatting at a fly.

If she only concentrated on the kids, she thought, she could induce amnesia where Ted was concerned; or imagine he'd gone to fight in some forlorn war and that she'd received a telegram concerning his death in battle. A drastic measure, sure. But what else did this situation call for?

She followed Frankie into the kitchen.

"Morning, brother," Charlotte said.

Frankie grunted and sat down sleepily at the table.

2.

Quayle's wife, a woman who rarely moved from her chair in front of the TV, whose life was dictated to by the schedules of *TV Guide,* looked up from the morning paper and stared at her husband across the breakfast table.

"Can you believe they're showing 'No Time for Sergeants' on Channel Five tonight? It was on Channel Three last Monday." She rattled the newspaper in an irritated manner. Quayle, who had become accustomed to this kind of conversational gambit merely nodded his head. He was thinking: If she was left alone in the apartment, even for a short time, she could have taken the gun. But why? Why would she take the gun anyhow? And even if she had, it didn't explain the guy's disappearance—unless you forged some unlikely link in your head.

Quayle's wife said, "Phyllis Diller and Kaye Ballard are on Merv Griffin tonight."

"Yeah?" Quayle said. He pushed the remains of his breakfast aside, staring morosely at the rasher of black bacon.

"What was Kaye Ballard in?" his wife said. "What was the name of that series?"

Quayle shrugged. He was trying to think of a reason for going back to see the woman. Trying to think of something good. You couldn't just go in and say: OK, did you steal the goddam gun? That would be Steadman's way. You had to go back almost apologetically and say: There's something I forgot to ask, something you can clear up for me. . . . He peered at his wife for a while.

"They keep repeating Rockford," she said, shaking her head. "I mean, once is enough."

Quayle got up from the table and looked around for his shoes. It was funny, he thought, how obsessive you could get at times. His wife and her TV schedule. Him and the missing gun. Then he tried to imagine what it would be like to lose a kid in a swimming-pool drowning accident and he shuddered inwardly. He'd never had kids, but it was easy to imagine. It was easy to feel the grief. And grief could unhinge you quicker than anything else. He knotted his shoelaces. Maybe later, when he had a spare moment, he'd make a last visit. Maybe. If there was time.

His wife said, "Will you be home in time for 'Mannix'?"

"I hate 'Mannix'," he said. "If there's anything I hate more than 'Mannix', I don't know what it is."

" 'Mannix' is OK," she said.

" 'Mannix' is shit."

"Well, you're a cop," she said in a vague way.

He looked at her, puzzled. Sometimes he couldn't get a handle on the kind of connections she made. Like she was in her own world, a place where sentences didn't have to mean anything logical. Maybe that came from sitting in a chair with a remote-control device in your hand, forever pressing the button and watching the channels switch meaninglessly.

"I don't know exactly when I'll be home," he said. "I'll call."

"OK," she said.

He went outside, having kissed her quickly on the cheek. He knew as soon as he left she'd be transfixed by the soaps or early reruns of *Bewitched,* or *I Dream of Jeannie.*

3.

A baby-sitter, Emily thought. She stood in the back yard and looked at the fallen trellis, folding her arms under her breasts. A baby-sitter —but if Marylou said she wasn't available, that left a choice between Carole and Susan. She didn't want to think about telephoning either of them, not just yet anyhow. Restlessly, she walked around the yard. The midday sky was gray, like some stretch of flannel. She paused outside Ted's toolshed and she thought how unfamiliar it seemed to her all at once, as if what Ted had done were to knock all the props away, undermine things, impart to the familiar a kind of sheen of strangeness. She'd felt it in the house too, after the kids had gone. A sense of the rooms being different. A sense of not being *in her own home*. Maybe that was too weird—but it was what she felt, and she could only lay the blame for that on Ted.

She went indoors when she heard the telephone ringing. Ted. Maybe Ted. Ted with a damn good excuse. But it was Adrienne. She sounded drunk, her words slurred, her speech just a little too fast.

"I've been thinking things over, dear," Adrienne said. "You know? Kind of turning them over in my mind and . . ."

There was a long pause. Emily tried to think of something to say, something to fill the void. Why was Adrienne calling anyhow?

Adrienne said, "Did you mention my . . ."

Fumbling for a word. Emily was embarrassed for the woman.

"Did you mention my *situation*, shall we say, to any of the other women?"

What did she imagine? Emily wondered. That some kind of emergency meeting had been called to debate the fact of her lies? Some kind of extraordinary general gathering of the co-op women for the purpose of considering Adrienne's facade.

"I haven't said anything," Emily answered.

"Good. I'm glad of that." Another pause. "You see, I'd still like to be a member, dear. I'd still like to take part somehow."

"I don't understand—"

"Obviously, I wouldn't need anybody to baby-sit for me, but I still have something I can contribute, and I *do* like kids, I enjoy them—"

"Well." Emily shifted her weight around. What was she supposed to do? Police the cooperative? Vet the members on moral grounds?

"I know it's hard for you to understand," Adrienne said. "I really like kids, I like looking after them. . . ."

"I do understand," Emily said. And it crossed her mind that she should feel sorry for the woman, she should perhaps even bandage whatever kind of wound existed by inviting Adrienne to sit for her tonight—but she put the thought out of her mind. How could she trust her now? It was the final step she couldn't quite make. "What can I say, Adrienne? The other women have your number. I guess somebody will call you, ask you to baby-sit. As far as I'm concerned, I won't say anything. I wouldn't do that."

Adrienne laughed. "Between the lines, dear, I get the general drift that it would be OK for me to sit other people's kids, but when it comes to yours—forget it. Forget it. Right?"

"I didn't say that, Adrienne—"

"You didn't have to."

"I didn't say it. Oh, shit. I'm not sure."

"But it's obvious from your tone, Emily—"

"I didn't mean to sound that way—"

"OK OK. The picture's quite clear. It's perfectly obvious. Anybody else can look after your precious kids except me. Right? Right so far?"

"Adrienne, please—"

"Skip it. Forget I ever called. Just forget it."

And the line was dead.

Emily put the receiver down and wondered why other people's lies could bring such a heavy trip down on your own head. It didn't make sense. For a moment she was taken by an urge to call the woman back, to say she hadn't meant to take any kind of moralizing attitude or whatever it was that Adrienne accused her of—but she didn't. Good Christ, my life is falling apart all around me and I stand here worrying about that woman and her lies. There was a line to be drawn somewhere, if she could only find it.

She shook her head and picked up the Book of Points and flicked the pages. The class. I shouldn't go. Despite what Charlotte said, I shouldn't go. Because this time I don't know how I'll react if Hamilton asks me for a drink. Because this time I might be spiteful enough, vengeful enough, to accept and to hell with what the consequences might be. She put her hand on the receiver, hesitated. There was an angry echo of Adrienne's voice in her head still.

What have I got to lose by going? she wondered.

4.

Something woke him with a dreadful surprise. An external noise that had stopped before he came to awareness, so that now he wasn't sure what it had been. Then he could hear her moving around downstairs, pacing, it seemed, pacing forever up and down, up and down, like some caged thing. His mouth was godawful dry and his tongue stuck to the roof of the mouth where there were lumps like clotted saliva. He turned over, facing the bedroom door. He listened to the way she moved. An animal. A cat in a zoo. Then she stopped and everything was still and in the stillness he realized he'd lost track of time again and that time was the only map he really had and without it he was adrift. He rubbed his eyes, pressing the knuckles hard into the soft core of the sockets so that he'd see some kind of inner flash, like jagged lines of color, colors he couldn't identify. Nick. Where the hell was Nick? Without Nick, he didn't have much of a chance. It might be today. Some time today. He couldn't be sure. There was the smell of his own waste products in the pan on the floor. He turned his face away and tried not to gag, but what difference would it make anyhow because there wasn't anything in his stomach he could fetch up if he tried. And he was sweating, sticking to the clammy sheets. Day or night? When? He pushed himself into a sitting position. She was moving around again below, back and forth, forth and back, like her madness prevented her from stopping, like she was a volcano surging around and ready to erupt.

She might do it today.

She might choose this day. This day in which to kill him.

And this could be the last day of his whole life.

He panicked and pushed the bedsheet aside and tried to raise his aching legs. Nothing. Move move move goddam you, goddam you. Nothing. He breathed hard. You start to feel sorry for yourself. Lying here like a baby, like a goddam baby, not able to do a thing. Let her come, he thought. Let her come. Let her try. Somehow I'll be ready for her.

But even as he thought this he realized he was filled with dread,

dread of the sound of her feet on the stairs, the creak of his door, the hush as she entered the room—it was all dread, and it congealed in his brain and turned to liquid and came out through the pores of his skin in cold sweat. He couldn't live any longer with this feeling.

Let her come, he thought.

Let her try.

He turned again, trying to get comfortable, hearing the creak of the mattress beneath him. He'd be ready. Somehow he'd be ready.

Then maybe he slept again, maybe he drifted off into sleep, a fitful shallow kind of sleep in which he imagined the touch of his dead wife's hand on the back of his fingers and he woke expecting her to be in the room but she wasn't, of course she wasn't, the room was silent, the house silent, all around him stillness in the air, like the kind of sound you might imagine at the bottom of some deep dark aquarium tank. The sound of zero.

He tilted his head, tried to lick his dry lips, waited.

Waited.

Whatever happened, it had to be fair. It had to be balanced somehow. He lived in darkness. So, if she wanted to kill him she'd have to try in the same kind of darkness as the one that was his life.

He turned over, moaned, wished with the kind of wishing that hurt, that caused a pain in your heart, wished he could see, wished he could see just this time.

5.

Emily watched the school bus stop on the corner, saw her kids get off and cross the street. She went to the front door, opened it, waited for them. Charlotte, as usual, was the first. She kissed the girl lightly on the forehead, then watched Frankie come across the lawn, passing under the oak, pausing a moment to reach up and knock at the branches with his hand. The boy came inside, Emily closed the door. She followed the kids into the kitchen.

"So. How was school?" she asked.

"Dreary," Charlotte said. "I wasn't into it today."

I understand that, Emily thought.

Frankie opened the refrigerator and took out a can of Pepsi, which hissed as he popped it. "I had incursive writing," he said. "You know what that is?"

"Sure I do," Emily said.

"They teach you how to join letters." Frankie sat at the kitchen table and sipped from the Pepsi. "You make these loops and stuff."

Emily watched the boy, then the girl, noticing now that there was a hesitancy about them, and she knew what it was, she knew that a simple question lay unasked in the room, as if it were the center of gravity, some kind of force that pulled them but one they wanted to avoid. *Did dad call?* And she realized she'd been waiting most of the day for the same thing. That one telephone call that would explain everything. The last chapter of the detective novel in which everything was explained away. *What you didn't realize, Em, was he didn't say the Silver River Lodge in Chapter Seven. No, he said the Silver Falls Lodge. So that's where you went off the track, see. Right there.*

But he gave me the wrong number, didn't he?

Not quite, Em. See, he took the number off the wrong piece of stationery. Simple mistake.

That was total bullshit. The wrong piece of stationery. Tell me about red herrings made out of paper, please do. She moved to the kitchen table and she sat down, lit a cigarette, felt a certain tightness at the back of her throat, a dry quality. Too many smokes. All day long, cigarette after cigarette. So she crushed the one she had in her hand.

Charlotte looked at her, frowning. "Did you decide about class?"

"Class?" Frankie said. "What class?"

"Her night class, dummy," Charlotte said.

Dummy. Emily wondered why that simple word, appended without any malice, any insult, stung her. She was about to say *Charlotte, you shouldn't call your brother that* when Frankie said, "Oh, yeah. The poetry. I forgot, that's all."

"Well?" Charlotte said. "Did you make up your mind?"

Emily nodded. "I thought it over. You're right. I'll go."

Charlotte smiled in a weak way. "It's gotta do you some good, you know."

Emily patted the back of the girl's hand. "I take your advice, Abby."

"Abby?" Frankie said. He raised his Pepsi to his mouth.

"She's somebody who gives advice in the papers," Charlotte said.

There was a slight edge to the girl's voice, a vague impatience with her brother. Emily thought: I should make a little speech. I should tell them about the value of love, about how important it is that we all stick together. We three. But she wasn't in the mood for that and besides she understood that Charlotte did care for her brother. A certain amount of carping, the little verbal snipes, didn't matter.

"Did you get a baby-sitter?" Charlotte asked.

"I called Carole—"

"I hope you stocked up on beer."

"If you'll let me finish, I called Carole but she wasn't available, so I asked Susan, and Susan happens to be pleased to come—"

"Which one's Susan?" Frankie said.

"Is she the one with the pretty face?" Charlotte said.

"Kind of, I guess."

"She's OK," Charlotte said.

"Well, I wouldn't have asked her if I thought she wasn't OK, would I?"

"I guess," Frankie said.

"But I won't be late," Emily said. "Ten maybe. Not much later than that."

There was a silence in the kitchen now. Charlotte went to the refrigerator and poured a glass of milk, then stood at the back door and looked out.

"It's a yucky day," she said. "I wish it would snow or something. Anything but this kind of . . . nothing."

Another moment of quiet, this one broken by Frankie who asked: "Did dad call?"

Emily looked at the boy. He was watching her innocently. How could you tell what lay beneath that look? Deep down, what he was feeling? Thinking?

She shook her head, smiled, then said, "Hey, maybe he'll call tonight."

"I want to tell him about his trellis," Frankie said.

"You can, if he calls," Emily said. She looked at the litter in the ashtray a moment. *He isn't going to call.* But she wouldn't say that to the kid. It was the empty sack on Christmas morning. Or all the lights burning out on the tree at the same time. Wet tinsel. Ted, Ted, Ted. You disappoint.

She got up from the table and said, "Any ideas on what you want for supper?"

"Not hungry," Frankie said, slipping out of his chair, going out of the room. After a moment the TV was playing.

"Charlotte? You?"

"I don't mind. Really. Something simple."

"Macaroni and cheese?"

"Sure, fine," Charlotte said. She turned from the back door and added: "You know, it's pretty funny that he put so much work into that thing out there and it only took one storm to blow it over."

"Isn't it," Emily said flatly. She took a packet of macaroni from the pantry and she thought: macaroni and betrayal. The perfect menu. But then there were dark pictures, dark bedrooms of her mind, two faceless lovers playing out their frenetic melodies—one of them, on closer inspection, being Ted. She drew back from the image, stepped away, shut the door behind her. I refuse, I refuse point-blank, to look, to think, or even to feel. Consider the virtues of numbness, lady. They can take you quite a long ways.

Charlotte was watching her. "Listen, have a good time tonight. Promise?"

"I promise," Emily said.

6.

It was twenty past six when Susan arrived. Remembering the antiseptic appearance of *her* kitchen, Emily had made a vague effort to tidy up—altogether halfhearted. What did it matter if Susan lived in a world without lint, without screwed-up empty potato chip packages stuffed down the sides of chairs, without ash-stained ashtrays? You could be the Princess Domestica, for all I care, Emily thought, letting her in through the front door.

"Am I late?" she asked. She had a somewhat hushed, timid voice.

"Right on time," Emily said.

The kids emerged from the TV room. Susan smiled at them in a shy way.

"Susan meet Charlotte. And Frankie."

"Hi," Susan said.

The kids smiled. Susan looked away a moment, as if she were examining the room. There was a pile of books on the coffee table. An appearance of disarray. A stub in an ashtray. Even, God forbid, some withering flowers in a vase.

"You play checkers?" Frankie asked.

"Not very well," Susan said. She took off her blue coat and held it, as if she were afraid to sling it on the sofa or over the back of a chair, and Emily thought: A place for everything, everything in its place. She's looking for a hanger. Emily took the coat from her and went out into the kitchen, draping it over the back of a chair. She heard Susan saying, "I'd like to play, though. But you'll beat me all the time." And then Charlotte was laughing, saying, "He couldn't beat anybody." And Frankie was protesting this: "I can too. I beat Eddie Smithers." Charlotte said, "Eddie Smithers! He's a retard." And then Susan said, "I don't think I can even remember *how* to play." They were all laughing now—and Emily wondered why, she couldn't see any joke, anything funny in the dialogue, maybe Susan pulled a funny face or something, or made a spastic gesture. But the sound of the kids laughing encouraged her. God knows, there hadn't been much of it around the place lately.

She picked up her own coat and put it on and as she did so she realized, with some slight surprise, that she wanted to get out of the house, she wanted to get away, she didn't want to be stuck here with the kids and waiting for the goddam telephone to ring. She went back inside the front room.

"You'll be OK, Susan," Emily said, a half-question.

"Oh, sure."

"Anyhow, Charlotte knows where everything is."

"So do I," Frankie said.

She watched them a moment, this little group of three, and she felt displaced somehow, like she'd been usurped, like she wasn't needed all at once. Charlotte smiled at her encouragingly.

"Have a good time," she said.

Emily opened the front door. She said her goodbyes, closed the door behind her, and she thought: I'd like to have a good time.

Chapter Ten

1.

The poem, being read aloud by the same elderly woman who'd done a number on Paul en route to Damascus, concerned a supposed conversation between Christ and Pontius Pilate—although Emily hardly listened. The reedy voice grated on her. The rhymes were barbarous. She stared at the floor most of the time, trying to avoid Hamilton's occasional glance, the bemused way he would sometimes look at her —as if they shared between them a large secret. As if he were saying: *I told you so, didn't I?* It was a curious sense of intimacy in some way, like that of lovers who could communicate across crowded rooms without speech. And it embarrassed her. She raised her face for a moment and watched the poet, thinking, this old bird has something of a monopoly on the class. That shrill noise. She looked like an irritated finch. Any moment now she'd be trying to find something to rhyme with Nazareth. "You say you're the King of the Jews/But I see you don't even have shoes."

Dear God, no, Emily thought. It wasn't so much the doggerel that made her want to laugh, it was the burning sincerity of the reader, the hand motions through the air and the shaking papers. When the old dear sat down Hamilton prowled around the podium, silent, thinking, his hands deep in his pockets. Then he faced the class and asked for comments. Profound silence.

Emily knew it was coming. She could feel it like an arrow.

"Mrs. Allbright," he said. "What did you make of the poem?"

She stared at him. When she spoke she heard a slight crack in her voice. "I didn't care for it."

There was a stare, of the heavy duty variety, from the poet, who turned around in her chair.

"Why, Mrs. Allbright?" Hamilton said.

"It lacked . . . conviction," she answered.

"And what is conviction?"

Damn him, she thought. She felt herself sink, a stone through air. "I can't explain it," she offered.

"She doesn't know what she's talking about," the poet said.

"Is conviction one of those subjective things?" Hamilton asked.

"Well, maybe," Emily said.

"Something we feel?" Hamilton said. "For example, a man says to a woman . . . oh, let me think . . . a man says to a woman, listen, would you care to have some wine with me, something like that—does the woman *feel* whether the offer has any conviction in it or not? Something along those lines?"

"That's a bad example," Emily said.

"Give me a good one then," Hamilton said.

Before Emily could think of anything, a man seated at the front of the room was mumbling loudly, complaining about the class, about whether they should be discussing such abstract notions instead of the "nitty-gritty" of poetry. And Emily, to her relief, saw the conversation swing away from her. She sat back in her chair, doodling on a scrap of paper, making little rings that interlocked. It was a roundabout way Hamilton had of asking her for a glass of wine again, she saw that much: and something in the way he'd done it, obliquely, in front of a class, reinforced the impression of a shared thing, a secret between them, as if intimacy already lay in the past. Intimacy, she thought. Chalk that one up to the Victorian novel. So, she thought. He's asked again. You knew it was coming anyhow, didn't you? What do you do now?

She looked up to see him go through the motions of passing coins between his hands, rattling them as he talked. The same weird intensity was there, striking right into the empty heart of the poem they'd just heard, going down into the core to find nothing—then coming back up again with suggestions, clues, hints, as to how the thing might be improved. Poor Hamilton, she said to herself. Flogging the dead horse, no twitch of life even. It had to get discouraging. Sweating up there—and for what? She picked up her pencil and doodled some more, sometimes tuning in the discussion that was taking place, sometimes not. The man in the front, as if he were demented, was still going on about the "real function" of a poetry-writing class.

Hamilton entered into a brief debate with him, then somewhat abruptly ended the class. He gathered up his papers and left the room, leaving the door open behind him. The woman who sat next to Emily, a small middle-aged person with a face as fuzzy as the surface of a peach, said: "I think he's pretty good. But strange. *Strange.*" And she rolled her eyes up as she said the word "strange."

Emily smiled and went outside the room, looking for some sign of

Hamilton but not seeing him—and wondering if he'd just decided to leave without talking to her; and if her wondering that meant she was disappointed or relieved. She went down the stairs quickly, along the hallway, then outside to the parking lot.

He was standing beside her station wagon, a cigarette cupped in one hand. She hesitated, then moved slowly towards him.

"Terrific class, huh?" he said.

"I enjoyed it—"

"I could tell from your face."

"OK. I enjoyed *some* of it—"

"That gives you a better percentage than me." He laid his hand on the roof of her station wagon. He turned his face a moment, looking towards the building where a couple of students were coming down the steps, passing beneath the electric lamps. She rattled her car keys in the palm of her hand.

"Got a baby-sitter?" he said.

"Sure." She smiled, leaned against the car, dangled the keys so they reflected lamplight, and she thought: My God, I'm flirting with this man. *I'm flirting with him.* Ah, Ted.

"A glass of wine," Hamilton said.

"Are you asking me?"

"Do you want me to?"

She hesitated. Maybe this particular bridge swayed over some dark crevice. "Ask," she said. "Ask me."

"I thought I had."

She looked at him. Where is this leading, Emily? Where is this going? "I accept then," she said.

Hamilton seemed to relax all at once. She watched him for a moment, realizing she hadn't thought about the kids. She hadn't thought about the kids once.

2.

Charlotte thought that there was something nice about Susan, except "nice" wasn't really the word she wanted. What was it then? A kind of peaceful quality? There was a word lying on the tip of her tongue. Serene? She watched the baby-sitter's face as the TV played. In the soft light, Susan was quite beautiful, Charlotte thought. Beneath a more harsh light you could see small lines, tiny wrinkles—but right now, as she sat on the sofa beside Frankie with her hands lying loosely in her lap, she looked good, her skin smooth, her eyes kind. Maybe something in her manner had affected Frankie too because he was unusually subdued and quiet, watching the flicker of the TV picture—some terrible comedy about a divorced woman raising two daughters.

"Do you like this show, Charlotte?" Susan asked, smiling.

Charlotte shook her head. "I don't like TV much."

"I do," Frankie said.

"In small doses it's OK," Susan said. "The educational channel is usually all right."

Charlotte shrugged. She wished they could do something other than watch the box—but what? She tried to think of a game she could suggest, but nothing came immediately to mind. Cards, maybe. She remembered that somewhere she had a game of Pit, but she wasn't sure where she had put it. Susan got up from the sofa and went to the bookshelf and looked at the titles.

"Are these your father's books?" she asked.

"If they're about carpentry and stuff they are," Charlotte said. She watched Susan kneel in front of the books, running the tips of her fingers idly over the spines. Then she turned her hand around and gazed at her fingertips, as if she'd gathered dust from the books. She rubbed her hands together. Charlotte thought for a moment about her mother—she loved her mother more than any other person in the world, but she wasn't much of a housekeeper, was she? When I have my own home, she thought, it will shine. (You're kidding yourself. You're too lazy. So you marry a rich man and hire several maids to do the dirty work, right?)

"He must like building things," Susan said.

"That's what he does best," Charlotte said.

Susan turned her face and smiled at the girl again. The sofa creaked as Frankie shifted his weight around. And Charlotte noticed he was sucking on his thumb, the old baby thing, something he only did these days when he was nervous, or anxious. And she understood what it was: it came back to their father, it came back to him, a situation compounded by their mother going out. Maybe, poor kid, he felt he was being abandoned. She tried to catch his eye, offer some look of comfort, but he was staring absently at the TV picture although you could see his mind was miles away.

Susan stood up, turning away from the bookshelf. Frankie watched her for a second, then went back to staring at the situation comedy.

"Do you help your daddy build things?" Susan asked.

Frankie seemed not to hear her. He watched the commercials come up, something to do with contact lenses, and he thought: *Somewhere* . . . It was the feeling of a dream that he had suddenly, when you wake out of a dark room, a cold place, in the light of your own bedroom, and for a moment you can't remember, you can't say where the dream stops and the world begins. *Somewhere* . . . He realized his thumb was wet. He felt embarrassed now. Charlotte was staring at him and he knew she was going to tease him about the thumb sucking.

"Cat got your tongue, Frankie?" the baby-sitter asked.

Frankie looked down at his hands. "When he lets me help him, yeah, sometimes. . . ." His voice trailed away quietly.

"Is he away somewhere?" Susan asked.

Charlotte said quickly, "He goes away on business."

"I'm sure you must miss him."

"Yeah," Frankie said.

"Where is he now?" Susan said. She passed in front of the TV, creating a dark square shadow.

"Not sure," Frankie said.

"Pennsylvania," Charlotte said.

Frankie watched the baby-sitter move out of line of the picture and he thought: *Pennsylvania. It sounded so far away. So far away he couldn't be reached by telephone.* But it wasn't his father that was troubling him now. It was something else, like he had a shadow falling at the back of his mind, the same kind of feeling you get when you know there's something you have to do only you can't remember what it is. The itch you can't scratch. Like that.

"I'm going into the kitchen," Susan said. "Can I fetch you guys anything?"

Charlotte asked for milk. Frankie didn't want anything.

Susan, smiling, went out of the TV room and shut the door behind her.

A moment of silence. Then Charlotte said, "What's the matter?"

The boy gazed at his sister. "I don't know," he answered. Then with some mild defiance he added: "Nothing. Nothing's the matter, OK?"

"I *know* you, Frankie."

He returned his eyes to the TV. Charlotte sighed and crossed her arms and thought: If he doesn't want to talk, I sure can't make him.

3.

She'd taken the pins from her hair and brushed, hard, causing the beehive to collapse. Then she'd picked the pieces of stupid glitter out of the red strands. And after that she'd looked at herself in the mirror and what she saw was a certain haggard quality, a slackening of the skin, a sagging. Now her hair lay untidily over her shoulders, but that didn't matter to her—not now. One kind of illusion, another kind, what difference did it make? *She thinks you're ridiculous. They all must think you're ridiculous.* But a lie was only harmful if you let it be, it was only like a piece of reality you'd taken and inflated and twisted out of shape, that was all. Nothing more.

On her way out she slammed the door loudly but it didn't satisfy her. She unlocked her car and she thought: Emily Allbright doesn't have to lie. She doesn't have to make things up. *But she won't let me look after her precious goddam kids, will she?* No, she won't do that. Do I have to beg? You already did that, didn't you? You already went *crawling* to her on the telephone—

She drove. She drove in circles. She drove through the dark streets of West Pastorville, hating the place, hating it more than she'd ever done. She drove with no particular destination in mind, except maybe—

But what good would it do now to go to Emily Allbright and talk with her face to face? She'd built a wall, a thick goddam wall, and you couldn't hope to find any weakness in it. And then she remembered what she'd felt that night in the supermarket when she'd turned round to see the woman staring at her, the utter look of confusion on her face—she remembered feeling some empty black embarrassment, humiliation, shame: and, behind these things, lying there at the center of her mind like a pit, an abyss, her own loneliness. *Emily Allbright isn't lonely, is she?* No, goddammit, she isn't lonely.

But I am.

Her precious kids.

God, her precious little jewels. And she won't let me near them. So what good will it do to go and talk with her? No damn good at all.

She was on Larue Drive now, passing the house with the yellow outside light, passing it before she'd realized it. She pulled in towards the sidewalk and killed the engine and sat silently in the car, her mind blank now. Loneliness. Sheer loneliness. What did you do with that condition?

Self-pity.

Yeah, self-pity was terrific. It helped you when you wanted to crawl, when you wanted forgiveness and absolution, when you had to ask Emily Allbright for something she wasn't prepared to give.

Don't do it, she thought.

You don't have to debase yourself, not for her, not for anyone.

She backed the car up close to the driveway of the house, then she noticed that the station wagon wasn't there, that a Ford of some kind was parked in the drive. And she thought: *A baby-sitter*. She's found herself a baby-sitter. And it isn't me.

She stared at the yellow light and the cluster of moths that flew around it pointlessly—and what she felt, more than anything else, was a profound sense of having been shut out, of having been excluded, as if she were herself one of the fall moths beating against the heart of an unattainable light.

4.

Emily had expected a bar, a tavern, but Hamilton—sitting in the passenger seat of the wagon—had given her directions to a Victorian house. She waited for him to say something like *My place,* but he didn't say anything for a long time, nervously drumming his fingers on the dash, as if he were uncertain himself of the next step. The next step, Emily thought, in whatever the process might be. I won't go inside, she told herself. It was like a line she had to draw somewhere, a boundary between what she was prepared to do and what she wasn't—and it was so damned hard to find that line. She stared straight ahead along the dark street, the lamps dim between branches of trees, the rows of old houses gaunt and shadowy. She felt she was waiting, just waiting, for something to happen. (Such as? A clumsy kiss? Come on. Then what? *Come up and see my drafts?*) She turned now to look at him; he was watching her, one hand lightly rubbing his moustache.

"You live here, right?" she said.

"Right. Top floor."

She gazed at the house, ornate even in the dark. "This is all somewhat . . . up front, isn't it?"

"Like how?"

"You invite me inside. That's how it goes. You invite me inside and we drink some wine and perchance you put on a little music and . . ." She paused. Pictures in the mind. A whole scenario unfolding.

Hamilton laughed. "You're a married woman, kid."

"And you're a highly moral poet," she said.

"My morals are impeccable."

Impeccable: by what standards? she wondered. And what was this anyhow but some game designed to obliterate Ted and his . . . adventure? *I don't know how to play it,* she thought. I don't know where it goes from here on in. She suddenly wished she could open some internal window, smash some interior glass, and let freedom blow through her life. You're not built that way, she thought. Some people, maybe: not you. Not you, Emily.

"You think I have this plan to, ahum, *seduce* you?" he said.

"Ahum, maybe."

"I like you, in a world where I find most people despicable," he said.

"Despicable?"

"You find that a sorrowful outlook on life, Emily?"

She wanted to say something like Hey, there's a little bit of good in everybody, but it was too banal even to utter, and Hamilton would only laugh at her anyhow.

"I happen to like you," he said again.

"I don't know why—"

"Analyze. Dissect. Do what you like, you keep coming back to some simple emotional statement. The power of intuition."

She looked at him, wondering: What was that *tone* in his voice? Cynicism? A weariness? What was he tired of? And then she thought maybe it was a front of some kind, a veneer. The man shies away from his sensitivity.

"OK," she said. "You like me. I accept that. But then you've got this gap, see, between you liking me and me coming up to your apartment, and it's a hard gap for me."

"I'll tell you what. I'll sit at one end of the room and you sit at the other, and the closest I'll come to you is when I pour some wine in your glass. How does that grip you?"

She wanted to laugh. The only thing missing from Hamilton's vision was a chaperone sitting in a corner complete with crochet on her lap. She looked up at the house again. Shadows, dark corners, a few windows lit in a pale way. I don't want to go inside, she thought.

Hamilton laid his hand on her arm. "I'm only dangerous at feeding time. But then any old lump of raw meat keeps me content. Besides, the only risk you'd run coming up to my apartment is the possibility of a coronary climbing the stairs. But you look pretty fit."

He was silent for a second. Then he said, "Maybe I've got it wrong. Maybe you don't like *me*."

"I hardly know you—"

"What could be a better time?"

She took the key from the ignition and turned to look at him. What am I? she wondered. The Last Virgin on the Block? The Cheerleader Tease? The Girl Least Likely To? It was stupid. What the hell.

"I couldn't stay long," she said.

"I wouldn't expect you to."

Already, Hamilton was getting out of the car. She stepped out, slammed the door, and thought: Go back. Go back now.

Hamilton was waiting for her on the sidewalk.

5.

When he'd risen from the bed he'd supported himself by leaning against the wall, moving as quietly as he could even though he was sure he'd heard her close the door some time ago and go out. His legs trembled as he slid forward towards the door of his bedroom where he paused, listening, hearing only the silences of the house around him and yet conscious of how easily that quiet could be broken by the sound of her coming back, a thought that panicked him. He turned his head this way and that, listening, waiting, then he found the door handle and turned it and moved out on to the landing. Darkness. Complete, total. Again he paused, trying to create some kind of diagram of the house in his head, wondering how close he might be to the top of the stairs. There was a sharp pain in his calves, pulse beats rippling through his muscles. He put one foot forward tentatively, then the other, and with an arm extended in front of himself he felt the wood surface of the handrail. Careful now. Careful and nice and damn slow. But he couldn't afford to be slow. She could come back and see him standing there at the top of the stairs and . . . It crossed his mind that maybe she hadn't gone out at all, maybe she was standing there right now watching him, watching him as he tried to fumble his way down the steps. No, he couldn't afford to go slow. Hurry, he told himself. Hurry. But he couldn't get the legs to move faster, he couldn't get rid of the pain that came with each slight movement. It's a damn stupid plan, he told himself. It's not too late to go back to the bedroom. And then what—just wait there for her to kill you? Forget the plan. How's it going to help you anyway? A plan of darkness. He counted each step. Three, four, five. How many before he made it down to the bottom. He wished he knew. Five, six, *his hand trembling on the rail,* six, seven, *his whole body hurting now.* Seven. Eight. Nine. He could hear his own rapid breathing. Then there were no more steps, no handrail to guide him, only a smooth-surfaced wall that led through the rest of the house. But what good did that knowledge do, what good did it do to know that you only had to follow the goddam wall if you didn't have a remote idea how big the rooms were or what kinds of obstacles might lie under your feet? He felt hopeless, resigned to remaining where he was in the darkness at the bottom of the stairs. But he couldn't go back up again. He wouldn't do that. Damn her. He wouldn't climb back to his room. He had to go on. Waiting, all the time waiting for her to come back. Move, damn you, move move move. He stood close to the wall. Then it turned, there was a corner, and his foot knocked against something that was lying on the floor and he tripped, spilling forward, arms spread to brace himself for the fall. A goddam stool. A chair. He fell over on his side, jarring his arm under his body. *Shit, shit, shit.* He sat upright and he thought: I can't go on. It's hopeless. I can't make it.

You don't have any choices, do you?

Count them.

Either you go. Or you stay. And if you sit here in the fucking dark and she comes back and finds you . . .

He struggled to his feet and felt for the wall again and then there was a door, a door half open, and he knew from the faint odor of food that he had to be in the kitchen now. The smell made him feel faintly sick, reminding him of how hungry he was, but he couldn't stop to grope around for something to eat, he didn't have time for that, he didn't have time. He had to move. He collided with the kitchen table, the sharp corner of the thing catching him in the hip, causing him to moan aloud. Be quiet, he told himself. No sound. Make no sound. *What if she's just sitting there with a smile on her lips and watching you? Watching you right now?*

He couldn't afford to think like that.

He'd heard the door slam, hadn't he? The car go out of the driveway. He stumbled across the kitchen floor, reached the back door, paused, feeling all his strength diminish, feeling it all just drain out of him. But he had to find more from someplace. His legs were numb now. It was like he wasn't walking at all. Floating, floating through some sticky liquid, something like that. He opened the back door. The night air, with a thin rain falling, was chill against his face. He could feel the wetness spread through the cotton of his pyjamas. Around here, around here somewhere.

He remembered this was where Nick used to come when he had a repair to do. Around here— And he remembered sometimes when he'd be sitting in a lounge chair by the pool, he'd hear Nick work at the fuse box. The fuse box. Where?

There were sharp pebbles under his feet, pebbles that cut into his soft soles like misshapen razors. But he could hardly feel them now. He put his hand against the wall of the house, pausing, listening, hearing the rain fall on the surface of the pool, trying not to remember that day when . . .

He had it!

His fingers encountered the cold metal of the fuse box. Trembling, he opened it. He ran his fingertips carefully over the interior, feeling for the switches. And there, situated at the top, was the main switch. He waited for a second, feeling some tiny triumph, and then he pulled the switch.

And he thought: Darkness.

Darkness for me.

Darkness for her.

Now they were almost equal.

6.

She walked around the side of the Ford. She put her face against the side window of the house, trying to look in. The front room was in darkness. She brushed her hair from her shoulders and moved towards the back, wondering who Emily Allbright had asked to look after her kids . . . who she'd asked instead of me, she thought. Somebody. And then she felt foolish doing this, prowling around a house in the darkness, and all because of her own jealousy. Because that was what it came down to: She was jealous of that stupid woman, Emily. A house. A husband. Her precious kids. And at the core of this jealousy lay the various strata of her own loneliness: a quarry, something she'd mined year after year after year. Something she knew so damned well, this quarry, this great hole in the ground that had never yielded anything precious. . . . She closed her eyes. A light fell from the kitchen window, a small square of yellow. *My model agency's such a big success*, she thought. *That's really going places, all the way out into the galaxies. . . .*

She saw a figure move across the kitchen floor.

One of those damned women. That's who—a face she recognized, only she couldn't remember the name now, but she couldn't recall *any* of their names. Wait.

Susan.

That was the woman's name.

Susan. She watched Susan a moment, enjoying the idea of observing without being seen, like you were invisible. (All your life you've been invisible, so what?) The woman was touching the telephone. And then, suddenly, as if she intuited the fact she was being observed, she swung her face around quickly, taking in the kitchen, the window, and then the back door—all in a series of quick nervous glances.

She didn't see me.

She just didn't see me.

But then Susan was gone from the kitchen, moving quickly, the door swinging shut behind her.

7.

Charlotte looked up from the TV when Susan came back from the kitchen. The baby-sitter put her finger to her lips for silence and Charlotte, puzzled by the gesture, stared at her.

"What—"

"Don't say anything," the baby-sitter said. "Sshh. Don't say a word."

Charlotte got up from her chair. "Is—"

But Susan was shushing her again and this time Frankie was rising, wondering what was going on, turning his face to look at the woman. Susan switched off the TV and the sudden silence was unnerving.

Susan looked from one kid to the other and then said in a whisper, "Don't get upset. OK?"

"Upset about—" But Charlotte didn't have time to finish her question because Susan cut her off, saying, "There's somebody outside. Out back. Please don't get alarmed."

"Who?" Charlotte asked.

"I don't know who," Susan said. "I was out in the kitchen and I heard a noise and I saw somebody outside the back door—"

"What are we going to do?" Frankie said.

Charlotte stared at her brother: the small face was suddenly white. A prowler, she thought. *A prowler.* But what did prowlers do? What did they want? She couldn't think, trying to remember what she'd read about prowlers.

She said, "We should call the police."

Susan watched the girl. "That's the worst part, Charlotte. We can't call the police—"

"What do you mean?"

Susan hesitated. She made a nervous gesture with her mouth, reaching up to touch her lower lip with a finger. "We can't call the police because . . ."

"Because what?" Charlotte said, aware of herself still whispering, like she was in the school library where the signs all said Silence.

"Because the telephone isn't working, Charlotte."

"Not working?"

Susan went towards the window, fiddled with the curtains, but didn't look outside.

"Not working?" Charlotte said again. What did the woman mean? *Not working.* She felt the rise of a small panic inside her.

"Maybe the person outside cut the wire or something, I don't know," Susan said. "Maybe he just took a knife and cut the wire."

Frankie stared at the baby-sitter. There was something still stirring at the back of his mind, something he was on the point of reaching, of settling . . . but now it didn't matter, it didn't matter because there was a prowler outside. Nothing mattered now. He felt scared, startled by a shadow. He wished his dad was here. They were always safe when his dad was home. Nothing like this ever happened when he was around the house.

"What are we going to . . ." He let his question fade away because it didn't need to be asked. He stared at Susan, who was still pulling on her bottom lip.

"I don't know," Susan said.

"We've got to do something," Charlotte said, no longer able to keep her voice low, imagining the shadow moving around the house, shears in his hands, clipping wires, dreaming insane thoughts.

"Let me think, let me just think," Susan said.

Silence. Like deep thoughts needed long silences. Deep thoughts. How deep would the thought have to be in this case? Maybe nothing would happen. Maybe it was only Mrs. DeSantis next door. The old snoop. Maybe that's all it was. Yeah, sure, Mrs. DeSantis would cut telephone wires. Oh, sure. You could see her going around the neighborhood slashing people's wires. Maybe whoever it was would just go away, just drift off into the night. That was always possible. She watched Susan and realized she was listening for a sound from outside the window, the crackle of a leaf underfoot, a movement, anything. But all she could hear now was the soft rattle of rain on some broad-leafed plants outside the window. Nothing else. Nothing else.

"My car," Susan said suddenly. "We could go out to my car and leave—"

Silence again.

"We could just make a run for it," Susan said. "We could drive down to the police station."

Make a run for it, Charlotte thought. Like in a movie. Only this wasn't any movie, this was the real thing, this was where you really had to make a run for it.

"Or we can just wait here real quiet until the person goes away,"

Susan said. "We could do that. Except . . . well, it doesn't seem like a lot of fun knowing there's somebody outside and all we can do is sit in here and wait for something to happen. Maybe even something awful. I don't know."

"Could we get to the car?" Charlotte said. "Could we get that far?"

"It's just outside. In the driveway," Susan said. She looked uncertain all at once, as if she weren't really sure. "I mean, it's only a few steps from the front door."

Charlotte stared at the curtains drawn across the window. No, it wasn't exactly a lot of fun just to sit around and wait. And you never knew what you were waiting for anyhow—maybe the glass would break and somebody would come rushing into the room, somebody who'd hurt them, kill them even, and suddenly she understood she was thinking more of Frankie than of herself, she was thinking of protecting Frankie. It wasn't anything heroic, she realized, it was more like a gut instinct. Then she looked at Susan. The baby-sitter had an expression of terrible uncertainty, of indecision, like she'd forgotten where she'd put something. No, Susan wasn't any good in this kind of situation. Susan wasn't cut out for this sort of thing at all. She could see that.

"We'll go to your car then," Charlotte said.

"We can make it," Susan said. "I mean, it won't be difficult."

"OK. That's what we do," Charlotte said. "Do we try it now?"

"I think we better."

Charlotte put her arm around Frankie's shoulder. Followed by Susan, they left the TV room and went quickly along the hallway to the front door. Then Charlotte paused. *The prowler might be out front,* she thought. The prowler might be standing right outside the front door. . . . And she couldn't remember ever having been this afraid before, she couldn't remember ever feeling anything like this strident sense of alarm, of fear.

She looked at Susan. "The car keys," she said.

"I've got them," Susan whispered. "Don't worry."

Don't worry.

How could she not worry? Susan looked like she'd gone into some indefinable place beyond fear, beyond panic. Her skin was pale, her eyes glazed and empty: it was like she just wanted Charlotte to tell her what to do, how to behave.

"Open the door," Charlotte said.

Susan put her hand out slowly and Frankie began to cry. It was a strange soft cry. Charlotte put her hand over his mouth and could feel him trembling.

There was nobody outside the front door, nothing but the yellow light and the rain falling in the oak tree.

"Quick," Susan said.

And then they were running across the grass to the driveway and getting inside Susan's car and she was fumbling with the key in the ignition, twisting it, twisting it as the engine of the big car growled, then the tires grated on the wet concrete as she put the car into reverse, and the headlights came on, burning, white and burning—

Burning against a figure that stood in the shadows at the side of the house.

Adrienne put her hand up to her eyes against the sudden brightness. She stepped close to the wall of the house, surprised, blinded. Where were they going? Where were they running to? What had made them run like this? She watched the car spin around and heard the tires scream on the wet concrete. What were they running from like that? She let her hands fall to her sides and she walked down the driveway, seeing the red taillights of the car vanish in the rain.

Charlie. Oh, Charlie.

8.

Another man's apartment: and Emily felt a strange sense of disorientation, the feeling she didn't belong here, that she shouldn't have come. It was a large studio room, barely decorated, a long sofa, an unvarnished desk under the slope of the window, a typewriter, papers, shelves of books. The wall that faced the window was covered with framed photographs of a woman—a lovely woman with a bright intelligent face and dark eyes, a wide forehead surrounded by fair hair; and she knew without having to ask James Hamilton that this was Deirdre, this was the Deirdre of the dedication. Hamilton had gone out into the tiny kitchen and come back with a bottle of chilled wine and two glasses.

"Ah, the shrine," he said. "You probably think it a morbid obsession, don't you?"

"Morbid? Why? She's very beautiful."

"Yeah." Hamilton poured wine and handed her a glass.

"It's Deirdre," Emily said.

"Right." He sipped his wine and made a face.

"You dedicated the poems to her."

Hamilton was silent for a while. He was gazing absent-mindedly into his wine. "You've got a good memory, Emily."

"Where is she?"

"She's dead."

Dead? Emily turned from the series of portraits and looked at Hamilton. "I'm sorry. I mean . . ."

"She died just after that book came out. Some form of blood cancer."

Emily tasted her wine. Her hand shook. Blood cancer. She couldn't connect the vital young woman in the photographs with any kind of disease. It didn't make sense.

"You were married to her?"

Hamilton shook his head. "It didn't go that far. I sometimes think I should take the pictures down and destroy them. What the hell good do they do?"

Emily shrugged: What was there to say? She tasted some more of her wine, aware now of how it burned inside her chest.

"It probably is morbid to keep her on display like a goddam mummy or something," he said. "But some mornings when you get up and it's shitty outside, and the sun doesn't look like it'll ever shine again—well, the photographs produce a little light of their own, you know? Surprises you, does it—this sentimental streak in me?"

"I thought some of your poems were sentimental," Emily said. "So I guess I'm not really surprised."

"Cheers," Hamilton said, and he lightly knocked his glass against hers, a gesture she thought clumsily intimate, as if the rap of glass on glass were a kind of substitute for a kiss, lips touching. She turned away from him, crossing the room, standing under the sloping window and staring at the mess of papers on his desk.

"Botched poems," he said.

"Why botched?"

"I remember how to start them, but I can't remember how to

finish them," he said. He moved after her, stood alongside her, set his wine glass down on a sheet of stained paper that had the typed words . . . *the doors along the street are* . . . Unfinished.

"Maybe all your creative energy goes into teaching," she said. It was the wrong thing to say, she understood that at once.

Hamilton laughed and, reaching out so that he touched her lightly on the neck, said, "Creative bullshit. Poor Emily. You don't really understand, do you?"

"Do you expect me to?"

He shook his head. "Not really. Maybe it's magic. Maybe there's some kind of magic involved and after a while you lose your wand and you can't make the transformations. Then again, maybe that's bullshit too."

She wondered why he sounded so bitter, how far that bitterness had gone down deep inside him. She took another drink of the wine, glancing at her wristwatch. (*Ted, she thought. Where is Ted now? What is he doing right now?*) She drained the glass, which Hamilton immediately refilled.

"One for the road," he said. He took his hand away from the side of her neck, reached for the bottle, poured. She already felt slightly inebriated, flushed, a faint glaze falling over her perceptions. Danger signals, she thought. Little fiery signs. She watched him fill the glass again, this time almost to the brim—and then, quite suddenly, he was leaning down towards her, kissing her directly on the mouth, his breath warm against her face. And what she felt more than anything else was some sense of strangeness. Another man's mouth, another man's taste, as if the geometry were all wrong, as if it weren't a matter of morals but one of spatial shapes. Not Ted's mouth, but someone else's. And almost as soon as he'd kissed her he pulled his face away.

"Do you want an apology?" he said.

She felt wetness against the front of her blouse, spilled wine.

"I'll send you the laundry bill—"

"I broke my promise," he said. "For that I'm sorry."

Flustered, she leaned against the edge of the desk and watched him. "This isn't going to work," she said. "Do you understand what I mean? This isn't going to work out. For you. For me. It's not going anywhere."

"I didn't ask for a map, Emily," he said. "I didn't ask for direc-

tions. And I didn't mean to bring you up here under what we sometimes call false pretenses, OK?"

"OK," she said. OK, and she thought: The loneliness must bite
into him. It must eat away at him. The photographs of a dead
woman, a dead love. It was like a sickness, a heartbreaking sickness.
And what she wished suddenly was that she *could* console him, comfort him, reach out and touch him. But I'd have to be a different person, she thought. I'd have to stop being Emily Allbright. I'd have to
be somebody else, somebody with that kind of courage.

She put her glass down. She stared at him.

"You're going," he said.

"I have to," she said.

"You haven't finished your wine."

The kids, she thought. The kids.

"Finish your wine first," he said.

She picked up the glass and held it, but she didn't drink from it.
There was an expression of sadness on his face and she thought: *No,
sweet Christ no, I'm not going to fall for that. Not for that little lost
boy look. No way.*

"You could always call home," he said. "Tell your baby-sitter
you'll be late."

"I won't do that," she said. "I won't do it because it isn't going to
lead anywhere. You get my point?"

"I get it, but I don't like it."

She stared at the surface of her wine, sipped some more, then put
the glass back down on the desk. She stuck her hands into the back
pockets of her jeans, still staring at him, as if she were waiting for
him to come up with an argument that couldn't be refuted. But he
was silent, watching her, half-smiling now. She looked down at the
floor. She felt something in her right back pocket.

A piece of paper. A crumpled piece of paper. A creased piece of
paper she couldn't remember putting there. She took it out and un-
folded it and looked at it.

Hamilton said, "What's that? Your appointments calendar?"

Puzzled, she stared at the paper.

It was the address of an antique dealer in Pastorville. And then
she remembered. Susan. It was the address Susan had given her.

But that wasn't it at all.

There was something else, something that hit her like the echo of a voice thrown a long long time ago, something that came back with a cold feeling of fear. Think. Just think. Hold on tight to what you have and think. *Goddammit, think.*

"What's wrong?" Hamilton said.

She looked at him, forgetting why she was here, what she had come for, an amnesia of surroundings.

What's wrong? he asked again.

She shook her head slowly from side to side.

9.

When they reached the end of Larue Drive Susan swung the Ford westward, away from the entrance to the freeway. In the back seat Frankie said, "We should take the freeway. It's quicker."

"I know a short cut," Susan said. "I know a quick way to the police station. Believe me."

Charlotte, in the front passenger seat, stared at the tightness of Susan's knuckles on the wheel. She wanted to say, relax, we can take it easy now, we made it out of the house, but she didn't say anything. Something in the way Susan drove, some grim determination, made her keep silent.

Frankie said, "I never heard of any short cut. The freeway's quicker. . . ."

Susan shook her head. "No, no, it isn't."

Outside, the streets were getting darker, the buildings thinning out. Frankie sat back and stared out of the window. A prowler, he thought. They'd escaped the prowler. They'd be OK. Everything would be fine. Everything would be all right now. Except . . . except what? They'd go to the cops, the cops would come back to the house with them, the prowler would be gone, mom would come home, and then it would be like nothing had ever happened. Except . . . except this same small ghost kept playing around inside his head, bothering him.

They passed a diner on the edge of the freeway, then Susan swung the car again, this time to the left, away from the blinking neon that flashed the word Diner Diner Diner like a slash of pale blood in the darkness. A short cut, Frankie thought. He only knew one quick way to Pastorville, and this wasn't it.

Something else.

Some other thing.

One afternoon . . . why did he keep losing it like this? He saw Charlotte turn and smile at him and her look made him feel a whole lot easier. If Charlotte thought it was OK, then it *was* OK. So he could relax.

An afternoon, he thought again. One afternoon. When? Why did he keep thinking like this?

He looked out of the window again. The suburb was gone. Out there everything was in darkness. There were no street lamps now. No lights. Nothing he recognized except for the faint glow in the rainy sky of the suburb they'd just left. Where were they going now? What kind of short cut was this?

One certain afternoon, he thought.

You putting us on, Frankie? You sure you really saw somebody?

He shut his eyes, confused, tired all at once.

How big? How small? What color clothes?

I don't remember. I don't remember, honest I don't.

You're making this up, Frankie.

He opened his eyes when he heard Charlotte say, "Do you know where you're going, Susan?"

"Sure I'm sure," she said.

"I don't recognize any of this," the girl said.

Susan lifted one hand from the wheel and reached out across the dark and lightly touched Charlotte's hair.

"I know where we're going," she said. "Just trust me."

Charlotte felt cold, watching Susan's hand fall from her hair to the glove compartment, watching the fingers turn the lock of the compartment, take something out, something dark and heavy, something she laid in her lap as she drove. Something. *Something.*

"Susan," she said.

Susan didn't answer, just kept watching the dark road carved by the headlights.

Frankie sat upright. No, he thought. It's wrong. I have to be wrong.

But it kept coming back in on him, like a wave, wave after wave.

The afternoon in the woods.

That afternoon. That time in the woods.

Then.

"You were in the woods, weren't you?" he said, his voice shrill. "I saw you in the woods, didn't I!"

Susan smiled.

"You were following us in the woods!"

Charlotte turned around, as if to seize the door handle. But she felt Susan's grip around her wrist and she realized, even though it was dark inside the car, impenetrably dark, that the heavy thing Susan had taken from the glove compartment was a gun.

"Susan, please . . ." She heard a catch in her own thin voice. You want to cry. You want to cry. Don't cry, Charlotte. Hold back the tears.

Susan smiled. "Just take it easy, kids. Just take it nice and easy now."

"Where are we going?" Frankie said.

Susan was silent for a time before she answered: "We're going to see your daddy. That's where we're going. You'd like to see him, wouldn't you?"

10.

James Hamilton said, "What's wrong? You pull a piece of paper out of your pocket and—wham—it's like the end of the goddam world. *What is it?*"

She felt numb. She fumbled for something to say to him. She couldn't think of anything.

An antique dealer. A piece of paper with handwriting on it.

Handwriting. Susan's hand.

No. There's a mistake here. I'm confused. Mixed-up. A mistake, that's all. But then her mind was racing away in all kinds of directions, moving through all kinds of empty avenues.

A slip of paper under the windshield wiper of your wagon.

A simple slip of paper with a scrawl on it.

What the hell had it said? What?

You think you've got it all, don't you? But nothing lasts.

Why was that handwriting the same as this on the crumpled scrap of paper she'd found in her jeans? No, it had to be a mistake. Plain and simple. Because if it wasn't a mistake, it didn't make any kind of sense. . . .

You think you've got it all don't you but nothing lasts.

Oh, dear Christ.

She picked up the telephone on the desk and she dialed her own number, her hand shaking, her fingertips hardly finding the digits, her mind barely conscious of Hamilton's continual questions. *What's wrong? What the hell is wrong? Won't you tell me what the hell's going on?* She got an unobtainable signal, a steady whistling whine, so she pressed the bar and tried again and got the same sound a second time. She slammed the receiver down and she thought Think. Try to think. Just try to make it yield some kind of sense. Hamilton was holding her by the shoulders and she looked at him, not seeing him, not really aware of him. Conscious only of her voice saying *I have to go home I have to go home,* conscious only of how her words formed a steady incoherent stream, like the sounds of a dreamer, the sounds of nonsense. And then she was opening the door and Hamilton was coming after her, still trying to get answers to his questions, but she was moving by then towards the stairs, running downwards, down and down, hearing the echo of her own feet and her own exhausted breathing, no longer listening to the sound of Hamilton calling after her, no longer hearing his shouts as they reverberated in the stairwell. And then there was rain and cold air and the spilled wine chilled her blouse as she rushed towards the wagon, getting inside, pulling the door shut, turning the key, listening to the labored motor turn over—but all these sounds were killed and deadened by the noise she'd heard on her own telephone, that dreadful chill whistling like somebody whining in a place of the dead. She drove blindly, blindly, trying not to think, hitting the freeway entrance without looking, swerving around a truck, hearing its Klaxon scream at her, then coming off the freeway at the West Pastorville ramp and driving through the red light without looking, without caring, her thoughts scattered like so many marbles in some lunatic game—Ted, where is Ted, why isn't the telephone working, why the words on a scrap of paper, and the kids, where are the kids, where are the kids. Then she was hurtling through the dim-lit streets of the suburb, suddenly unaware of her surroundings, suddenly afraid to find her own home, to open the door, to go inside, to find . . . to find what?

Wait. It's a mistake. It's nothing. You're scared. But it's nothing. And then she saw the yellow light of her own house on Larue Drive.

She saw the yellow light.
She saw an unfamiliar car parked outside.
She saw the front door was wide open.
And she knew everything had gone wrong.

Chapter Eleven

1.

She found Adrienne standing in the kitchen. She heard herself say *The kids where are the kids* and Adrienne was trying to tell her they'd gone in a car with Susan, that they'd rushed outside and taken off wildly into the darkness. For a moment, Emily sat down at the kitchen table and lit a cigarette and listened to Adrienne make consolatory noises, soothing little sounds. But they weren't getting through to her. They weren't reaching any center of understanding. Adrienne might have been talking in an alien language. They're dead, Emily thought. My kids are dead. My little kids are dead. And then she reached for the telephone, thinking she'd call the police, but she noticed the cord had been hacked, the loose wires bared and glistening. Think, she told herself. Think of possibilities. Something mundane. They went for ice cream. They just went to the store, maybe for candy, soda, whatever. Think all you want along those lines. But there isn't any consolation in that direction.

And then she stared at Adrienne and said, "What are you doing here?"

"I came down . . ." Adrienne paused. She ran a hand in a fatigued way across her face. "I came here to talk with you and . . ." She didn't finish the sentence.

Emily stubbed her cigarette carelessly: "How do I know you didn't have something to do with this . . . how do I know that?"

Adrienne put out her hand and touched Emily lightly on the arm. "I saw them go—"

"You just *happened* to see them go?"

"No," the other woman said. "It wasn't quite like that. I was looking . . ."

But Emily wasn't listening now. She was walking up and down the kitchen. Every rational explanation seemed groundless. Every possible explanation seemed to have no merit. *The kids are gone.* With that hard fact, against that cold hard fact, reasons and explanations had no place. The kids are gone. She covered her face with her hands, wanting to cry, wanting to give in to a merciless despair, but she didn't.

"You know where Susan lives?" Adrienne asked.

"Somewhere. I can't remember."

"Where would you keep her address?"

Emily pointed vaguely towards a drawer. Adrienne found the Book of Points and opened it at Susan's address.

"She might have taken them over there for some reason," Adrienne said.

"Like what?"

"I don't know. Maybe her husband got sick. Maybe one of her own kids is unwell. I don't know."

Emily could feel the harsh edge of hysteria, something that moved at the back of her head, something sharp as a blade. "No," she said. "It isn't anything like that. It isn't anything like that." And she picked up the useless slashed cord of the telephone, as if to make the point.

"I didn't do that," Adrienne said. "If that's what you're thinking, I didn't do that."

"OK. So Susan did it. Right? Susan cut the wire. People don't do this kind of thing unless . . ." Unless what? Emily thought. Unless they mean harm. Unless they mean a terrible kind of harm. She stared at Adrienne, still holding the useless cord in her fingers, not really seeing her, but seeing instead some frightening inner vision of two small children lying dead in some night-black field, hearing them cry out on the point of their slaying, hearing them call out to a God that wouldn't listen, wouldn't protect them, to parents who weren't around to save them. And the terror of those sounds filled her head.

"I didn't have anything to do with it," Adrienne said. "I swear it. I only came here to talk with you. . . ."

Emily let the cut wire fall from her fingers to the floor. She gazed at Adrienne. Ted, she thought. Ted would know what to do. If she knew where he was. If. She went to the window and opened the drapes, then she pushed the back door open and stared out into the yard. So much blackness out there. The kids. Dear God, the kids could be out there, they could be out there anywhere, and that was the worst of it. Knowing they were out there someplace. *Out there*. She felt something slip inside her, something just yield and give way, an overwhelming sensation of powerlessness, of uselessness.

Susan's house.

Maybe there was a rational explanation.

Sure. Forget the ripped cord and maybe all kinds of explanations were possible. And then she thought: She's taken my kids. *She's stolen my children.*

And that was the emptiest thought she'd ever had in her whole life.

That was the most total void she'd ever faced.

"Look, maybe I can help," Adrienne said. "I'll go next door and use the telephone. I'll call the cops. You want to let me help?"

Emily felt herself shake, a trembling that began in her lower limbs and flowed jarringly through the rest of her body. She felt a darkness encroach upon her, something that buzzed inside her head like any number of lights about to pop, to explode. She turned to Adrienne and nodded and watched as the other woman left the room. Silences. Silences as deep as bottomless wells. *I'll go upstairs. I'll look inside their rooms. I'll find them fast asleep. That's what it'll be like.*

And then I'll wake.

Ted will be sitting on the edge of the bed, watching me.

That's how it will be.

But the silences crawled through the house. They crept, they slithered, they undulated with the cunning of snakes, seeking every opening, every aperture, every sliver of space. *I won't find them upstairs, I won't find them in any part of this house.*

And I can't just wait here for the cops to come. I can't just wait here for that to happen. She picked up the Book of Points and looked at Susan's address, trying to remember how she'd got there the last time.

I can't wait.

She went out of the kitchen, through the front room, and out into the rain towards her car.

2.

Charlotte watched the lights of the car illuminate a fence of barbed wire and a sign, seen briefly, that said Keep Out, and for a moment it seemed to her that Susan was going to stop the car, but she didn't, she didn't even brake slightly, she just kept on going, ramming the front of the Ford through the wire so that the fence was ripped away, the wire bent this way and that and wood support posts uprooted and tumbling across the hood of the vehicle. In the back she could hear

Frankie cry and she thought: Whatever I do, whatever happens now, I can't let him hear me cry like that, I can't afford not to be brave somehow. She reached over and held his hand while the car bounced and jarred through some long grass, and the springs whined and the shocks groaned. And Frankie, through his tears, kept saying something about his daddy and how could Susan possibly know where his daddy was. Then the grass was growing longer, so long it seemed impossible to go on driving, but Susan didn't stop, she just kept grinding the car through the tall grass. And then she couldn't go any farther, because mud sucked at the wheels, and although she shoved her foot down on the gas pedal the wheels only spun more and more madly. Then she stopped and she picked the gun up from her lap and told them to get out, it wasn't much farther to the place where their daddy was now, they wouldn't have far to go at all.

They got out. Susan didn't even bother to shut the car doors. She walked behind them through the rain. There wasn't even a moon, only a mass of rain clouds touched by something silver, something that gave out barely any light at all.

"Stop crying, Frankie," she said. "I want you to stop crying. You're going to see your father. So what are you crying about?"

Charlotte held his hand tightly. See, Frankie, I'm not scared. Why should you be? Take some strength from me, go on, take as much as you need. Now the air was filled with the smell of musty water, of dampness, of something festering in the darkness.

"Make him stop crying, Charlie," Susan said.

Charlie? Charlie? "He's scared," she said. "Don't you know he's scared?"

"He doesn't have anything to be afraid of," Susan said. "Doesn't he understand that? Make him understand that, Charlie. He doesn't need to be scared. We're all going to be together again."

Charlotte stumbled through the long grass. Now she could hear water lapping through reeds and she realized they were moving towards the edge of the old canal and suddenly she was very afraid of their destination—that black water, that place where nobody went any longer, that same place where every summer they pulled out the body of some drowned kid and it was written up in the newspapers. I don't want to go near that place, she thought. Don't make me. She felt Susan's hand on her hair, the fingers stroking lightly, touching in such a way that all she could feel was some deep chill. And the rain, the rain was falling heavier. She thought of her mother, her mother coming home, finding the house empty, finding them gone. And then her panic, her blind terrible panic. She tightened her hold on poor Frankie's fingers, hurting him the way she gripped.

"Make him stop, Charlie—"

"That's not my name—"

"I'm your own mother. I ought to know your name."

"No—"

"Don't talk back to me, Charlie."

Charlie was never disobedient. Charlie was never a disobedient child. Always polite, always charming. Except only once, only once when she was disobedient about going to the deep end of the pool. . . . But that hadn't happened, that was only some silly dream, a long nightmare, and she'd wakened up out of that now, because here was Charlie walking alongside her. And the boy too, the boy she hadn't lost, hadn't miscarried. It was strange to think how real a dream could be sometimes. But that was all in the past. Past and dead. And now, now there would be a reunion. There would be happiness. There would be joy again.

She remembered the woman who'd been looking in through the window tonight. Maybe that hadn't happened either. But she'd had to cut the telephone wire, she'd had to do that, because suddenly all the pieces fitted, it was like some wonderfully easy jigsaw, all the tiny shattered pieces came together again in a beautiful mosaic. A prowler. A shadow in the window. And you had to cut the cord so you couldn't call the police and if you couldn't call the police then you had to get your kids out of the house. But that was the beauty of it all now. That was the way things fitted, even in the dark moments when you thought they weren't going to work. But they did. They had a way of working out.

"I love you, Charlie. But don't talk back to me," she said. "A daughter shouldn't talk back to her mother."

Charlotte tried to see the woman's face in the dark, but it was all shadow now. Sometimes she talked to herself in a low voice, words that ran together without much sense. . . . Which meant she was crazy; which meant she was capable of anything.

And Frankie wouldn't stop crying.

Susan shook him by the shoulder and he said *I want to see my daddy* and she said *That's where we're going* and then he cried some more. She hit him then. She hit him across the mouth with the butt of the gun. He slipped down on to his knees, howling there in the darkness. Charlotte kneeled alongside him and put her arms around his shoulders. It was that dream she'd had, it was like that terrible old dream coming true, the one where somebody hurt Frankie and where her own anger was a brutal thing rising in her mind like her blood was turning hot.

"It's OK. There, Frankie. It's OK."

Susan stood over them. "It's not far now," she said. "Get up. We don't have very far to go now. It's been so long . . . it's been so long that you've forgotten how much I love you."

Suddenly she was crying, standing there in the rain and crying as if her heart had just broken in two. And she was saying over and over *I didn't mean to hurt you, I didn't mean to hurt you.* . . . She bent down and helped Frankie up, kissing his face, touching him, pressing her lips against his forehead, his cheeks, his mouth. Charlotte stepped back, feeling Frankie's blood on her fingertips. She was seized by the terrible impulse to hurt this woman, to do to her what she'd just done to Frankie—Frankie who was limp and stunned and silent—but the chance passed, the opportunity evaporated, because now Susan was no longer crying, she was pushing Frankie forward in whatever direction she intended to take him.

"It isn't much farther," she was saying. "Then you'll see your father . . . you'll be home at last. And he's going to be so proud of you both. Believe me. He's going to be so proud."

Charlotte listened to the slip of water pass through the rushes and up ahead, as a faint sliver of moon broke the cloud bank briefly, the squat shape of some small dark building. She didn't want to go near it. She was suddenly afraid of getting too close to it, of going inside.

But Susan was stroking her hair and saying, "This way, my love. This way. Only a few more yards."

Charlotte reached out to touch Frankie, who mumbled something inaudible, a word she didn't understand but a tone she did—one of inexpressible fear.

3.

Emily didn't remember driving to Susan's house, she didn't remember the quick ride through slick dark streets, nor did she recall except as one might a dream figure the shape of Adrienne rushing out of Mrs. DeSantis's house, waving her arms and trying to get her to stop—because stopping didn't matter, only arriving where she wanted to go, that was all. Her mind was empty. Her heart was an absence. The kids, that was all she could think. The kids. To lose the kids— there wasn't a goddam thing that could make living worth it after that. To lose them. *But she wouldn't lose them. She wouldn't. If she had to spend the rest of her life looking for them, if she had to search everywhere, she'd do it.*

She parked outside Susan's house. Darkness. An absence of life signs. But this is where you begin to look now, in all the dark corners you can find. No matter how dark, that's where you go. She understood she was crying. She could feel cold tears cross her cheeks. If they're dead, she thought. If they're dead. I could murder. *I could bring myself to kill.* She got out of the car and ran up the driveway and stopped outside the front door, turned the handle, felt the door yield, and then she was inside a dark hallway. A light switch. Somewhere there had to be a switch. She fumbled forward, touching the wall. She paused. She thought she heard something. Maybe it was only the rain falling outside the open door, the rustle of the night draft that shifted along the hallway. She moved forward, knocking against something, almost causing it to fall and then catching it before she realized it was the goddam coat tree. And then she found a switch and flicked it and nothing happened, no light, nothing. Ahead of her she could faintly make out the door that she remembered led into the living room—or was it the kitchen? Her memory was gone now, shot—and she went towards it. She encountered another switch and touched it, moving it up and down several times, but still there was no light.

She waited silent in the dark, listening.

Something moved. She was sure of it.

Charlotte? Frankie?

She heard her own whisper, the sound of her own fear.

No answer. *Charlotte? Frankie?*

Answer me. Please answer me.

Waiting, he listened. He understood. They were strange names. But that didn't matter. That was part of her killing game. And she'd made her voice different too. It was all part of her scheme to confuse him.

But he wouldn't be goddam confused. He wouldn't be upset by her. He would kill her. As soon as she pushed the kitchen door, as soon as she stepped inside the dark kitchen, he would strike her through with the knife.

Patience, that was all.

Already he could hear her come towards the door.

Already he could hear the sound of her breathing.

I'm ready, he said to himself.

I'm sure as hell ready for you.

Charlotte? Frankie?

None of the lights worked. She stumbled across the living room to a lamp but when she turned the switch she got the same dead response. She paused, certain she could hear something nearby—certain she could feel the presence of somebody else. But not her kids, because they'd have answered. They'd have tried to answer. Then who? Susan. It had to be Susan. And if it was Susan, then where were the children?

Where?

Scared, she went towards the door that she thought led to the kitchen, but she didn't open it at once. Closing her eyes, she concentrated on listening, on just listening, as if for the sound of a child breathing, or some muffled cry, some restrained moan. Listen. Listen. Listen. She heard a faint scraping sound, then it was gone. Like what? What did that noise remind her of? Metal on wood? She wasn't sure. She rubbed her eyes and she thought: *Please, God, if you care, please don't let anybody harm the children.*

There was a smell now, some kind of disinfectant. Pine or Lysol. She wasn't sure which. She pressed her ear to the wooden surface of the kitchen door and listened. I might as well be blind, she thought. Seeing nothing. Groping out into darkness, ignorant of what I'll touch. Please God. And she pushed the kitchen door slightly and the smell of disinfectant was all at once stronger.

She heard the door creak behind her, the hinges squirming, and then it happened, a sound of air rushing around her head, a man's choked cry, something that came from the back of his throat, and she felt flesh move against her, some kind of weight that pushed down on her and a sharp piercing pain slice through the flesh of her upper arm. She slipped down on her knees, conscious of how the suddenness of the pain made her want to be sick, aware of a smell of stale sweat and urine, and then the weight was directly on top of her, pressing her to the floor, and the strange choked cries became louder, only now they were shapeless words, incoherent to her, except for the name *Susan Susan Susan* being repeated over and over. . . . There was a sigh, a mouth open in front of her face, the smell of rancid breath, and another sickening sharp pain stabbing at her hip. She rolled over, screaming, feeling at her side and trying to contain the wetness she felt there, the damp of her own blood. And what flashed through her mind was the senseless vision of her own death and the weird disembodied feeling that it didn't matter if she died, it only mattered that she find the kids. She heard again the swish of air. A knife. It sliced past the side of her face and she could hear the blade snap against the tiled floor. She pushed against the weight that lay on top of her and, clutching her side, stemming the flow of blood, tried to rise. But the hands that held her were claws, dragging her back down into the darkness. And the claws were firm around her neck, firm, tight, tightening, until she felt dreamlike, until she felt she was being lifted away by some taloned predatory creature in a nightmare. *Christ, no.* She had to fight this. She had to fight this somehow. She heard the broken knife skitter over the tiles, then the sound of the man groaning, his fingers fumbling out for what was left of the blade, then again there was something sharp being pressed against her hand, sharp and ragged, and she twisted away, conscious of her own slick blood being spilled around her, smearing the floor, slithering across the tiles. The hand at the throat. The claw. The claw. She couldn't scream. She could hear only the silence of her own blood. *You go out like this. Without a fight. With nothing. You go out into some kind of weird tranquillity.* As if death were a downer, a pill somebody prescribed, something you unwrapped and swallowed and it took you all the way down into a quiet placid darkness. . . . *No! No! Goddammit!* She tried to push him away, tried to roll out from under him, but he held her so tight she could hardly move. She shut her eyes and twisted her head to one side and she thought: The kids, the kids, it has to mean something, you have to live through this to get to them—

Susan Susan Susan, he was saying.

Susan.

Susan.

Suddenly there was a brilliant beam of light, and somebody was standing in the kitchen doorway with a flashlight. She turned her eyes away from it. Somebody else. Somebody else come to kill her. She was conscious of the striped cotton material of pyjamas, the shadows in the creases of the material, the bright eyes of the person who'd attacked her—and what she read there, before she closed her own eyes, was a madness. Then somebody was helping her to rise. Somebody was helping her. She didn't understand this at first. But the man with the flashlight was helping her to her feet and speaking to her in quiet tones. And she thought: Maybe this is a trick. Maybe it's a trick before they kill me.

And then she found she couldn't stand, her legs no longer existed, the joints in her bones yielded, became liquid, and she slumped against the body of the man who held the flashlight.

4.

There was a smell of dampness inside the building, but Susan didn't notice it. It wasn't some old canal lock house now, it was home. She ushered the two children ahead of her and then shut the door. In the darkness something scampered away and she heard Charlotte say, "What was that?"

Susan didn't answer. She waited until her eyes had become accustomed to the dark, then she herded the kids towards the door that led down to the cellar. Nick, she thought. Nick will be pleased. He'll be pleased with me now. He won't want to leave me now.

"Where does this door go?" Charlotte asked.

"To a little room downstairs. Where your daddy is."

Frankie said, "My dad's in Pennsylvania—"

"Of course he isn't," Susan said. "Don't you think I know where he is?"

Frankie shook his head in the darkness. He was standing close to his sister, holding the sleeve of her blouse, trembling. He was cold and wet and scared. And his mouth hurt where the woman had hit him and he was sure a tooth had been broken because his gum was numb and bleeding.

"I don't want to go down there," he said.

"Of course you do," Susan said. "Doesn't he, Charlie?"

"I told you my name is Charlotte," the girl said. I'm not going to be frightened. I can't let Frankie know how frightened I am.

"That isn't your name, dear," Susan said. "But if you want to play that game with me, fine. It's fine. I don't care. All that matters is we'll be together again. Isn't that the only thing that really matters, Charlie?"

Charlie. They said you were dead. They told me you were dead.

The girl put her arm around Frankie's shoulder and said, "I don't want to go down there either."

"But your father is waiting," Susan said.

"He is *not* waiting," Charlotte said. "He's in Pennsylvania, like Frankie said. He is *not* down there."

"You used to be more pleasant, Charlie," Susan said. "I guess the woman you lived with didn't teach you very well. That happens sometimes when a child is stolen from her natural mother. Somebody else just doesn't care the same way. Doesn't *love* the same way. The way I love you, Charlie. But you'll learn. You'll learn to love me again. You really will. Then you'll forget all about this Allbright woman who stole you."

Stole me? Charlotte closed her eyes, feeling dizzy. She didn't want to go through that door and down to whatever it was that lay in the room below. She wouldn't go. Damn, she just wouldn't go. Let her make me move. Just let her make me.

"I'm not going," Charlotte said. "I refuse to go down there."

"Charlie," Susan said. "Open that door."

"No—"

Susan stepped forward and caught Frankie by the shoulder and pulled him away from his sister and struck him, deftly, abruptly, on the side of his face with the gun. Charlotte cried out, seeing her brother slip to the floor, rushing towards him, holding him, hearing the terrible way he moaned.

"Why'd you do that?" Charlotte screamed. *"Why the fuck did you do that? You must be some kinda fucking crazy—"*

Susan lashed out with the palm of her hand, catching Charlotte on the mouth, silencing her. That language, she thought. Where did Charlie learn that foul language? Charlotte bent over her brother, squeezing her eyes tight shut so she wouldn't cry, biting on her lip so she wouldn't moan. She wasn't going to give this woman the satisfaction of causing pain. No way. She wasn't going to let her hear the noise of pain. Damn her.

Susan opened the cellar door. She said, "I don't want to hear you talk that way again. Ever. I don't want to hear that kind of language coming out of your mouth, Charlie. And I know your father wouldn't want to hear it either. Are you ready to go down now?"

Charlotte, holding her sore lip, stood up. She helped Frankie to rise too and they went slowly towards the door.

"Be careful of the steps," Susan said. "I don't want you to fall, either of you."

Charlotte went forward first. Her hand touched a banister of rotted wood. She held Frankie close, drawing him after her. And she thought: Maybe it could be a game, a game where you have to humor somebody, you have to play along and see how far it goes. Maybe it would help to do that. Maybe.

Susan shut the door as she put her foot on the top step.

"Your father's expecting you," she said. "I know he'll be expecting you to kiss him. After such a long time, I think that would be a nice thing to do, don't you?"

And then she called out, *"Nick? Nick? We're home."*

But there was no answer from the blackness below.

5.

There was a car and somebody called Quayle and then a slow ride back to her own house and after that Adrienne and some men she didn't recognize and one of them must have been a physician because she felt a needle going into her arm and bandages being applied to her cuts. And then after that she was drifting in and out of sleep, chasing her own shadow through confused images, sometimes turbulent, sometimes placid—and yet the same darkness lay on the landscape and the same questions were asked by the man who called himself Quayle and she tried to answer because he was kind and gentle, patient and slow.

I don't know where my husband is.

There was a telephone number. But he lied to me, see. He lied.

She wasn't in her bedroom. She was lying on the sofa downstairs. She could sometimes hear people move in the kitchen. Maybe they'd repaired the telephone. She was sure it rang from time to time. She was sure, but she couldn't be sure. She drifted. And in her drifting there were the shallow graves of two small children and she felt as if her blood were being drained away, devoid of all feeling. Empty. But sometimes, too, she wanted to scream, like she was trying to tell somebody not to throw dirt into the graves yet because it was too soon, because they could still be alive, because you couldn't bury the living.

Quayle would sit on the edge of the sofa and hold her bandaged wrist: "You think he's in Pennsylvania? Is that where he might be?"

And she'd say: *He lied. I don't care where he is now. Just find the kids.*

Then there were other times when she'd open her eyes and the kids would be sitting in the chairs and watching her with concern but she knew these were the dream times, the moments when she was floating out again on the dark ship of whatever drug they'd pushed into her blood. The dream times. But then she was beyond pain, no longer knowing about the kids, no longer caring about the places in her body where she hurt, where she hurt badly. The drug took panic away.

"We're trying to find him," Quayle would say in the dream.

And she'd answer: Find the kids. Not him. Just the kids.

"He has a right to be told," Quayle would say.

Sometimes the dreams were filled with other shapes, with terrors, and she'd sit upright on the sofa and look around for her coat and shoes because she had to go back out and look for them, but Adrienne was always there, always, just sitting like some contented nurse.

"The police are looking," Adrienne would say. "They'll find the kids, Emily. They know what they're doing."

But it seemed in the dream times that they didn't know what they were doing, that they were looking in all the wrong places. And she'd force her eyes open and call out their names, *Charlotte, Frankie, where are you?* And she understood, faintly, if there were any understanding to be had, that all the strings that had kept her tethered to reality were snapped and cut as surely as the telephone wire had been.

Once, Ted appeared beside her in the room and said he was sorry, sorry he'd lied, sorry about the kids, but that was only a mirage, something she dreamed up between the noise of the telephone ringing and Adrienne clucking over her. Then Quayle would come back and say something like: "His employers don't know where he is. . . ."

And she wondered why it was so fucking important to find fucking Ted when it was the kids who were missing.

Dreams. Dreams. Dreams.

The walls of the room melted. Upstairs, mechanical toys went off by themselves, beating on drums or marching pointlessly up and down or toppling off the edges of tables. Dreams. Dreams. Dreams. She shouldn't have let them stick a needle into her. She wanted reality. She wanted substance. She didn't want this sense of floating endlessly on some tide.

Once Quayle tried to ask her about Susan but she hadn't any answers. Did she know about the girl who'd drowned in the swimming pool? Did she know about the missing husband? Did she know Susan didn't have any kids? Did she know about the blind father? These questions tore through her consciousness like lead pellets through some flimsy target—and they had nothing to do with her lost kids, her poor loved lost kids.

In the kitchen Quayle said to Steadman: "It seems she was seeing a shrink. Some guy Spassky. An asshole. The usual head sessions and painkillers. I asked him if he knew of any place where she'd take two kids and he gave me some bull about how she couldn't tell the real from the unreal. I ask you. Does that help find the goddam kids?"

Steadman hawked into a handkerchief. "Shrinks need shrinks. They don't need people as patients."

Quayle drummed his fingers impatiently and jerked his head in Emily's direction. "She's shook up pretty bad. Even so, she doesn't know anything we don't know."

"We're looking," Steadman said. He reached for the telephone and dialed a number, asked a question, got some negative response, then hung up. "Fucking lucky you went to that house, Quayle."

Lucky, Quayle thought. Maybe. A few minutes later, they'd have had a corpse on their hands. A numbered tag in the Pastorville morgue.

"The old guy thought it was his daughter about to kill him," Quayle said. "Obsessed she was poisoning him."

"Maybe she was," Steadman said.

"Yeah. Could be." Quayle got up restlessly from the table. He went to the window and gazed out into the darkness. "I figure she killed her old man."

"Yeah," Steadman said.

"Took the gun. Blew him away. Stashed him somewhere."

"Like where?" Steadman said, looking into his handkerchief.

"That's the question," said Quayle. "That's the big one."

In the silence that followed they could hear Emily Allbright moan in the front room.

"Sedative's wearing off," Quayle said.

Steadman was quiet a moment. "Figure her old man's dipping his wick on the side?"

"You've got this turn of phrase, Steadman. We still haven't found him, have we? So wherever he is, he's well and truly stashed away."

"Say this much," said Steadman. "I wouldn't like to be him, coming home to face the old music."

The telephone was ringing. Quayle answered it. "Nothing, huh?" He was quiet a moment then said, "Keep at it," and then hung up, drawing the palm of his hand across his face in a weary way, as if nothing surprised him but the bottomless well of his own disillusionment.

"I better try and talk with her again," he said.

Steadman said, "If you want me, you know where to find me."

Quayle listened to Steadman leave the house, then he went back inside the front room where the red-haired woman was sitting on the edge of the sofa; and where Emily Allbright, lying flat on her back, looked dazed and mournfully indifferent, her face the color of chalk.

6.

There was an indescribable smell in the small cellar room—it was more than just damp, more than the smell of old rusted metal, but something else, something that reminded Charlotte of bad meat, like the time when they'd gone on vacation and her mother had left some ground beef in the refrigerator and when they'd come home the kitchen was filled with the sickening rancid smell, as if the badness had managed to slide out through the shut door of the refrigerator; or another time, when Frankie had brought home the carcass of some bird riddled with worms. She tried to hold her breath against the smell, wanting to be sick, but not wanting Frankie to feel how the odor upset her. She paused in the middle of the floor, realizing that there was a tiny pane of filthy glass set high in the wall and that moonlight, in some faint burst, had come through the clouds and was tingeing the little room with a cold silver. Shapes, shapes all around her, things she couldn't make out—all she could think to do was to draw in on herself, make herself small, to concentrate only on keeping the scent out of her nostrils. Like, imagine you're not here, imagine you're dreaming this; in a moment, any second now, you'll wake up in your own bed.

But Susan just kept talking, talking and talking.

Charlie, do you remember that time when we all went sailing on the St. Lawrence and you nearly capsized the boat because you saw a big fish and you got so excited and your dad had to grab you, do you remember that, Charlie?

I remember, Charlotte said.

How could I ever forget?

Then there was that other time when the three of us went camping up in Vermont and it snowed overnight when we didn't expect it and we could hardly get the tent flap open because it was so stiff?

The three of us? Charlotte said. Where was Frankie?

Frankie?

Yeah, Frankie. Was this before Frankie was born or what?

Silence.

Something rustled in the cellar. The small pane of glass became dark, then silver again, the coldest silver Charlotte had ever seen.

It must have been before he was born, Susan said. *Yes, it must have been. You must have been very small.*

Charlotte listened to her brother sobbing in the dark. She reached out for him, touched him. She thought: Mom will have come home by now, she'll have called the police, the police will be looking for us. And then suddenly Susan was singing softly to herself, a strange little tune. *Clap your little hands, Daddy's on the stairs, What's he got for Charlie, Apples or pears!*

I remember that, Charlotte said.

Yes. I knew you would. Your dad liked to sing it.

"I wanna go home," Frankie said.

"But you are home," Susan said. "You *are* home now."

"This isn't my home," the boy said.

"But it *is*. Isn't it, Nick?"

Nothing. No answer. Silence. Charlotte stood motionless. Nick, she thought. Who was this Nick supposed to be? There was nobody else in this little room but the three of them. Or maybe this Nick, whoever he was, didn't have much to say. But that was stupid. *There was no such person as Nick down here.*

And still Susan was calling to him: "Nick? Don't play games, Nick. I've brought them to you. Come on, Nick. Say something to us."

> *Clap your little hands*
> *Daddy's on the stairs*

That weird crooning, like the voice in some demented dream. The moon became the color of new frost, brightening the cellar room, illuminating a variety of old objects—gloves hanging on hooks, an ancient glass lantern with its panes smashed, a sou'wester, some tarpaulin stuff, a pile of sacks in a corner.

Why is she going towards the sacks? Charlotte wondered.

> *What's he got for Charlie*
> *Apples or pears*

The sacks. Why the sacks? Why the sacks? Was that where she imagined this character Nick was sleeping or something? Charlotte watched, then the moon went away again, and the room was dark, so dark that even the shadows filled. Why the sacks? She listened. Slither. One by one. Slither slither. The sacks were being pulled away and then the moon shafted through the dark and she could see the woman bent over the heap, still singing, still breaking the lines of her song with the name of this Nick. And Frankie, poor Frankie, was shivering and crying, and there was a dark stain of blood on his face. Then there was no more moon.

"We've got kisses for you, Nick. Come on. Don't be shy. We've got kisses." Susan waited for an answer. "I even brought you the little boy, my love. You thought I'd forget him, didn't you. Oh, Nick, I wouldn't forget that much."

And then she heard Nick whisper: *Bring them over to me. Bring them nearer. So I can see them. So I can let them kiss me.*

Of course, love. Of course.

"Charlie. Frankie. Over here."

"Don't wanna," Frankie said.

"Over here," Susan said again. They're a little shy, Nick, that's all. A little shy. "Over here. Didn't you understand. I asked you to come over here."

Charlotte held her brother's hand. They moved forward towards the woman, towards the pile of sacks. *Daddy's on the stairs.* And then the room was all silver again, the scaled silver of a landed fish, something twisting in death, in the death struggle for air, the room was a terrible silver and unbearably bright and something lay amongst the sacks, something Charlotte didn't understand, didn't recognize, something black and shapeless and stained and webbed by the workings of spiders.

Those might have been eyes.

Once.

That might have been a mouth. Not now.

The blackened hand twisted in the air might once have held things. No longer.

Charlotte shut her eyes. She shut all her systems down. All she was conscious of was the retching smell of decay and the unbearable shriek of Frankie screaming, screaming and screaming again, until more than his voice filled the small room—more than his voice, his whole being.

And Susan said, "Come along, kids. Come along."

Kisses for daddy.

Don't you have at least one kiss for daddy?

7.

Quayle said, "Look. We'll find them. I want to get that through to you. We'll find them."

Emily, barely listening, watched the big man's expressionless face.

He tried again: "I got men out there. A whole lotta men. And we'll get those kids back for you. Am I getting through to you, Emily?"

Emily nodded. *They're dead,* she thought. *Bring me back coffins.*

"Now this woman, er . . ."

"Adrienne," Emily said.

"She's agreed to stay here with you for as long as you want her to, OK? You shouldn't be on your own. I figure she should stay until we locate your husband. You're gonna need some company. OK?"

Emily nodded absently. Locate my husband, she thought. Drag him out of whatever bed he's lying in. She wondered what time it was now, whether it was before midnight or after, whether it was drawing close to dawn. She'd lost her watch someplace. Now she didn't know if it was dark outside or light. And she didn't care. She didn't care about anything except for getting up from this sofa and going outside and looking for her kids.

"I know this is tough," Quayle said. "I know you don't want to sit around here. But I don't think you're in any shape . . . you know what I'm telling you?"

She opened her mouth. She was dry. "That old man," she said.

"You don't want to concern yourself with him," Quayle said. "He's going to be OK. He's going to be taken care of, OK?"

She nodded her head and glanced at Adrienne, who was watching her with concern. Suddenly she felt she wanted to be alone, she didn't want Adrienne's kindness, her attentions, she wanted to be alone in this house. But she didn't say anything. Adrienne went out into the kitchen and came back with a glass of water and a pill.

Quayle said, "The doc says you should take this pill."

"So I can sleep again? Is that it? I don't goddam want to sleep."

"It's not a sleeper, Emily. It's a mild trank. Nothing more."

Adrienne held it out and Emily put it in her mouth, swallowed it down with some cold water, and felt sick. They're no more than babies, she thought. They're babies, they're vulnerable, and they're going to die. And I'm supposed to lie here and wait, like somebody in a terminal ward watching a patient fade out. I'm supposed to do that. Dear Christ.

"And we're working on getting your husband," Quayle said. He looked at his watch. "I have to go out for an hour maybe, then I'll come back, check things out. OK?"

She said, "I don't care if you never find my husband."

Quayle patted the back of her hand. He sighed deeply, then stood upright. She didn't see him leave. She only understood that after a while she was alone in the house with Adrienne. Adrienne and silence.

Adrienne said, "I'll stay. Don't worry. I'll do anything I can."

She looked at Adrienne for a moment, thinking, she wants to help. She wants to be useful to me. And I don't deserve it. I don't deserve her. Then the pill hit her suddenly, beginning with a queasy feeling in her stomach, then flowing through her limbs so that she felt weak, disoriented. A tranquilizer, Quayle had said. But it felt like something way stronger than that. She sat upright, swinging her legs to the floor.

"You shouldn't move," Adrienne said.

Emily laid the palms of her hands on her knees. "They're out there somewhere . . . and all the pictures I keep getting are black. Just black nothings. Do you know what that's like?"

Adrienne nodded. "I'm sorry," she said.

Emily sat back, her head tilted to one side. The fear had been eclipsed by a sick emptiness. A zero condition. It was like she didn't exist all at once, she no longer had a body, only a mind barely capable of the thinnest perceptions, the most facile understandings. They're dead, she thought. *I know they're dead.*

"You want anything, you ask, dear," Adrienne said. "You just ask me."

Emily closed her eyes, fumbling to make some response. But the pill was working its way through her now, funneling, altering her perceptions. They want me to sleep, she thought. They just want me to sleep until this nightmare, one way or another, is over.

But I can't.

I can't sleep my children's lives away.

8.

Charlotte watched in horror as the woman, cradling the man's face in the crook of her arm, raised the mouth upwards and laid her own lips against it—and then turned, looking at Charlotte, smiling.

A kiss. You see. A simple kiss, that's all.

Charlotte stepped back, stepped away. She put her hand over Frankie's mouth to stop the noise he was making. And then she shut her eyes, trying to block out the hideous thing she'd just seen, the lips of the woman pressed to that emaciated dead grin, the touch of the mouth against the dark-stained face. But now she felt Susan's hand tugging on her own, drawing her towards the sacks, towards the dead man.

The way I did it, Charlie. Just like that. With your mouth. He's pleased. Can't you see how happy he is to have you back?

Charlotte wrenched her hand away and, going down on her knees, was sick on the floor, her stomach turning over, her mouth filled with a sticky fluid. There was a loud buzzing in her head, like a gnat was trapped in there, flapping its wings in a mad way for release. A gnat. A horsefly, something trying to get loose. Help me, she thought. Somebody help me.

Kiss your father, Charlie. Don't hurt his feelings.

Oh, poor Nick, don't be angered, don't be mad at her she's shy, that's all it is, she hasn't seen you in so long, don't be mad with her.

Charlotte crawled towards the tarpaulins, lying flat on her face, feeling the same dreadful sickness rise inside her again. Help me. Somebody, please. Then she felt Frankie bending over her, his small cold hand pressed against her forehead. Frankie, she thought. Get out. Run. Get up those stairs and run. I'll find the time for you. I'll make the time. Just run.

Then Susan was pulling her by the hand again, smiling, laughing, telling her she didn't need to act this shy, this was her father after all, this was her own flesh, her own blood.

"Yes," Charlotte said. "Yes."

"Kiss him. He's waiting."

"Yes," Charlotte said. Yes yes yes. She felt herself being drawn towards the figure that lay, stiffly propped up, in the corner of the silver room. She floated outside of herself, like she was drifting on a cloud, drifting even as she was being drawn towards the corner of the room—and then the smell was worse, the terrible perfume of dead flesh. She held her breath and tried not to gag. Yes, she thought. Yes yes yes.

She pulled her hand away from Susan's again and yelled at her brother: *Go, go, for Christ's sake go!*

The room darkened, the silver became silence.

Go go go why don't you run Frankie just run!

He wouldn't move he wouldn't move he wouldn't get his body to work he just stood there like he wasn't a part of anything anymore just stunned and catatonic and indifferent, as if he'd stumbled into a play and he didn't know his lines.

For God's sake run Frankie run!

Frankie hardly heard her. In the silver corner of the room his attention was transfixed by the appearance of the thing, of what must have been a man once—the thing she'd kissed, kissed with her lips, kissed like he was alive and not dead, not decayed like this . . . and then his sister was yelling at him but the words didn't make much sense. Go—go where, go how?

There was the awful sound of the gun clicking in the darkness.

And Charlotte was still yelling at him *Go run get away do it now* and Susan was laughing, saying, *He's not going anywhere, Charlie, he's not going anywhere, I don't know why you won't return our love.*

A simple kiss.

Then Charlotte was drawn towards the corner, being pulled by Susan, seeing the reflection of the gun in Susan's hand. And she felt her head being pressed down by Susan's hand, her face being pushed to the thing that lay there in the corner and she screamed, she screamed at Frankie again, trying to twist away, trying to struggle with Susan, to knock the gun from her hand—but Susan pushed her forward so that she fell on top of the dead man, and then the smell was overwhelming.

You've forgotten how to love, Charlie.

You've been gone too long from me.

Remember how to love. Remember.

Yes, Charlotte said. She closed her eyes. Yes. Yes, I'll try to remember how to love. I'll try.

I'll try.

The stench rushed up through Charlotte's nostrils. Her eyes smarted; and even with them closed she could see that terrible face looking up towards her lips.

Frankie! Frankie!

Kiss him, Susan said. It's you, Charlie. It's you that has to love him. Nobody else.

Yes. Me. Nobody else.

Susan ran her fingers through the girl's hair. *There never was any Frankie, Charlie, I made him up. He never lived. Don't you see? I invented him.*

Charlotte felt her mouth against the stiff cold flesh, the whole sick anguish of love and loving, the whole nightmare of love and death that obsessed this woman, that tethered her to the dead man, that made love linger after the grave, after the darkness, she felt the kiss of poison, the kiss that meant everything and yet meant nothing to this corpse, and she was consumed with a sense of sadness and fear and hatred, as if what she'd come to understand, in one grotesque moment, was the destructive nature of the human heart.

You see, Charlie. You see how happy he is now. Now we're together again.

Charlotte raised her face and wept and Susan put her arms around her, rocking her gently back and forth, saying: *My poor baby, my poor poor baby.*

Charlotte saw the outline of the moon on the glass pane, saw it flood the cellar, saw it illuminate everything in the cellar. Everything except Frankie.

But she couldn't remember Frankie now. She couldn't remember anything.

He was running through the dark rain, running and running, not knowing where he was going, understanding only that if he went in a direction away from the edge of the canal he might come eventually to the car, and after the car the broken fence, and somewhere beyond that road, a dark road, and at the end of this road there would be lights, maybe even a place he recognized. To run, just to run, to get help for his sister—that was all he understood now.

9.

She thought Quayle came back once.

She wasn't sure when.

She seemed to remember him standing over her and looking down, saying something about a search. She opened her eyes, then shut them again. There was a place, she told herself. There was a place she could reach for, she could find—like a space far inside herself where she'd be safe, where nothing would have happened. Where everything would be the same as it had been. The same, the same, the kids asleep upstairs.

Then maybe she only dreamed Quayle.

Another time, when she opened her eyes, she saw Adrienne asleep in the chair in the corner of the room. She didn't recognize her. Reality was a maze, trails you followed, little landmarks you recognized or failed to recognize—and yet they were all in some way familiar.

Then she was conscious of a very faint light pressing against the drawn curtains. She wanted to move, haul the drapes back, look out,

but she couldn't face the light because light meant a further passage
of time, more time in which they hadn't been found yet. So she listened to the rain and imagined tunes in the way rain splattered
against oak leaves.

Sometimes Adrienne changed position, twisting her head to the
side, then to the other side, her mouth slack and open as she slept.
The last pill she'd been given—but when had that been? She couldn't
remember. She listened to the rain. She couldn't remember. Maybe
they were out in the rain. The kids. She hoped they had coats. But
she didn't think they did. Maybe they were out there in the dawn rain
because it had to be dawn by now, hadn't it? It had to be that first
glimmer of morning. The last pill she'd been given—more of the same
dreams. Hallucinations. Take the edge off the situation, Emily.

But the edge of the situation was razor sharp and you couldn't
ever blunt that, could you. Then she dreamed a conversation with
Ted.

I didn't want to love somebody else, Em.

It just happened like that.

I never asked for it.

I betrayed you.

And so you lied, Ted, to spare me the hurt. But you don't know
where hurt begins, where it ends, how long and bloody that line is.
You don't know.

Ted evaporated somewhere along the way. The trellis was
upraised, then it fell down again. And Ted came tumbling after. The
pill in her bloodstream made her coast, then she was out on some
placid sea, or a quiet lake, and there were gulls making distant cres-
cents high overhead.

My kids! My kids!

What are they doing to find my kids?

She tried to rise at one point and Adrienne woke from her sleep
and made her lie down again.

Think of the good times.

Think of the good times when you had the kids.

When they were yours to love.

More dreams.

And this time there was a dream of Frankie standing beside the
sofa, touching her, shaking her arm. She opened her eyes and stared
at him and although he was talking to her she didn't understand any-

thing he was saying to her, but Adrienne did, Adrienne seemed to understand, Adrienne took control, took the boy out into the kitchen and drenched a sponge with water and wiped stains of blood from his face. Why was he bleeding? she wondered. But the timbre of this dream was different, harder, cleaner, because then she was outside, she was following Frankie and Adrienne to Adrienne's car, she was outside crossing the lawn, moving under a dawn light that was growing stronger, more terrible, carving fresh shadows out of houses and trees. And Adrienne was saying—*Hurry hurry we must hurry*— Then it seemed to her she'd missed something, something Frankie had told Adrienne, but Adrienne knew anyhow, and that was all right. They were in the big Olds now and Frankie was talking about the canal, kept talking about the canal, about Susan, about going to get Charlotte. And Adrienne was saying *Don't worry we'll get her, we'll get Charlotte*, then Frankie was crying, holding his mother, his tears warm against the side of Emily's face, so warm they had to be real.

But if it wasn't a dream. If it wasn't a dream, what was it?

Adrienne drove. Emily held the boy tight and stared through the window, watching the sullen houses of the silent suburb, seeing Frankie point down one street, then another, like he really didn't know where he was going. And that had to be a part of a dream, that lack of direction, that twisted sense of unreality, of hallucination.

I know where the fence is, Adrienne said.

I know where the canal is, Adrienne said.

Emily listened, glazed. It was getting harder, the edges sharper, the corners more clean. It was beginning to feel like some hallucination disintegrating. Just falling apart. Adrienne's voice. That was real. The boy's tears. They were real. But the rest of it—the silent streets and the blank houses and the streetlamps glowing against the first slashes of dawn, none of that seemed real.

There's a fence. There's a hole in the fence. Then you'll see a car. Then this funny kinda house.

This is Frankie, Emily thought. This is Frankie. He isn't dead.

She thought her heart might break then.

I know it, Adrienne was saying. *I know the fence.*

There's a Keep Out sign. A hole in the fence.

Through the thin drizzle of rain there was the spare flat disk of the morning sun now. Hardly any glow. Just a meager suggestion of warmth up there someplace.

A fence, Emily thought. I have to look for a fence. Adrienne was driving very fast, taking corners so that the tires burned, squealed, the big wheel spinning in her hands.

It isn't a dream then.

It's real. It isn't a dream.

Then Frankie was talking about a gun and a dead man and what Charlotte had had to do.

But Emily didn't believe that part of it. So it was a dream. It had to be a dream. Nothing like that happened except in the world of a nightmare, so this wasn't a car, and this wasn't Frankie, and Adrienne was really sleeping in the chair.

Then there was a fence and Adrienne drove the Olds straight through it, and after the fence there was long grass, and some way beyond the long grass a car with its doors hanging open. Adrienne drove round the empty vehicle, then the Olds wouldn't go any farther in the soft earth.

Hurry, Emily. Hurry.

They were out of the car now, following Frankie through the long grass. Emily was fighting for breath. Her lungs moved inside her like two clenched fists. In the distance there was the sound of rain on water, then a smell of dampness. A smell. She couldn't ever remember *smelling* anything in any of her dreams, like it was a sense she never took with her into her dream world, so if she smelled something now then this wasn't a dream, this was real, this was long grass and rain and a canal nearby and Frankie shouting hoarsely *This way over here this way* and Adrienne holding her by the elbow so she wouldn't fall over in the mud.

This is real, she thought. And the thought was like something snapping inside her head. It was like a scalpel scraping along the surface of bone. Real. *This is real.*

Dear God. This is real.

In here, Frankie was saying. *In here.*

A small building, like some kind of misshapen house. She stopped, watching Frankie push the rotted door back.

No, she thought. I can't go in there. I can't go in there.

But she followed Adrienne inside, she followed Adrienne who'd gone in after Frankie. The kid was pointing across a littered room to another door. Something, she thought. Something beyond that door.

Charlotte's down there, Frankie said.

But it was Adrienne who moved first, who went across the floor, who opened the other door. And Frankie was still saying something about a gun. She went after Adrienne. She stood outside the open door, conscious of a flight of stairs going down. Below, a dim room. A terrible smell. It blew up from the bottom of the stairs, filled her nostrils, permeated her. And something moving in the dimness at the foot of the stairs.

She pushed past Adrienne and began to move down the stairs.

She heard the sound of her own footsteps with perfect clarity. She heard them as if she were hearing for the first time after a life of deafness. Hard and steel and real.

She saw the locks of blonde hair first, shining like gold in the dimness. She saw Charlotte's face turned towards her. She saw the empty unseeing eyes stare at her.

Then someone else moved in the weak light.

She heard herself say, "Charlotte."

Adrienne was crying behind her on the stairs. She was crying in short stifled sobs. She heard her own voice come back in a thin echo. "Charlotte, Charlotte."

And then her attention was drawn inexorably away from the blank face of her daughter, drawn to the far corner of the room, drawn to the dark heart of the room. Something moved. Somebody moved.

And what remained of the dream broke and splintered, it came crashing down like a guillotine and she knew that what she was looking at was real, that nothing would ever reduce that reality, soften it, buffer its hard edges.

Susan was holding something in her arms, rocking it back and forward, crooning softly to it.

Something.

Emily didn't move for a time. And then slowly she crossed the floor. "Charlotte," she said. "Charlotte. Charlotte, love."

Susan said nothing. She just kept rocking, kept moaning.

"Charlotte, love. It's me."

The child smoothed a lock of hair from her forehead and looked at Emily. *Please let it go back to being a dream,* Emily thought.

"Charlotte, baby. It's me. It's time to come home."

The girl twisted her head to the side, looked at Susan, made a sound, something unintelligible.

Susan stared up from what she was holding and said: "But she is home."

Emily moved forward, understanding for the first time what it was that the woman held in her arms, understanding with a consciousness of horror, of pain, realizing that what she saw now would come back, time after time, in her darkest dreams. She closed her eyes, wanting to scream aloud, but staying silent. Dizziness was like some great black bird that hovered around her, settling its awful weight on her shoulders.

Behind her, Adrienne was still crying.

"Charlotte," Emily said. "I'm going to take you home now."

Charlotte.

The girl looked at Emily for a long time in silence before she said: "I'm Charlie. And I am home."

Epilogue

There was the sea and the sand and the transmutation of fall into winter, there were sea-changes in the rise and tumble of the surf, in the way it pounded senselessly against the outcroppings of rock. There was a rented house, a ramshackle affair above the cove and mornings spent walking the wild sands. There was the physician who came a couple of times a week to look at Charlotte, to prescribe this or that medication, to offer the primitive salves of science, or to utter platitudes that came down to: *It'll take time, Emily. Time and patience. You don't forget an experience like this easily.*

There was a bedroom for Charlotte at the top of the house. The window had a view of the cove. Sometimes, when the girl slept, Emily would come and sit on the edge of the bed and hold her hand and hope she'd be returned to her. Just Charlotte again. Not this other lost person, this stranger. Just Charlotte. *It'll take time.*

There were calls from Ted, terse conversations.

Once or twice he visited. She never asked an explanation for his lie. It didn't matter to her. Only Charlotte mattered to her now. Ted paid the bills. Ted did his best. But she hadn't anything to say to Ted anymore.

On one visit he mentioned the fact that he'd like them to get together as a family again. She didn't answer him. Another time he was on the point of blaming her for what had happened, he was on the edge of saying *I told you so*—but he had the grace to draw back from the accusation. And on another occasion he railed at the crazy woman who'd caused Charlotte such pain, how she deserved to be hung instead of languishing in a psychiatric institution.

Sometimes Emily woke from nightmares she couldn't describe. Sometimes she could hear the surf roar through her nightmares, and what she saw at these times was a great tidal swell filling a small cellar room. And something moving in a dim corner . . .

When the weather was good outside she'd walk along the beach with Charlotte and Frankie, all of them dressed in their parka jackets, zippered up against the bonechilling Atlantic wind. And then there were good days when Charlotte seemed like her old self again, smiling, talking in an animated way about going back to school, seeing her old friends. These were the times when Emily felt optimistic. When she felt that a phase was passing, a horror starting to disintegrate.

It was going to take a lot of love, she thought. It was going to take all her love. And maybe even more than that. She hoped she had enough.

Especially on those nights when, sitting downstairs in the front room and listening to the surge of the sea, she'd hear Charlotte singing up in her room, singing monotonously, tonelessly, the words of a song that went:

> *Clap your little hands*
> *Daddy's on the stair*
> *What's he got for Charlie*
> *An apple or a pear?*